The Evolution of
Hospitals in Britain

The Evolution of Hospitals in Britain

Edited by F. N. L. Poynter

Librarian, The Wellcome Historical Medical Library

London

Pitman Medical Publishing Company Ltd

First published 1964

© Pitman Medical Publishing Co. Ltd, 1964

PITMAN MEDICAL PUBLISHING COMPANY, LTD.
46 CHARLOTTE STREET, LONDON, W.I

ASSOCIATED COMPANIES
SIR ISAAC PITMAN & SONS, LTD.
PITMAN HOUSE, PARKER STREET, KINGSWAY, LONDON, W.C.2
THE PITMAN PRESS, BATH
PITMAN HOUSE, BOUVERIE STREET, CARLTON, MELBOURNE
22–25 BECKETT'S BUILDINGS, PRESIDENT STREET, JOHANNESBURG
PITMAN PUBLISHING CORPORATION
20, EAST 46TH STREET, NEW YORK
SIR ISAAC PITMAN & SONS (CANADA), LTD.
(INCORPORATING THE COMMERCIAL TEXT BOOK COMPANY)
PITMAN HOUSE, 381–383 CHURCH STREET, TORONTO

MADE AND PRINTED IN GREAT BRITAIN BY
THE GARDEN CITY PRESS LIMITED
LETCHWORTH, HERTFORDSHIRE

Contents

These papers were read at the Third British
Congress on the History of Medicine and
Pharmacy on 26-28th September 1962.
The Congress was organized by the Faculty of
the History of Medicine and Pharmacy of the
Worshipful Society of Apothecaries of London
and sponsored by John Wyeth and Brother
Limited.

Illustrations

PREFACE

THE HISTORY OF hospitals in Britain has long been neglected as a subject of serious research, despite its obvious importance in the development of modern society. The increased attention now being given to all aspects of medical care in Britain and the change in the status of the hospitals brought about by the establishment of a National Health Service have shown how little was generally known of the origins of one of the most important institutions in our welfare system. The committee which had the task of choosing the theme of the Third British Congress on the History of Medicine and Pharmacy was familiar with the several historical monographs on some of our famous teaching hospitals and knew of the vigorous and even exciting research in the subject then recently embarked upon by Dr. Brian Abel-Smith at the London School of Economics. However, it considered that a general discussion of the various types of hospitals and hospital services which had grown up in Britain would be a useful complement both to the individual histories and to Dr. Abel-Smith's sociologist research and would show up the areas where further research was most needed. The Congress theme was accordingly taken as "The Evolution of Hospitals in Britain".

The papers read at the Congress, to which Dr. Abel-Smith himself contributed, are published here for the first time.* The Congress was organized by the Faculty of the History of Medicine and Pharmacy of the Worshipful Society of Apothecaries of London, and sponsored by John Wyeth and Brother Limited. With the permission of the Master and Wardens of the Society of Apothecaries, their ancient Hall in the City of London was used as the Congress Headquarters and for the Inaugural Session, other sessions being held at the Royal College of Physicians, the Royal Society of Medicine, and the

* The substance of his paper is included in Dr. Abel-Smith's forthcoming book to be published by Heinemann, and is not available for publication here.

9

Royal College of Nursing, by courtesy of their governing bodies. Members of the Faculty are grateful to their Honorary Secretary, Dr. F. N. L. Poynter, for organizing this Congress at short notice and for his subsequent editing of the Proceedings; to all the contributors for the time and care which they spent in the preparation of their papers; to Mr. Eric Gaskell for preparing the Bibliography on the History of British Hospitals which is published as an appendix to the Congress proceedings; and, finally, to the Pitman Medical Publishing Company Limited, and its Managing Director, Mr. David Dickens, for publishing this volume.

W. S. C. COPEMAN

Chairman of the Faculty

Monastic Infirmaries

LORD AMULREE

LITTLE KNOWLEDGE HAS been preserved of what life was like in the hospitals of the Middle Ages. There are only scanty records of the patients who entered their wards, apart from a few accounts of cures, some of which border on the miraculous. There are, however, full details of their possessions, charters, endowments, staffing and the like, as can be seen among the archives of St. Bartholomew's Hospital in London. We do not even know what type of patient entered these mediaeval hospitals, but there is some evidence that the buildings were more a mixture of chronic sick wards and homes for the aged than the acute general hospitals we know now. The difficulty of transporting an acutely ill patient to a hospital across crowded and narrow fourteenth-century streets must have been formidable.

All monasteries and nunneries had infirmaries to which went those monks and nuns who were unable, owing to illness, to take their usual place in the choir. These infirmaries were not quite like hospitals in our sense of the word: a monk who was ill brought with him to the infirmary his own bed and bedding from the dormitory, and this was certainly so until shortly before the dissolution of the monasteries by Henry VIII: the Infirmarer, however, kept a number of flock and feather cushions for the comfort of his patients. In its original form the infirmary was like any other mediaeval hospital—a long hall, with an altar at the east end, and the beds arranged in two rows with their backs to the side walls: the Hospice at Beaune, the former hospital at Angers and, in this country, St. Mary's Hospital at Chichester, although now used as an almshouse, are good examples of this type of building. The ruins of the infirmary buildings at Christchurch, Canterbury and Castle

Acre, in Norfolk, give an impressive picture of what these buildings were like when intact. At Westminster Abbey the hall was replaced by a small cloister with the sick men's rooms opening off it, but the chapel, dedicated to St. Katherine, remained at the east side of the cloister.

The Infirmarer was not a doctor, but was one of the obedientiaries of the monastery whose task was an administrative one. He kept an annual record of his accounts: his income was drawn from properties which were attached to the infirmary and from certain monies coming from nearby churches. With this money he had to maintain the sick monks and pay for any medical attention and for any medicines which were needed. This account was audited and entered on a parchment roll, which was preserved among the archives of the monastery. Most of these rolls have not been preserved, but those of the infirmary at Westminster Abbey are among the most complete in the country: they run from 1297 until 1536, and for the fourteenth, fifteenth and sixteenth centuries are seventy per cent complete: the monastery was dissolved in 1540. It is from a study of the Westminster rolls that the material for this paper has been drawn.

Although the Infirmarer's rolls do not go back before 1297, the monastery was founded in 1049 for an establishment of a prior and fifty monks. These figures were rarely attained, so the sample at risk to be considered is not large and is a highly selected one. The monks belonged to the Benedictine order, which was not one of the most strict. They slept, at first, in a dormitory where each monk had a straw mattress, blanket, coverlet and pillow: in later years each monk had his own cubicle. They wore reasonable clothes, properly fitting and adapted to the season: these were changed regularly and washed every two weeks in the summer and every three weeks in the winter. The monk wore stockings and a linen shirt and underpants, with his black habit on top: in the winter a leather cloak was provided. Each monk was allowed two baths a year— this was at one time increased to four, but sterner counsels soon reduced the figure once more to two. Tablecloths and napkins were washed regularly and there was a hand lavatory next door to the refectory. Water supply from springs in Hyde

Park was good, and there was enough head of water to flush the sewers: the buildings were interspersed with gardens. It is probable that conditions were not in fact so good as this description would imply, but on the whole sanitary and hygienic conditions were satisfactory.

Some of the Infirmarers may have had some medical knowledge and experience: there was probably a large textbook of medicine among the books in the library. In some monasteries the Infirmarer was allowed to treat minor illness, in others, he was forbidden to do so. It was laid down that the Infirmarer shall be

> "gentle, good tempered, kind, compassionate to the sick, and willing to gratify their needs with affectionate sympathy. It should rarely or never happen that he has not ginger, cinnamon, peony and the like in his cupboard, so as to be able to render prompt assistance to the sick if stricken with sudden malady. . . . He should provide in a spirit of fraternal sympathy a fire on the hearth, should the state of the weather require it, a candle, or a cresset, and a lamp to burn all night: and everything that is necessary, useful and proper."

While on one occasion the Abbot was enjoined to

> "oft times visit the brethren in the Infirmary and shew them all human kindness: supplying the same with more delicate food that is suitable for them and with medicine wherewith they may more quickly recover."

The amount of information to be found in the rolls varies with the different infirmarers. But the duration of sickness of each monk is recorded, and its cost—3d for a meat day and 2d for a fish day—is reckoned. From these figures a pattern of illness in this small and highly selected community can be evolved: biographical details of 706 monks have been recorded, of these one or more illness is recorded for 484. There is rarely any mention of the disease itself, so we learn nothing of what the monks suffered: not that any medical records, if they existed, would help a great deal, so empirical and magical was much of late mediaeval medicine.

Until the middle of the fourteenth century illnesses among the monks were divided into two types—those which kept a monk out of the choir and those which took him into the infirmary. This distinction was soon lost, and I have, therefore, taken both types of illness together. I have, however, classified the illnesses as long or short, having chosen, quite arbitrarily, two weeks as being the dividing line. There are twenty-three admissions to the infirmary recorded where the length of the illness is not given, and ninety-seven deaths are also recorded where there has been no previous period of sickness in the infirmary. Further, among the short illnesses are included forty-six terminal, or fatal, illnesses.

TABLE I

1297/8–1535/6

Number of monks recorded as being ill	484	
Short illnesses	1,746	3·5 per monk
Long illnesses	807	1·6 per monk

Some monks had more than one long illness, and this is shown in Table II.

TABLE II

Illnesses of over 2 weeks	Number of monks
1	110
2	74
3	34
4	31
5	16
6 and over	24
	289

It is interesting to note what a large number of monks suffered from more than one long illness—some of these illnesses must have been serious and some were of long duration, up to seventeen or eighteen weeks.

It is useful to have some idea of the age of this community, but this information is not easy to obtain. Very rarely is the date of birth and of death recorded for any one monk. But it is possible to obtain some idea of the average age from the fact that, until the reign of Edward IV, 1461–1473, a new monk could not celebrate his first mass until he had reached the age of twenty-four; after this reign the age dropped to twenty-one.

The number of years that passed between the celebration of their first mass and their death is recorded for 187 monks: the figure could be obtained, probably, for more than this: death can often be assumed from entries in other rolls, but sometimes when no further record is given it is because that monk left the convent for some reason other than death: these have, therefore, been omitted.

Table III gives the number of years which these 187 monks lived after their first mass.

TABLE III

1297/8–1535/6

Time between 1st mass and death	Number of monks
1– 5 years	19
6–10 ,,	20
11–15 ,,	23
16–20 ,,	11
21–25 ,,	17
26–30 ,,	20
31–35 ,,	19
36–40 ,,	14
41–45 ,,	21
46–50 ,,	12
51–55 ,,	4
56–60 ,,	7
	187

The average number of years between the celebration of their first mass and their death for these 187 monks is twenty-seven years.

If the age of twenty-four be taken as the age reached for this first celebration, this will give a mean age at death of at least fifty-one years. It is unlikely that a large number of monks were over the age of twenty-four when they were able to celebrate their first mass, and the number of those who did so after the reign of Edward IV was not great, and any difference they may make to the mean age at death will be slightly to increase it rather than to reduce it. It has been estimated that during the late Middle Ages the expectation of life of a man of twenty-five varied, from 1276 to 1450, between twenty-one and twenty-seven years: this would give a mean age at death of something over fifty years: a figure very comparable to that of the monks included in this sample. A smaller sample has been collected from the rolls of the monastery of Christchurch at Canterbury—another Benedictine house, but one whose rolls are not so complete as those at Westminster.

TABLE IV

Date	Number of monks	Average time spent as monks
1285–1309	64	30 years
1415–1432	45	27 ,,
1457–1471	48	33 ,,

These figures are roughly comparable to those of West-minster and, assuming that the first mass was celebrated at the age of twenty-four, give a mean age at death of something over fifty years. It does not look, therefore, as if the average monk could look forward to a longer life in the protected environment of a monastery than his fellow man could in the outside world. This may be, of course, because the man who chose the monastic life was more prone to disease and early death than the man in the outside world.

In the early rolls the records are kept by quarters, but later on they are kept by months. This makes any attempt to assess the incidence of disease by seasons a little rough, but Table V shows the quarterly incidence.

TABLE V

1297/8–1535/6
Incidence of disease by quarters

	Admission to infirmary	
Michaelmas quarter	417	29·1%
Christmas	370	25·7%
Easter	379	25·8%
St John's	267	18·6%

As might be expected the summer quarter shows the lowest incidence, but there is no great difference between the other quarters: the Michaelmas figures are the highest, but only slightly so.

The Ministry of Pensions and National Insurance publishes tables which show the proportional incidence of sickness by certain arbitrary periods of time. The figures for 1957 have been compared with the overall figures of incidence of illness drawn from the rolls, and the two sets of figures are given in Table VI.

TABLE VI

Sickness periods by days Infirmarer's Rolls 1297/8–1535/6		Ministry of Pensions and National Insurance Report 1957/8
0– 3 days	10·1%	3·8%
4– 6 „	24·7%	21·5%
7– 12 „	26·9%	33·2%
13– 18 „	9·4%	16·4%
19– 24 „	7·1%	7·5%
25– 48 „	11·0%	10·0%
49– 78 „	4·4%	3·4%
79–156 „	2·2%	2·3%
157–312 „	0·9%	0·9%
312 & over	1·9%	1·0%

Although the comparability of these two sets of figures cannot be pushed too far, the similarity between the general picture now and the general picture in the late Middle Ages is interesting and rather suggestive: the biggest differences being in the shorter periods of sickness.

The Nuffield Provincial Hospitals Trust published, in 1954, an analysis of the fate of 705 men discharged from the medical wards of four general hospitals in Glasgow. Their survey showed that about one third of these men had already had one or more spells of in-patient treatment in hospital and the conclusion was drawn that a considerable number of available hospital beds were used by a comparatively small number of patients who broke down in health repeatedly and needed regular re-admission to hospital. When the sickness records of the monks are studied, it is found that the greatest demands on the services of the infirmary came from a small group of monks, about one third of the total, whose health apparently broke down at regular and frequent intervals. This figure is comparable with that already quoted from Glasgow.

The infirmary was used partly as a home for monks who, either because of long term, chronic disease or because they were afflicted by the infirmity of old age, could no longer maintain their place in the choir. Eighteen such monks, who were known as "stagiarii", are mentioned as living in the

2—TEOHIB

infirmary for more than a year before they died, the longest stay recorded being for seven years. On the other side of the scale, however, it is recorded that ninety-eight monks were admitted to the infirmary before celebrating their first mass, that is as novices, who were, for the most part certainly, under the age of twenty-four years. Those who were admitted during the same year that they celebrated their first mass are not included in this figure, because it is uncertain which came first, the illness or the celebration.

To complete the pattern of disease the length of the fatal, or terminal, illness is recorded for ninety monks, and is shown in Table VII.

TABLE VII

Length of terminal illness in weeks
1297/8–1535/6

Weeks	Number of Monks
1	32
2	14
3	11
4	4
5– 8	9
9–12	9
13–16	7
17 and over	4

This table shows that the last illness of over sixty per cent of the monks in the sample lasted for three weeks or less.

It is not possible to find out from the rolls from what diseases the monks suffered or of what they complained when they entered the infirmary. But a certain number of the monks were submitted to surgery, and some on more than one occasion.

TABLE VIII

Total number of monks treated by surgery, 89
1297/8–1535/6

One treatment only	74
Two	10
Three	4
Four	1
	—
	89
	—

While we do not know a great deal of the nature of the surgical treatment performed, we do have an occasional glimpse—one monk was treated for "rupture of the stomach", one for an injury to his foot caused by an axe, one for a disease of his arm, one for his hand and one for his privy member. No further details survive.

Occasionally methods of treatment are mentioned—cuppings, administrations of clysters. Sometimes they were on the advice of a physician, but sometimes, particularly in the later rolls, as part of the infirmary routine. Electuaries, oxymels, cholagogues, plasters and ointments were made in the infirmary, and regular purchases of honey and liquorice are noted. Occasionally individual treatment or prescribing is noted—milk for one monk, pork for another, tench, apparently, for one monk suffering from jaundice. A suppository of honey, salt and "yra beneditae" is ordered, and white wine in large quantities, a depilatory powder, and a sharp wine made from crab apples. A stove is bought for one monk and another is ordered to take a bath. Treatment of the shins, either by surgery or by the application of white wine, is common. It is uncertain what disease this could have been. Some writers have maintained that it was caused by kneeling—but the tibia is not generally involved in this: the monks, presumably, sat in the stalls for their services, and it is unlikely that their tibiae would be in contact with anything sharp or irritating. Their complaint might have been a form of housemaid's knee, or even a varicose condition of the legs caused by long standing in the choir.

Mentally sick monks who suffered from the irksomeness of the cloistered life, or who found the silence of the monastery and the fasting and long services too much for them, and who suffered from the work, sleeplessness, heaviness in the head or pains in the stomach were sent to dependent houses in the country, usually to Battersea, Wandsworth or Hendon.

Among the staff of the infirmary were male nurses who took care of the sick monks. In 1372 it was laid down that these men shall "wait upon the sick, get their water ready" and they were also bidden to "endure the foulness of sick persons, whether in vomiting or other matters". Between 1402/3 and 1408/9, it is recorded that a special male nurse was called in to help to serve the sick brothers on five occasions, and during 1411/12 and 1412/13 the male nurse was called in to help in the ill-nesses, fourteen in number, of individual monks, whose names and the duration of whose illness, from nine to forty-four days, were recorded.

The first mention of a doctor attending at the infirmary is in the roll for 1297/8, and for the next twenty years there are several records of doctors visiting individual monks and pre-paring medicines. But in 1320, Master Robert of St. Alban's was appointed doctor to the monastery at a stipend of 53s. 4d. a year. St. Alban's Abbey, another Benedictine house, had a great reputation for scholarship and learning at that time, and it is likely that Master Robert had received some of his training in that Abbey. Although the doctor to the monastery remained a post paid by stipend, with the addition of an annual gift of a robe trimmed with fur, until the dissolution in 1540, there were many instances where another doctor is called in, at a fee, to see an individual. Most of these doctors remain shadowy figures, but two at the end of the fourteenth century, John de Wyke and John Middleton, were both graduates of Oxford, were both in holy orders and were both royal physicians, the first to Richard II, and the second to Richard II and Henry IV. Both were called in to see monks with what may be called a bad sickness record, and both were paid a fee for their work.

At the same time there are several references to a woman doctor, "mulier fisicus", being called in to see several monks on more than one occasion and being paid the appropriate fee for her work: in one year she saw ten monks and was paid 40s. as her fee. Women doctors were not uncommon at this time, although their place in medical history remains obscure.

Study of the Infirmarer's rolls of Westminster Abbey will not give much new information on the methods of treat-ment or on the diseases suffered during the late Middle Ages. But some useful information on the pattern of disease at this time can be found: how far this can apply from the small sample which has been investigated is not sure. But it is pos-sible from these rolls to form what are almost case histories for some hundreds of monks, and this in itself is of some use in illuminating an obscure period in the history of medicine.

Eight typical "case histories" of monks, selected from the Infirmarer's rolls of Westminster Abbey, are given below:

Jordan de Wratting

Born—1238
Novice—1261

1297/8	6 days, Michael.*
	1 week, Xmas
	Medicines, 5/- & 17d. Medicine by hand of Master Lawrence.
1305/6	6 weeks, Michael.
	6 days, do
	4 days, do
	Medicines, 2/-, 9d, 7/7
	6 days, Xmas
	5 days, do
	6 days, Easter
	13 weeks, do
1309/10	1 week, Michael.
	1 week, do
	2 weeks, Xmas
1310/11	10 days, Michael.
	4 weeks, Xmas
1320/1	12 months, Michael.
1322/3	6 months, do Obiit.

Adam de Lalham

1297/8	3 days, Michael.
	14 days, do
	1 week, do Medicine at the hand of
	1 week, Xmas Master John of Kent.
	Surgery, 4/-
	Medicines, 15d.
	Medicines, 2/9—Easter
1305/6	6 weeks, Michael.
	4 days, do
	"being in jaundice for tench 17d."
	Medicines, 6d, 3/2, 20d, 13/1, 8d, 19d.
	Surgery, 3/4

* The period spent in the infirmary and the quarter within which the illness occurred.

1305/6	7 weeks, Michael.
	6 weeks, Xmas
	7 days, Easter
	6 days, do
1309/10	5 days, Michael.
	? days, do
	4 days, Xmas
	3 days, do
1310/11	4 weeks, ?
	3 weeks ?
	2 weeks—or more—?

John de Walyngford

Novice—1336
First Mass—1339

1339/40	1 week, Michael.	
	5 days, Easter	
	2 weeks, do	
	9 days, St. John	
	1 week, do	to Hendon, *per licencium Prioris.*
	Surgery—6d.	
	Medicine—2/-	
1347/8	3 days, Michael.	
	5 days, Xmas	
	3 days, Easter	
	3 days, do	
1351/2	6 days, St. John	
	4 days, do	*because he took one clister fever.*
	7 days, do	
1352/3	1 week, Michael.	
	4 days, Xmas	
	6 days, do	
	12 days, Easter	
	? days, St. John	
1354/5	6 days, Michael.	
	Pro tibia sua curanda—12d.	
1357/8	*Bath for J. de W.—8d.*	
1364	—no further mention.	

John Sandon

Subdeacon—1378
First Mass—1381

1378/9	6 days, ?
1381/2	3 days, Michael.
1382/3	3 days, Xmas
1383/4	9 weeks, Easter
1385/6	1 week, Xmas
	2 weeks, Easter
1391/2	*Medicine—16d.*
1398/9	9 days, Xmas
	9 days, do
	9 days, Easter
1401/2	27 days, Easter
1403/4	9 days, Easter
1405/6	96 days, do
1406/7	364 days, Michael.
1411/12	48 days, St. John
1412/13	13 days, Michael.
	Man to look after J. S. for 13 days & nights
	102 days, St. John

William Asshewell

First Mass—1381

1378/9	3 days, Michael.
	13 weeks, Easter
1379/80	6 days
1380/81	2 weeks
1381/2	2 weeks, Easter
1382/3	3 days, Easter
1386/7	2 weeks, Easter
	2 weeks, St. John
1387/8	2 weeks, Xmas
	1 week, St. John
1388/9	3 weeks, St. John
	7 weeks, do
1389/90	9 days, St. John
1390/91	9 days, Xmas
	11 days, St. John
1391/2	7 days, Easter
	Medicines 5d.
1392/3	3 days, Michael.
	10 days, Michael.
	11 days, Xmas
1394/5	9 days, Xmas
	4 weeks, Easter

1395/6	9 days, St. John
1396/7	3 days, Xmas
1397/8	9 days, Xmas
	6 days, Easter
1398/9	3 days, Michael.
	9 days, Easter
	9 days, St. John
1399/40	9 days, Michael.
	26 days, Michael.
	6 days, Easter
1401/2	58 days, St. John
	80 days, Xmas
1402/3	32 days, Michael.
	3 days, Xmas
	In surgeria solut' Johanni
	Brademoor pro fratre
	W. A. 6/8.
1403/4	6 days, St. John
1405/6	3 days, Michael.
	9 days, Xmas
1407/8	20 days, Michael.
	6 days, Xmas
	24 days, Easter
	Medicine 5/-
1408/9	6 days, Xmas
1409/10	9 days, Xmas
	6 days, Easter
	9 days, Easter
1410/11	19 days, Michael.
	6 days, Xmas
	2 plasters 2/9
1411/12	9 days, Michael.
	22 days, St. John
	Man to look after W. A.
	for 22 days & nights
1412/13	6 days, Michael.
	Man to look after W. A.
	for 6 days & nights.
	17 days, Easter
	Man to look after W. A.
	for 17 days & nights.

Robert Athelard

Coquinus [cook]—1380-1

1386/7	2 weeks, Easter
1398/9	3 days, St. John
1399/00	9 days, Xmas
1406/7	3 days, do
1407/8	6 days, St. John
1409/10	58 days, Michael.
1411/12	59 days, St. John
1412/3	365 days, Michael.
1416/7	365 days, do
1417/8	74 days do obiit.

John Snellyng

Novice—1384

1386/7	3 days, Easter
1388/9	9 days, St. John
1391/2	3 days, Michael.
	Medicines, 16d.
1392/3	117 days, Easter
	9 days, St. John
	Medicines, 11d.
1393/4	3 days, Easter
1394/5	9 days, Xmas
	6 days, Xmas
1397/8	9 days, Michael.
	6 days, Xmas
	9 days, Easter
	9 days, St. John
	6 days, do
1401/2	3 days, Michael.
1402/3	6 days, Michael.
	6 days, Xmas
1403/4	9 days, St. John
	9 days, do
1405/6	9 days, Xmas
	9 days, Easter
·06/7	3 days, St. John
ˎ409/10	9 days, St. John
1410/11	15 days, St. John
1411/12	44 days, Michael.—obiit.
	Medicines, plasters, syrups & waters—9/10.
	Man to look after J. S. for 44 days & nights.

Reginald Shiplake

Priest—1398

1399/00	6 days, Michael.
	9 days, Xmas
1400/1	6 days, Michael.
1401/2	6 days, do
1416/7	6 days, Xmas
1440/1	16 days, ?
1443/4	all year—stagiarius
1444/5	do
1445/6	obiit.

BIBLIOGRAPHY

CLARK, J. W. (Ed.) (1897). *The Observances in Use at the Augustinian Priory of Barnwell, Cambridgeshire*, Cambridge, Macmillan and Bowes.

FLEMMING, PERCY (1929). The medical aspects of the mediaeval monastery in England, *Proc. roy. Soc. Med.*, **22**, 25–36.

KIRK, R. E. G. (Ed.) (1892). Accounts of the Obedientiars of Abingdon Abbey, *Camden Society*, N.S. **51**, pp. lx, 195.

PEARCE, E. H. (1916). *The Monks of Westminster*, Cambridge.

RUSSELL, J. C. (1948). *Expectation of Life in Mediaeval England*, University of New Mexico Press.

The Royal Hospitals before 1700

W. S. C. COPEMAN

PRE-REFORMATION

IT HAS ALWAYS been an injunction of the Christian faith to heal the sick, and from earliest times the medical art had been a near monopoly of the Church, priests having the privilege of the cure of bodies as well as that of souls. After the injunction by Pope Alexander III (through the Edict of Tours in 1163) surgical proceedings, as they involved the shedding of blood, had perforce been handed over to lay brothers and so found little part in monastic medicine as it evolved after that date.

All large monastic communities had of necessity an infirmary where the sick of their order, and probably from the local population, could be cared for. For this purpose one of their number would generally specialize in medical treatment, and was known as the "infirmarius". Doctors of medicine were very scarce, and their practice still lay mostly amongst the rich, so such men were seldom qualified by a university degree. Treatment largely consisted of the exhibition of holy relics, charms, exhortations, and herbal potions, all of which were considered more effective when administered by a priest on consecrated ground. A favourite potion of the time was known as Hiera Picra (Holy Bitters), and in its usual form contained about fifteen ingredients, which included aloes, mastic, saffron, Indian navel, balsam and assarum. Many other laxative, sedative and stimulating or "tonic" drugs of vegetable origin were known, often grown and used by them, and polypharmacy was the fashion. This entailed the need for an apothecary to tend, store, blend, prepare and dispense the prescriptions; and one of the lay brothers was generally taught this art through apprenticeship to some senior dispenser brother.

After the capture of the Arab Medical School at Salerno by the Normans in 1072, some priests from England were sent there

27

to brush up their knowledge. Later, after the foundation of the
Universities, they were sent first to Paris (1100), then to Bologna
(1113), Montpelier (1181), and Padua (1222). Such a one may
have been the celebrated Brother John Mirfield of St. Bartholomew's Hospital, who about 1387 wrote the *Breviarium Bartholomei*
in which he epitomized the medical knowledge of his time.
We know him to have been apprenticed in his younger days to a
physician, and although it seems that he sometimes practised
outside the hospital walls, there is no record that he ever took a
degree.

In time these monastic infirmaries came to minister also to
the medical needs of most of the poorer residents and itinerant
population, and the medical priests in charge had to be freed by
their superiors from some of their purely religious duties in
order to devote more time to their care of the sick poor. This
need became increasingly evident during the great epidemic of
the Black Death (1348), during which the pressure on the two
chief London hospitals of St. Thomas and St. Bartholomew
became enormous. Half of the population of the City, 20,000
persons, died and many of the monastic staff also.

The Order of Augustine Canons was at this time particularly
well adapted to run the Church's medical service, as the rule of
this order was much lighter in spiritual duties than was that of
the monks. It is for this reason that we find them staffing these
two pioneer City hospitals from a very early period. The first
clause of their rule reads: "Before all, dear Brothers, love God,
and next your neighbour." It is interesting to find that, according to Norman Moore, every Augustinian library contained
during the Middle Ages a copy of the fourth book of the *Liber
Etymologiarum* by St. Isidore, Bishop of Seville, containing a
digest of medical knowledge of the seventh century.

During their early existence City hospitals in this country
were designed as much to provide a shelter from the streets as
for treating the sick, as is exemplified in the preface to a letter
written by Sir Thomas Gresham to the King, in which he
states that these hospitals were "founded of goode devotion by
ancient fathers and endowed with great possessions and rentes
only for the relief, comfort and helping of the poore and impo-
tente people lying in every streete, offending every clene person

passing by the waye with theyre fylthy and nasty savors". St. Bartholomew's was the general hospital which served the northern portion of the City population, while St. Thomas's served the south. The latter, being situated near the point at which the great southern roads from the Cinque Ports and the important cities of Winchester and Canterbury entered London, also had to deal with large numbers of travellers and pilgrims— more especially after the canonization of St. Thomas à Becket and the hospital's change of name in 1215. During the earlier Middle Ages other hospitals of equal contemporary importance existed, such as St. Mary's-without-Bishopsgate, but they have left little record of their activities; while in 1370 there existed over two hundred leper hospitals or Lazar houses throughout the country, although most of these were turned to other purposes during the fifteenth century as a result of the disappearance of true leprosy.

It became obvious to the ecclesiastical authorities towards the end of the thirteenth century that the purely religious side of the Priories must be separated from their infirmary wings, which were now becoming specialized institutions for the care of the sick—hospitals in the modern sense. As early as 1200 the government of both St. Thomas's and St. Bartholomew's became vested in a Master, who although subject to the overall authority of the Prior, appears to have been largely autonomous. Both he and his staff of brethren and sisters were, however, enjoined by the Royal Charter of 1305 (Edward I) to continue to follow the rule of St. Augustine, and to eat together in common.

About this time we learn that the Master of St. Thomas's had as his staff four Augustine Canons and three Canonesses. The hospital had consequently, like the Priory, been accorded the official status of a "mixed convent". It appears that the ground floor of the hospital was taken up with the necessary offices, and that the sick in-patients, who numbered about forty, occupied the "solars"—the upper rooms. They lay at first on piles of rushes or straw mattresses, until beds began to be introduced late in the thirteenth century. It was then thought proper that they should be shared by two and sometimes three patients. Later each bed was provided with a bolster and a sort of canopy, as can be seen on the thirteenth-century seal of the St. Cross Hospital at Winchester.

In addition to the in-patients large crowds of sick and vagrant out-patients were dealt with daily, and the need for more staff grew. Lay brothers and sisters were recruited as porters and extra nurses, and it became the duty of some to visit the great houses to collect "broken meat" with which to supplement the diet of the patients. Some were also trained as assistants to the surgeon and the apothecary. Patients who died were buried in a graveyard within the hospital courtyard.

Rahere, Henry II's Court Jester who had turned Augustine Canon, when he founded St. Bartholomew's in 1123 largely copied the constitution of St. Thomas's—which was then named the Hospital of St. Mary the Virgin at Southwark—making the hospital subordinate to, but separate from, its Priory. He arranged for the care of the patients to be entrusted to four Augustine nuns who slept in a common dormitory and were liable for night calls, and who held their posts for life. A surgeon was appointed about 1308 on the advice of the Guild of Barbers, which had elected a Master for the first time in that year in order to supervise the conduct of surgery and barbery in the City. This man was probably a monastic lay brother, as the appointment to the refounded hospital of three Barber-Surgeons after the dissolution (1549) appears to have created a precedent.

St. Thomas's and St. Bartholomew's continued more or less unchanged until the beginning of the sixteenth century, when the new critical thinking of the Renaissance and its natural child the Reformation began to permeate English life.

That gross irregularities occurred both in the monasteries and in the two hospitals was, by the fifteenth century, common knowledge; an example lying in the long line of venal Masters at St. Thomas's which had culminated in one Richard Mabott, "a filthy and obscene fellow", who was said to keep a concubine within the hospital and who was proved to have been in the habit of selling the church plate and reporting that it had been stolen. This sort of thing helped to provide the excuse which eventually King Henry VIII required to justify dissolution of the foundations and the use of their considerable revenues for his own purposes. As Parsons points out, however: "The evils placed at their doors were more than counterbalanced by a long record of charitable, medical, literary and educational work since Christianity first came to England."

Accordingly, in 1540 both St. Thomas's and St. Bartholomew's hospitals, together with all their possessions, were surrendered. The former remained derelict until 1553 as the King pretended to see an additional cause of offence in this hospital's name, saying of St. Thomas à Becket: "There was nothing in his life whereby he should be called a Saint, but rather a rebel and traitor to his Prince." Parsons, recording its closure, says: "All that was bad about it came to an end; but so did all that was good, and huge numbers of helpless sick poor were now left unrelieved in the streets." Indeed, things got so bad shortly after that London's thoroughfares became blocked with "lazars and the lame", and the King ordered the Lord Mayor to have all these removed and confined. There is no record of where they were sent.

Of St. Bartholomew's we hear also that "the spital was vacant and altogether destitute of a Master, and all fellows and brethren".

AFTER THE DISSOLUTION OF THE MONASTERIES

The Lord Mayor, Sir Thomas Gresham, petitioned the King that the City should now have the governance of these two hospitals, together with Bethlehem, Christ's Hospital and Bridewell, "to bring them into a more decent and convenient ordre". He offered to replace the monks, who in the past had "refreshed, mayntayned and comforted" the inmates, with "phisicians, surgeons and poticaries which shall have stipende and salarie for the sole purpose of healing and curing their infirmities; so that all impotent persons not able to labour shall be relieved, but also that all sturdie beggars not willing to labour shall be punished". The King, who had intended to refound them himself for the care of wounded and diseased soldiers as "the King's Hospitals", as the result of this pressure felt obliged to reconstitute St. Bartholomew's by letters patent under the Great Seal in 1547, and convey it to the Mayoralty partially endowed.

Thomas Vicary was appointed as resident Governor, and was largely responsible for drawing up the famous "Ordre of the

Hospitall of St. Bartholomewes in West Smythfield in London"
(1551), in which the duties and terms of service of all those
associated with the hospital were laid down. This, according to
Price-Thomas, held sway until 1948. It was published "to
inform the public concerning the hospital, and to silence the
wickednesse of reporte".

Edward VI, on his deathbed in 1553, restored St. Thomas's
Hospital and incorporated it in a collective charter with
Christ's Hospital, Bethlehem and Bridewell as "the Royal
Hospitals"; and in 1557 St. Bartholomew's was added to this
group. All these he gave to the City, together with the revenues
of the Palace of the Savoy, decreeing that their governance
should be vested in the Lord Mayor and the Court of Aldermen,
and that the election of the Governors should take place annually
on St. Matthew's Day in Christ's Hospital. In spite of its Royal
title this group seems to represent the first great civic hospital
foundation in this country.

At the first meeting it was decided by the Governors to maintain Christ's Hospital for the purpose for which Edward IV had
founded it in 1247 (with the help of a public subscription)
namely, the maintenance of four hundred orphan children from
the City. Bethlehem ("Bedlam") was assigned for the accommodation of the lunatic poor; and the Palace of Bridewell, which
it is recorded "the Kinge did no longer like on account of the fylthy
stynkyng dytch which runneth alongside of it", was to be used to
segregate all idle rogues of both sexes who needed correction.

Officers and Surgeons

Under this charter seven paid officers were appointed to St.
Bartholomew's and St. Thomas's. These included a chaplain, a
renter clerk, a butler, a porter, a beadle, and a "matrone" who
should have under her strict governance twelve nurses (fifteen
at St. Thomas's). At St. Thomas's there was also to be an
apothecary with "a shoppe under the Matrone's lodging". No
apothecary was officially appointed to St. Bartholomew's until
1571. "There are also to be as in a kynde by themselves iii
experte chirurgeons in the wages of the hospitall, who shall
attend daily." These men were all members of the newly incorporated Barber-Surgeons Company; and it was laid down as

their duty, after dressing each wound, to advise the patient to sin no more, but to thank God for his recovery. They were forbidden to take in private patients, and were officially advised not to admit patients whom they judged to be incurable. Their salary was £15 p.a. and a livery, but they had to provide their own drugs and dressings. At times a bonus was added, and in 1620 it was the King's personal suggestion that their salary be raised to £36 p.a.

Physicians

It was probably on account of the expense involved that no physician was appointed to St. Bartholomew's until 1562, as charitable work by the medical profession was not yet expected. The first was the ill-fated Rodrigez Lopez, the original of Shakespeare's Shylock, who was later to be hanged, drawn and quartered for alleged complicity in a plot to poison Queen Elizabeth. The great William Harvey was elected as physician to the hospital in 1609. A physician, Dr. Palmer, was also appointed to St. Thomas's in 1566 at a salary of £13 6s. 8d., plus £2 for a livery. Both physicians were assigned a house near their respective hospitals at a low rental, and supplied with fuel. In 1649 the salary of the physicians was raised to £40, at which level it stayed until the eighteenth century.

During the Great Plague of 1665 it is sad to record that both the physicians of St Bartholomew's left London for their own safety. The Governors rightly suspended their salaries, diverting some of this towards a bonus for the loyal apothecary, and only one was subsequently re-employed. The physician at St. Thomas's, Dr. Thomas Wharton, however, was granted an honourable augmentation to his arms in appreciation of his devoted services during this time. In 1693 both the physicians and the surgeons were granted extra pay for treating casualties from Marlborough's armies.

Accommodation

Soon after their re-foundation both St. Thomas's and St. Bartholomew's were ordered to "harbor and receave" three hundred inmates; and we hear that St. Bartholomew's was not able to receive a tenth part of those for whom it should provide, "not havyng any place certayn whereyn they may be lodged, cheryshed and refreshed till they be cured". These numbers would probably include the numerous night lodgers, who slept on straw in a special ward and could earn small sums for crushing corn in the treadmill. It was the duty of the hospitaller to admit every in-patient and sign a warrant for the Matron to receive them. We hear that between 1547 and 1552 over eight hundred sick folk were healed in the hospital of St. Bartholomew, and that ninety-two died. An inventory of the former year lists one hundred beds as being in use.

It was usual from about 1560 to give each needy patient a small sum of money on discharge, generally 6d. (mutton and beef cost 1d. a pound); and surgical aids such as wooden legs and trusses, which cost the hospitals an average of 16d., were also generally supplied gratis.

From this time onwards the other old hospitals were mostly used as Almshouses to shelter the poor, and seldom undertook medical or surgical treatment. The exception were the six small hospitals on the outskirts of London known as the Outhouses, which were used to house chronic sick from the Royal hospitals. Each was under the care of a keeper or Master who received 40/0d. p.a., a house and garden, and free fuel. These may have been lazar houses put to a new use.

Both St. Bartholomew's and St. Thomas's had a special ward for the treatment of "the sweat" and other infectious diseases, as well as a "salivating ward" for the treatment of the pox by mercury. After 1630 there was a sharp decline in the purchasing power of money (the Matron at St. Thomas's went bankrupt!), and the Governors were forced to reduce the hospital accommodation to two hundred and forty patients in winter and two hundred and eighty in summer. During the Civil War, however, many wounded soldiers and sailors from the Parliamentary forces were sent for treatment to both hospitals, and we hear of bonus payments for the physicians, surgeons and some of the sisters. In 1650 a limited supply of piped water from the Thames was laid on to St. Bartholomew's at a cost of £6 p.a., to supersede the previous two wells, one of which was contaminated.

Matrons and Sisters

The Matrons' pay was £3 12s. 0d. p.a. in 1560, with the

additions of board wages of 18d. weekly at St. Bartholomew's and 16d. at St. Thomas's. The sisters received 40/od. and similar board wages. Their duties consisted of "ordering" the ten beds in their wards, "keeping them clene and sweete", and "purging and washing their patients' unclene clothes and other thinges". They had to sleep and remain in their wards after 7 p.m. in winter and 9 p.m. in summer, and their leisure time was to be set to some useful and profitable occupation, generally spinning. They had to attend to their patients "in all their griefs and diseases . . . and gyving them their meates and drynkes after the moste honeste and comfortable manner". They were also to be "alway obedient to the Matrone as their chiefe governesse and ruler". In lieu of the erstwhile religious habits they were provided with a dark blue livery to wear. For the sisters' entertainment the Governors at one time authorised payment for "a foole or zany".

By 1566, however, discipline at St. Bartholomew's was at such a low ebb that one of the sisters had to be "corrected" at the whipping post which the Governors had erected in the courtyard for the use of unruly patients; while the Matron had been before them on three occasions on charges of drunkenness. About this time the sisters obtained permission to take their meals in the Matron's room, but until 1586 they had to make their own candles from surplus fat from their meat. It was only in this year also that coals for heating the wards were authorized. Soap had been provided for the first time with which to wash clothes "for their better preservation" in 1557. It was not until 1666 that "assistant Sisters" (nurses) were appointed— and all able patients ordered to help them. It is pleasant to learn that all the sisters stayed at their posts during the Great Plague and were granted bonuses.

The Apothecary

We find the apothecary at St. Bartholomew's Hospital complaining, in rather a modern way, soon after his appointment in 1567, that he was unable to live on his wages although he also served St. Thomas's Hospital in the same capacity. This was no doubt because out of these he had to provide all drugs needed for internal use. This practice ceased at St. Thomas's only in

1684, although at St. Bartholomew's the hospital undertook to pay for drugs after 1613 and the sum subsequently paid to the apothecary became a true salary, possibly at Harvey's instigation. It seems from references in the Minutes of both hospitals that the apothecary also took part in the medical treatment of patients, at any rate in the absence of a physician.

By the beginning of the seventeenth century it became necessary for the apothecary at both hospitals to become resident; and at St. Bartholomew's a shop similar to that at St. Thomas's was built and equipped for him. These men had always been freemen of the Grocers Company until the foundation of the Society of Apothecaries in 1617. They were now members of a professional guild and so their status was augmented. In 1620 the apothecary's salary was raised to £45 at St. Thomas's, and a few years later to £60 p.a. As he still, however, had to find all the drugs for the hospital it became £180 in 1636, "as the beste medicines had not been given owing to the small salary of the apothecary". An "herb woman" was also appointed at £4 p.a. to assist him. By 1693 the apothecary's salary had risen to £250, but all his drugs had to be viewed by the staff twice a year. At the outset of the eighteenth century he was being paid £300 p.a. At St. Bartholomew's the apothecary's responsibility for providing drugs ceased in 1613, and by 1636 his salary was £50 per annum. In 1670 the two apothecaries produced a simplified pharmacopoeia for the use of the five Royal hospitals in which, to simplify prescribing, forty-six official preparations were given names; six pills were specified, as well as a number of ointments, powders, drops and lotions.

Specialization

The employment of outside practitioners, sometimes women, for special purposes dates from 1554, after when many references are made to payments to various outside persons, particularly for the treatment of "scald head, and lepersies"—probably eczema and other skin diseases. This was made a permanent appointment in 1632, and presumably represents the birth of dermatology.

In 1590 it was agreed that the surgeons at the Royal hospitals should be paid extra fees for particular operations, e.g. Moulins, surgeon to both hospitals "for his special skill in lithotomy";

and in 1609 the appointment of an extra surgeon for the stone was authorized for the staff at both St. Bartholomew's and St. Thomas's. Also a presumably non-qualified "bone setter", who received £8 p.a. plus "extras"; this appointment appears to have been regularized later by the appointment of a "surgeon for bone-setting, fractures and dislocations" in 1625.

In 1589 we hear of a practitioner "to cut and cure all wens and ruptures" who was employed at both hospitals at a salary of £4 p.a., and after 1630 this became a duty of the surgeons. In 1612 a lithotomist was appointed to St. Thomas's and soon afterwards to St. Bartholomew's, at a cost of £6 13s. 4d. p.a.; and in 1661 "a surgeon for the lock" was appointed, and a second in 1683. We also find unfavourable reference to the surgeons' apprentices, who evidently sometimes deputized for their chiefs, but who were now forbidden to do so on account of their bad behaviour. Finally we find the Governors making a contract (1666) whereby Elizabeth Bond agrees to kill and clean all the hospitals' beds of bugs at 6/od. per bed; also to clean and kill the bugs in the sisters' room at 40/od. A service of this nature remained necessary until the nineteenth century, when metal beds were introduced.

Running Costs

The actual costs of administration for the two hospitals are difficult to ascertain, as these are not differentiated from those which concern the maintenance of their considerable properties in the City and elsewhere. R. S. Roberts has done considerable research in this field and has given me the following brief estimate based upon the records of St. Thomas's Hospital:

1567—An average of 113 in-patients per week.
    Total expenditure upon the hospital .. about £600. 0. 0.
    Salaries of Physician and Surgeons .. ,,   £70. 0. 0.
    Cost of Apothecary and drugs .. ,,   £40. 0. 0.
Almost a hundred years later the comparable costs were:
1658–9—An average of 174 in-patients per week.
    Total expenditure upon the hospital.. about £2,000. 0. 0.
    Salaries of Physicians and Surgeons .. ,,   £225. 0. 0.
    Cost of Apothecary and drugs .. ,,   £200. 0. 0.
    Non-medical wages .. .. .. ,,   £225. 0. 0.

From this it will be seen that although the salaries and cost of drugs had risen three to five times and the number of patients by fifty per cent, the total expenditure had risen out of proportion to these, and it seems reasonable to conclude that the patients were by the latter period receiving better treatment in every respect.

In spite of the unitary provisions of the original charter the five Royal hospitals gradually came to regard themselves as autonomous units, each being presided over by an elected Treasurer; and after 1587 the statutory annual meeting originally decreed gradually lapsed. Every hospital nominated its own Governors, and merely transmitted their names to the Lord Mayor for confirmation. This quasi-independent status led them to a system of admniistration based upon an efficient system of committees, independent of the Corporation of the City. The aldermen unsuccessfully attempted on several occasions to reassert their supremacy, notably in 1603 after allegations of grave misuse of funds had been made, with particular reference to the Governors of Bridewell.

As influential laymen began to interest themselves in the affairs of the hospitals, so national politics began to assume importance, St. Bartholomew's remaining obstinately Tory, whilst St. Thomas's was favoured by the more powerful Whig influence until the eighteenth century. During the Civil War the City had supported the Parliamentary cause, and the hospitals had followed its lead. In spite of this Charles II, after his restoration, confirmed their charters.

With the onset of monetary inflation after 1620 the hospitals began to run into debt, and the large donations with which the Governors saved the situation probably gave birth to the ideology of public philanthropy which was to flower during the following century. The Great Fire of London exacerbated matters by destroying the bulk of the City property on which the revenues of the hospitals depended, and it became indeed hard for them to make ends meet. The Lord Mayor invited the charitable assistance of the public, and imposed a levy upon the great City Companies.

During the Civil and Dutch Wars the hospitals had been called upon to treat the bulk of the Parliamentary casualties, particularly the wounded "mariners and sea-soldiers", for which the Commissioners of the Navy gave a subsidy of 2d. per head, which they doubled in 1683. It was in this year also that a Royal Commission was appointed which laid down a new diet scale, which included a daily allowance of 10 oz. bread, meat four times a week, 2 oz. butter between May and October, cheese, and 1 quart of beer at all but St. Thomas's where the ration was 3 pts.; and a milk pudding twice a week (this is the first mention of milk consumption in hospitals).

In 1699 the City at last succeeded in regaining a modified degree of control, and an order from the Court of Aldermen was read in each hospital stating that "this Court being resolved to restore the government of these hospitals to their ancient constitution . . . agreed and ordered that for the future no person shall be elected a Governor of any that was not a free-man of the City, and that no-one other than the Aldermen should be admitted Governor of any more than one of the said hospitals."

Summary

The rise of public hospitals did little to advance the science of medicine during the period before 1700 recorded here. After the dissolution of the monasteries and during the period of the Reformation this country was so busy organizing its first medical institutions and establishing those rules of practice which were long overdue, that its intelligentsia were largely left behind by those on the Continent, where they were already making those drastic revaluations of long established tenets in medical theory which eventually led to medical science as we know it. These great advances in philosophical thought and science had scarcely begun to affect medical and surgical practice here by 1700. Nevertheless as regards hospital practice, several of the infectious and other diseases had been differentiated, and leprosy, the sweating sickness and bubonic plague had disappeared. As regards treatment some fresh air was now allowed into the sickroom, and a limited supply of piped water had become available. Quinine (bark) and iron were used medicinally in addition to the traditional herbal remedies, and mercury for syphilis. Amputations were often performed by the flap operation, and lithotomy had become a special branch of surgery. By the end of the seventeenth century patients in hospital were rather more comfortable and warm than they had been, the diet was good and on a generous scale, and each had a bed to himself. They were more adequately nursed, and decently buried.

It was during this period that the sense of public and personal responsibility for the proper treatment of the sick poor developed. Shortly before the end of the sixteenth century we find the Treasurer and two of the Governors in each of the Royal hospitals personally visiting the wards each month, and often admonishing the staff for negligence. A "dole" for maintenance was given also to most patients on their discharge. All this was the solid beginning of better things.

Finally, we can perhaps see the origins of the medical schools in the regulated employment and teaching of the surgeons' dressers and apprentices after the incorporation of the Barber-Surgeons Company in 1540. These methods of practical instruction remained beneath the dignity of physicians, however, for many years to come, for they were University graduates, learned men, whom tradition allowed to impart their knowledge only to students in recognized academic centres, the Universities.

BIBLIOGRAPHY

COPEMAN, W. S. C. (1960). *Doctors and Disease in Tudor Times*, London, Dawsons.

Memoranda, References and Documents relating to the Royal Hospitals of the City of London, 1836.

MOORE, NORMAN (1918). *The History of St. Bartholomew's Hospital*, London, Pearson, vol. I.

PARSONS, F. G. (1932). *The History of St. Thomas's Hospital*, London, Methuen, vol. I.

ROBERTS, R. S. Personal Communication.

THOMAS, C. PRICE (1962). Vicary amongst his contemporaries, *Ann. roy Coll. Surg. Engl.*, **30**, 37.

The Hospital Movement of the Eighteenth Century and its Development

W. H. McMENEMEY

"The devotion of life, or fortune, to the succour of the poor, is a height of virtue, to which humanity has never risen by its own power."

Samuel Johnson, 1758

THE VOLUNTARY HOSPITAL movement of the eighteenth century is generally regarded as a spontaneous expression of popular charity in an age which brought sudden and unwonted prosperity for a favoured few and a precarious existence for the artisan, leaving but squalor and misery for the unskilled and the unemployed. In the eyes of those who gave and of those who received, the support of hospitals and infirmaries was the embodiment of the Christian way of life.

Throughout thirteen or more silent centuries, the pilgrim, the wayfarer, the pauper and the sick had counted on the hospitality of abbots and friars. The Act of Supremacy in 1534 and its aftermath interrupted the natural evolution of our hospitals, but the Reformation appears to have had its effect also on hospitals in countries which still cherished their link with Rome. Nevertheless, by the end of the seventeenth century, England in the matter of caring for the sick poor seems to have lagged behind her neighbours and in particular France. Thus the charitable movement which in the latter half of the eighteenth century was to bring a measure of glory to our name was rendered spectacular because of our initial backwardness. If this apparent surge of goodwill and generosity gained rapid momentum it was because in the humane matter of caring for the sick there was in truth an unconscionable gap to fill.

The Act of 1601 for the Relief of the Poor (43 Eliz. cap 2) had aimed at inculcating discipline and self-respect into the disheartened poor and effecting an overall economy for the

benefit of the ratepayer: the basic idea however was doubtless
dictated by common humanity and perhaps in part by a post-
Reformation conscience. But the relief was strictly for parish-
ioners, and for those who sought work elsewhere there was not
even outdoor relief. Many had urged that work should be
found for the unemployed poor[1,2,3,4] and some schemes, as for
instance that of Cornelius for the establishment of common-
wealths, had envisaged medical care within the community.
Yet, we find Bishop Gilbert Burnet suggesting in 1708, at a
time when he thought his own end was nigh, that the Act
which charged every parish with the responsibility of maintaining its own poor should be reviewed, if not taken away, as
it encouraged the idle and the lazy. No such legislation had
been necessary in Scotland or Holland so why, he asked, was
it needed in England?[5]

It was not until the year 1722 that parishes were enjoined
by Act of Parliament to provide workhouses for their paupers:
to Bristol goes the credit for pioneering the scheme in 1696.
Before the reign of Queen Anne, there seems to have been little
attempt to classify the poor and to segregate the sick from the
fit. This would not have been easy, because the unemployed,
the unemployable and the vagrants were ignorant and often
verminous, usually undernourished and sometimes genuinely
sick. Disease must often have been overlooked in the overall
wretchedness of poverty. Richard Kidder, for instance, recommended to prospective donors five special objects of charity,
namely, diligent and industrious housekeepers, widows and the
fatherless, prisoners and especially debtors, slaves and finally
children in need of schooling.[6] He makes no mention of the sick.

After the Reformation religious hospitals in other Protestant
countries were mostly municipalized, in much the same way as
had happened at St. Bartholomew's and St. Thomas's hospitals. Indeed the same trend was apparent in Roman Catholic
countries. However the *Grand Bureau Général de l'Aumone des
Pauvres*, created by Francis I in 1544, was a more comprehensive scheme* than anything that was possible in England

* The edict of 1544 in effect strengthened a movement towards the control
of ecclesiastical hospitals by municipalities which had followed a decision taken in
the year 1505.

because France already had a greater number of hospitals, some of which had been established along the route of the crusaders, and others resulting from the endeavours of numerous religious orders. She had, too, to reckon with a multitude of "lepers", and the human tragedies of the Hundred Years War.

By the end of the seventeenth century this trend was well established in many countries of Europe but not in England. Under the guidance of Richelieu and Mazarin, France had prospered and this good epoch continued throughout the reign of Louis XIV. A visitor to France at that time would surely have been impressed by the facilities offered to the sick poor. Where in England was the equivalent of the Hôtel Dieu in Paris, already copied in Quebec (1637) and Montreal (1644)? But England had had to contend with a civil war and the uncertainties of the Commonwealth, an Irish rebellion, the plague, the Great Fire and the risings of Monmouth and Argyll. However, with the Restoration there came a social and cultural renaissance soon to be followed by an economic boom. Charles II requested his cousin Louis XIV to send particulars of the Hôtel Royal des Invalides[7] because he was envisaging a similar institution in London. These were the days of Anthony Hornbeck, the pioneer of the reforming society movement, and of Richard Kidder who had bidden his flock to visit the sick and personally dress their wounds, failing which they must content themselves by supporting good causes.[6] Soon there was an awakening of the public conscience to the need for more eleemosynary organizations to care for the poor. With the revocation of the Edict of Nantes in 1685 came the Huguenot refugees and in the year 1709 Lutheran refugees from the Palatinate. The Charitable Corporation was instituted in 1707.

THE EARLY VOLUNTARY HOSPITALS IN LONDON

The Treaty of Utrecht which in 1713 followed the expensive victories of Marlborough in the War of the Spanish Succession presaged a new age of prosperity. Thomas Guy was not the first to appreciate the need to augment the slender accommodation for the sick poor in London, whither both labourers and refugees were attracted, but he was the first to be able to finance such a venture and he lived to see the roof on his elegant building. Some others who were fortunate in their joint stock investments doubtless did likewise, for many small charities dated from this time: these were mostly residential hospitals for the aged. Joseph Addison in 1713 spoke of the need for a Foundling Hospital in London[8] but he had died before the benevolent Thomas Coram came to live there.

Thomas Guy, who was a friend of Dr. Richard Mead, had since the year 1705 been a governor of St. Thomas's Hospital and so was familiar with the problems of caring for the sick. He may have been influenced in his thinking by John Bellers, a Quaker who in 1714 had calculated that in England half of the deaths were probably preventable and that of the million or so who each year fell sick, three-quarters of them could not afford treatment. He advocated a state-supported service with hospitals at or near London, with one for "each capital distemper". In these hospitals clinical data, including the pulse, would be studied and, for the better information of the physicians, post-mortem examinations would be carried out. One of these hospitals would be under the care of the Queen's physicians to admit any patient suffering from an infirmity concurrently afflicting the Sovereign. In this way the medical advisers would be capable of prescribing for her Majesty "with the less Hazard of Mistaking". This far-sighted reformer wished to see "a Publick Laboratory" wherein blood, urine and saliva in every disease and age might be "chymically examined in the Texture, Quality and Tincture; and also by Microscopes, Air Pump, Hidrostatick, as well as by every sort of Drug, Mineral and Metal; as Spa water is tried by Gauls". He regarded it as imperative that there should be at least one hospital in each university town. It was impossible to secure a body for dissection at Oxford, he related, because "the Mob are so Mutinous to prevent them having one".[9] It is interesting that this was written in the year of Radcliffe's death. Addenbrooke died in 1719, and so he may have had an opportunity to ponder over the words of Bellers.

There was the example too of the munificence of M. de Gastigny who was once Master of the Buckhounds to the Prince of Orange. On his death in 1708 he bequeathed £1,000 for a hospital for poor French Protestants and their descendants in Great Britain.[10] It was opened in Bath Street, St. Luke's, in 1716 as a hospice for eighty inmates but by 1736 additional buildings had brought this number up to two hundred and thirty, to include many with minds disordered as a consequence of the tortures and privations they had suffered in France. Although it was more in the nature of a residential hospital for the elderly they probably admitted invalids because rule XVI states that the house visitors shall inquire "whether among the Poor, there may not be some who having been taken into the Hospital as sick in body and Disordered in Mind, are so well recovered as to be fit to be discharged". It differed from the new voluntary hospitals, however, in that the physician and surgeon as well as the apothecary were paid for their services.

Finally there was the example of the Westminster Hospital, founded in 1719 and opened in Petty France in 1720:[11] four years later, and a year before Guy's Hospital was opened for the reception of patients, it was moved to Caxton Street. Henry Hoare, sometimes known as "Good Henry", the banker, who along with others was instrumental in inaugurating it had attempted to do so three years earlier. Possibly it was a lack of decision as to the nature of the charity they wished to see established in the parish of St. Margaret's that had caused the earlier failure, and it may well have been the example of Thomas Guy's munificence as a governor of St. Thomas's Hospital which finally determined them on their plan.

In their public appeal the founders spoke of the need in those employed in the care of the poor for a "revival of the True Christian Spirit of Justice and Charity" as well as a voluntary effort on the part of others. It is not clear if their dissatisfaction with the conduct of churchwardens and overseers was local to Westminster or if a general callousness was noticeable throughout the country. It has been said that the advent of the Hanoverian dynasty coincided with a lowering of moral tone and a wave of religious indifference seldom surpassed, and this may have accounted for any complacency noted in those concerned with the management of the Poor Law. Dissatisfaction was sometimes voiced too over the management of the private charities and in the year 1728 James Oglethorpe, after ventilating his complaint over the sorry state of the Fleet prison, was duly appointed chairman of a Parliamentary Committee of Enquiry.[12]

St. George's Hospital was the next to appear after Guy's. It was inaugurated by a splinter group of the governors of the Westminster Infirmary following a difference of opinion in 1733 over the quality and prices of the drugs and certain other alleged abuses.[13,14] We learn that both St. George's Hospital and "the Infirmary" were supported by the public with "eagerness and alacrity".[15] By now there was a new building at St. Thomas's Hospital and a subscription for extensions was being opened at St. Bartholomew's Hospital.

The London Hospital, first opened in Featherstone Street near the Dog Bar on 3rd November 1740, was designed by John Harrison the surgeon and his co-founders to help, in particular, the manufacturers and merchant seamen together with their families. The management excluded from admission the dying, children under seven, and all who had the smallpox, the itch, scald head or leprosy. Six months later the hospital was moved to Prescott Street in Goodman's Fields.

THE SPREAD TO THE PROVINCES

The voluntary hospital movement spread early to the provinces, Winchester and Bristol claiming pride of place. Winchester was the first and the hospital owed its origin to the devoted labours of Alured Clarke, D.D., prebend of the cathedral since 1723. At that time Winchester was a small market town with no established industries. Clarke advanced the proposal on 22nd May 1736,[16] the first subscription papers were ready for distribution on 6th August and with contributions still short of £600 they were able on 18th October 1736 to admit the first patient.* On the following day he wrote to his friend Mrs. Clayton, "Yesterday, we opened our County Hospital with a very fine appearance of Gentlemen, who all did me the Honour to make part of my Audience at Church".[17] He promised to send her a copy of his sermon.[18]

---

*I am grateful to Miss H. Moore, of the Royal Hampshire County Hospital, Winchester, for confirming this fact from the Minute Book.

By 20th April 1737 the doctors had "cured" sixty-nine of the 176 patients admitted and seventy-five remained in the house. The founders, in a prospectus prepared by Clarke, believed that there was a greater case for an infirmary within their county than even in London "where every other help is always at hand".[16] They had set out to conduct the charity in as unexceptionable a way as could be expected "from Human Things". In some of the reports no less than sixteen reasons are advanced in support of the scheme and they include the advantages to the patients, the doctors and the ratepayers in centralizing the medical care of the sick. The patients were assured of an ordered life, neat surroundings, careful treatment and a diet which was simple and regular: there was too the inestimable benefit to everybody of religious instruction. Their policy in fact was to instruct the ignorant and reclaim the bad, while treatment of the physical disability was being carried out. By collecting these unfortunates under one roof the promoters of the charity believed that door-to-door vagrants would be discouraged in their tiresome activities and so too would be the quacks. The rates also would be lowered.

It is clear that Dr. Clarke was not without his critics and many objections were voiced against his well-meaning plan. It was even argued that the Infirmary would attract vagrants into the town: a workhouse was wanted, not an infirmary, and this was now permissive under the Act of 1722. But Clarke did not think this would suffice because although medicines were dispensed in some workhouses, it was never on the advice of physicians. He thought that there could be no stronger argument in favour of an infirmary than the fact that there was already a law to provide for the building of workhouses. Let them, he implored, at any rate make the experiment. If Parliament were ever to devise a better provision for the sick, then their public infirmary would cease to exist or would become part of it.

Clarke won the day and the governors ran this hospital for 210 years. Needless to say this learned divine had the ready support of the faculty in Winchester and so Dr. Browne Langrish, Dr. James Welch and Mr. Berrington King had the honour to become the pioneer hospital doctors of the provinces.

In the eighteenth century the higher ranks of the clergy had better opportunities than most to travel, and so to observe and make comparisons. Alured Clarke for instance in 1731 was installed prebend of Westminster where he would learn of the success of, and doubtless see for himself, the hospitals in Westminster and at Hyde Park Corner.* In November of the following year after delivering a sermon in Winchester he had an alarming haemoptysis and his house quickly filled with physicians and apothecaries. "My doctors", he subsequently wrote to Mrs. Clayton, "thought it the very stroke of Death", and he proceeded to describe his own feelings at the time. Part of a lengthy convalescence was spent in Bath and part in Bristol, but he was in London again before taking up residence in Winchester in the autumn of 1734. It seems not unlikely that Winchester's pride of place in the provinces as the pioneer hospital centre depended upon Alured Clarke's residence in Kensington Square and his personal experience of a grave illness. The sudden change from health to "an immediate Hazard of losing one's life" had doubtless left its mark on him.

Apart from local opposition the promoters of charities had to contend with the views of those members of the legislature who, often after careful consideration of all the facts and without being in any way callous, were clearly of the same mind as Bishop Burnet and others who had called for a tightening up of parochial relief. Thus in the reply on the Mortmain Bill of 1736 in the House of Lords it was stated:

> ". . . if you give a man any hopes of being well provided for in his old age or sickness, or of having his children educated, and his friends relieved . . . without putting him to any expense, I believe there is not one of a hundred will either labour so hard or live so frugally as he would otherwise have done."

The hospitals, this speaker thought, were themselves blameworthy, for "the custom of going thither to them upon every emergency is become so frequent that no contempt or ignominy attends it". It was not because there was insufficient public money for all charitable purposes that hospitals had been set

---

* The Winchester Infirmary rules, as Clarke explained, were based on those of St. George's Hospital.

up, and so, he believed, it must have been for some other cause. The number, he said, had increased prodigiously in the last century, and he spoke rather pointedly on the subject of governors and their privileges.

However, Alured Clarke, and others like him who refused to be deterred, knew what this other cause was. In 1741 this sick and failing man was elected dean of Exeter and within nine months was calling for an infirmary of 160 beds in that city. Three weeks later he preached on behalf of the Exeter Charity Schools and in the preface of the published version tells with a sad heart of the pains taken by some to prevent the execution of any good design by presenting its possible inconveniences in the very worst light.[19] He died in 1742 and Jeremiah Miller, in an anniversary sermon before the governors of the hospital, a few years later when they prided themselves on a new building, paid tribute to the memory of their charitable founder.* The hospital, he said, "now raised its Decent Head among the Publick buildings, and is become an ornament to our city, an honour to our county and a most extensive benefit to both."[20]

Jeremiah Miller was able to boast of the happiness which reigned in the Devon and Exeter Infirmary, uniting as it did men differing from each other in religious principles and private opinion. The same could hardly have been said of the early days of the General Infirmary at Bath where the callous behaviour of Archibald Cleland in his role as gynaecologist led to his dismissal and to undesirable publicity for the young charity. Cleland accused Dr. William Oliver, commonly regarded as the principal founder, and others of backbiting and calumny[21] but the governors vindicated their decision.[22] The objects of a hospital charity, they said, were helpless and liable to every kind of ill-treatment; therefore it was their duty to protect them.

The story of this hospital is unusual because an enactment had permitted "the diseased and impotent poor" of Britain to have free access to the baths. This Act expired in 1714 but the

---

* Alured Clarke was for long remembered as a pioneer of the voluntary hospital movement. The sermon he preached on the opening day of the Winchester Infirmary appeared in a third edition in 1769 and was printed in Norwich where it was hoped there would soon be a similar institution (actually founded in 1771).

"Beggars of Bath", as they were called, still continued to arrive. In 1716 Lady Elizabeth Hastings and Henry Hoare* proposed the founding of a hospital to cater for these poor unfortunates but subscriptions were not officially opened until 1723, Richard Nash, "the arbiter of fashionable taste", being an indefatigable collector on their behalf. There seems to have been difficulty in finding an appropriate site for this hospital but when the Act of 1737 for the suppression of playhouses was passed the trustees bought the playhouse at Bath together with adjoining property. Because it was the intention of the governors to open this hospital to all deserving cases in the three kingdoms incorporation was immediately sought and in 1739 obtained, but the premises were not opened until 18th May 1742. Prospective patients had to provide a description of their case written by a physician or a "Person of Skill". On admission they had to produce a certificate of poverty from their parish and £3 caution money as a contingency against return journey or funeral, whichever it should happen to be.[23]

Although Winchester was the first provincial town to establish an infirmary, Northampton has some claim to priority, the idea of county infirmaries having been put forward in 1731 by John Rushworth, a local practitioner.[24] He thought Parliament should be asked to encourage the establishment of such institutions throughout the county and as a measure of his sincerity offered £50 should others agree to support his plan in Northampton. It was left to the elderly Dr. Philip Doddridge, the nonconformist divine, and Dr. James Stonhouse, a young physician, to propose the scheme formally in July 1743, and some weeks later Doddridge preached on behalf of the proposed charity.[25] Although subscriptions totalled no more than £600, they had by December acquired a home at a cost of £750, the special fund for its purchase being headed jointly by the Rev. Dr. Richard Newton, founder of Hertford College, Oxford, and the Earl of Northampton, who each subscribed £100. The hospital with forty beds was opened on 25th March 1744 and in a sermon preached four days later in the parish church of All

---

* Presumably "Good Henry" Hoare, the founder of the Westminster Infirmary. In 1720 he purchased the Stourton estate in Wiltshire (see *Hoare's Bank 1672–1955*, London, 1955, p. 34) and so would not be far from Bath.

Saints, Dr. Richard Grey, prebend of St. Paul's, asserted that its government and direction were in the hands of men of character and fortune.[26] He reminded his congregation and readers that the principle of voluntary hospitals was economically sound because the cost of supporting patients therein was only a fraction of what it would be in their homes: he quoted a figure of "probably a tenth".

In the establishment of this Infirmary Stanford gives equal credit to Doddridge and Stonhouse, saying each without the other would probably not have succeeded.[27] Job Orton tells of Doddridge's real devotion to the cause[28] and of the assiduous way he studied the yearly reports from Winchester, Bath, Exeter, York, Bristol, London and Westminster. "He often reflected", wrote Orton, "with great satisfaction on the pains he had taken to establish this charity."

Doddridge moved his Dissenting Academy from Market Harborough to Northampton in December 1729 and in 1737 founded a charity school. W. P. Courtney[29] is clearly of the opinion that Stonhouse was the inspirer of the venture and so also is the anonymous writer of his biography.[30] Educated at Winchester, St. John's College, Oxford and St. Thomas's Hospital, Stonhouse later visited hospitals in Paris and elsewhere and, after one year in Coventry, moved to Northampton in April 1743, where he was remarkably successful in practice. Within four months of his arrival the plan for the Infirmary was advanced. It was said that he drew up the statutes, and although this has been denied it seems not unlikely for he claimed to have drawn up several of the annual reports, and he is believed to have compiled (in 1766) the statutes of the Salisbury Infirmary in whose cause he preached in 1771. Stonhouse had been greatly influenced by Doddridge who quickly converted him from atheism. In course of time he became ordained before finally succeeding to a baronetcy. The partnership of Doddridge and Stonhouse in this venture to set up a hospital proved entirely effective. It is of interest however to note that Doddridge once wrote of Stonhouse's work for the Infirmary "Dr. Stonhouse will hardly do anything without me"[25] and this is in line with the viewpoint of Stanford.[27]

The County Infirmary at York was the next after Winchester,

Bristol and Bath and owed its foundation in 1740 to the foresight of Marmaduke Fothergill. It was opened in the same year and therefore takes precedence over Bath in that respect. In the year 1809 it was known as the Public Hospital for Diseased Poor in the County of York.[31]

The story of these pioneer county infirmaries is often centred on individuals who were either members of the medical profession or prominent divines. An indefatigable worker in the cause of hospitals was Isaac Maddox[32,33] who was translated from the bishopric of St. Asaph to Worcester in November 1743, although his primary visitation was delayed until July 1745. He consulted Doddridge—whose wife came from Worcester—about the possibility of opening an infirmary in his new diocese, and found John Wall and others of the faculty at Worcester ready to support him. The idea was formally promulgated at the Summer Assizes in 1745 in a sermon, no copy of which has survived. Maddox was also president of the Smallpox Hospital* and at the London Hospital delivered the first anniversary sermon. He advised the governors to abandon the decrepit and costly premises in Prescott Street and in return for this sensible advice was voted chairman of the new building fund.[34]

Shrewsbury Infirmary, founded in 1745, was opened on 25th April 1747 and had as its first treasurer William Tayleur. Here again we can see the influence of the clergy in the establishment of a hospital, for Shrewsbury was the birthplace of the generous Job Orton who had worked with Philip Doddridge in Northampton from 1734 till the time when he succeeded at the High Street Chapel in Shrewsbury in the autumn of 1741. It was here that he received Presbyterian ordination four years later. Orton played a big part in organizing this Infirmary. The founders were fortunate in being able to make use of a mansion house originally intended for Corbet Kynaston, but in a guide

---

* This opened as two small houses not far apart, the one in Old Street Road and the other in Cold Bath Fields, in 1746. The first was reserved for persons being prepared for variolation, the second for patients with smallpox and those whose inoculations had taken. (See *An Account of the Rise, Progress and State of the Hospital for the Smallpox and Inoculation from its first Institution on 26th September, 1746 to 31st December, 1753*, London, 1754; also *A Historical Note on the Prevention of Smallpox in England and the Foundation of the Government Lymph Establishment* by J. R. Hutchinson, Ministry of Health Report for year ended 31.3.46, London, 1947, p. 110.)

book for 1809 more lines are devoted to the House of Industry which seems to have been a special source of pride to Salopians. This had its own infirmary and "a fever room" but we read that surgical cases were sent to the County Infirmary. The infirmaries at Shrewsbury, Northampton and Worcester were all instituted at a time of great uncertainty and potential danger occasioned by the Jacobite rising of 1745.

It is not surprising that of the larger cities Bristol should so soon have followed London. The large overseas trade made such an institution desirable and it has been said that the scheme was well supported by those who had an interest in manning the slavers. Subscriptions were opened on 22nd November 1736 and a conveyance of property was obtained in April 1737; they were ready for out-patients on the 20th June and for in-patients in the latter end of the year. Dr. John Bonython, then aged forty-one, appears to have been the principal promoter.[35]

Liverpool was the next of the seaports to call for an infirmary and it had a special problem because of the slave-trade and a steady influx of immigrants from Ireland, later to reach alarming proportions. This hospital, opened in 1749, had no restriction on selection of patients.

These then were the first of the voluntary hospitals to be established in England, and in the decade after 1745 several others were founded. The movement continued to spread through all major towns and finally to the peripherally placed towns in the shires. Promoters of new hospitals continued to stress the advantages of having many patients under the same roof, both on the score of economy and of the furtherance of the art and science of medicine. Hallifax[36] predicted that the voluntary hospitals would supplement the inadequate facilities of universities in the teaching of students. The profession was praised for its untiring efforts by such men as Secker[37] and Adams.[38]

HOSPITALS IN THE OTHER TWO KINGDOMS

In Scotland practitioners of medicine were foremost in the clamour for hospitals. John Monro, probably abetted by his son, Alexander *primus*, about the year 1721, is believed to have been the author of an anonymous pamphlet calling for a hospital wherein the art of medicine could be pursued while at the same time incapacitated workmen could be reclaimed for the good of the community.[39] The Royal College of Physicians of Edinburgh had, in the year 1682, detailed two of their number to attend the sick poor and in 1725 the fellows of the College launched an appeal for an infirmary. The Little Hospital in Robertson's Close, the first in Scotland, was opened in 1729. An important step in the establishment of a practical school of medicine was made when five years earlier four Scots who had returned from training in Leyden purchased a house as a chemical laboratory.

The Faculty in Glasgow were active too in the management of the Town's Hospital founded in 1733. The Infirmary at Aberdeen, which had but six beds when it opened in 1742, was a medical school from the start for it was regularly visited by the Regius Professor of Medicine and his students.

In Ireland the situation had been a little different because the British Army with its own medical service had been stationed there for many years. It appears that the corporation of Dublin had in mind to establish a hospital in 1699 and four years later the Irish Parliament passed an Act for the erection of a workhouse[40], on the same lines presumably as the Bristol Act of 1696. The position in Dublin had been rendered critical on account of a remarkable increase in population in the first quarter of the century, and by 1730 part of the workhouse had had to be set aside as a foundling hospital.

Grizel Steevens, who held money in trust from her deceased twin brother Richard Steevens for the building of a hospital for "the curable sick and wounded" encouraged the trustees in their efforts to see her brother's wish materialized, but although proceedings began in 1710 it was not until the year 1733 that it was finally opened[41]: it could well have been the first of the voluntary hospitals in the three kingdoms. The Charitable Infirmary in Cook Street, which owed its origin to the goodwill of six surgeons, anticipated the Steevens Hospital by five years although it was later in conception. Mercer's Hospital dates from a bequest in 1734.

The Irish Parliament in 1765 passed an Act (Geo. III 3, c. 20) to provide "receptacles" for the infirm and diseased poor in many of the larger towns in the form of public infirmaries or hospitals, as "a means of restoring the health and preserving the lives of his Majesty's subjects, of promoting labour and industry and of encouraging the manufactures". These were essentially rate-aided institutions but anyone wishing to contribute twenty guineas to any particular one of them was rewarded with a governorship. The surgeons and physicians were to be paid for their services to an amount not exceeding 100 guineas per annum and the three voluntary hospitals in Dublin were each to be allowed £150 out of the public money. Thus in Ireland the pattern tended to be one half-way between the true voluntary and the rate-supported institutions, whereas in England and Scotland a voluntary hospital was one maintained entirely by voluntary subscribers and attended by the consultants free of charge.

Eighteenth-century institutions for the infirm and the sick were usually called infirmaries if the community already possessed a charitable hospital for the aged. In some towns, especially those that acquired their voluntary hospital in the nineteenth century, the term "infirmary" was reserved for the poor law hospital and so was somewhat derogatory.

THE HOSPITALS AND THE PUBLIC

In spite of the supposed decline in religious zeal in the reign of George I there seems to have been no decrease in philanthropy and new voluntary hospitals continued to appear. There had been a great increase in foreign trade and under Walpole's ministry merchants prospered in an era of peace which lasted for a quarter of a century. The rich became very rich, profligate and often indeed reckless in pursuance of their pleasurable ideals. Gaming and gambling were popular and whisky and gin now appeared in the shops, the latter soon to well-nigh undermine the moral fibre of the country, as had French brandy a century earlier. But the poor remained poor and misery abounded.

The basis of charity is pity and a desire to help the less fortunate. A charitable act may however be dictated by ulterior motives and it often was. A subscriber to a hospital was in a privileged position because he acquired prestige in the eyes of his neighbours, his employees and his tradesmen. The right of admission to hospital was virtually in his gift and he received an excellent return for his guinea. His sick servants need never be on his hands. To segregate those with contagious or otherwise unpleasant diseases was only common sense. The subscriber to the Smallpox Hospital was in fact lessening his own chance of falling victim to the disease as well as that of all other Londoners, although this view appears not to have been shared, as Bishop Maddox soon learned, by those who lived close to it. Insurance companies were in vogue and what better insurance scheme was there than a hospital? It would be uncharitable of us to dwell unduly on these less worthy motives for supporting hospitals, but while not subscribing to the view that the seemingly worthy hospital movement was activated by panic rather than by piety it is likely that the hand that dispensed the guineas was often motivated by common sense. A man who subscribed five guineas could become a vice president and figure at the head of a printed list along with the nobility and landowners. Conscience also played a part and many a gambler and society miscreant found solace in channelling part of his ill-gotten gains to the cause of the sick poor. In the words of St. Peter, "Charity shall cover the Multitude of Sins" (1 Peter iv, 8). But Anthony Highmore (1814) was oblivious to all mundane considerations carried away by altruism and patriotism he asserted that

> "The English . . . are . . . the most devoted to sympathy and commiseration, most tenderly alive to the softest impression of every affection, most given to those emotions which flow from disinterested pity and concern . . . their courage is national instinct, and their charity is national refinement."[44]

Then there was the genuine feeling of gratification and pride when governors were acquainted with the annual statistics. Here was opportunity for hospitals to compete with each other. The governors of Winchester Infirmary boasted of having cured a paralytic who had lost the use of his leg for several years also of the recovery of a patient who had been totally blind in one eye, while at Exeter there was the story of the miraculous recovery of two men so far gone as to be admitted in open coffins.

Poverty was still regarded as more in the nature of a sin than a misfortune and the charitably minded were still on the look-out for the "sturdy beggar" of Elizabethan days* who was distinguished from the other poor by the severity of the punishments to which he was liable. Disease was commonly believed to be a visitation of God for undisclosed wrongs against His cause. This is to be noted in the writings of, among others, Bishop Maddox.[32,33,34] His remarkable success as a preacher of charity sermons was due partly to first-hand knowledge of poverty and partly to the fear he instilled into his congregations. Those who failed to subscribe to the cause he was pleading should think ahead to the Day of Judgement. How then would they find themselves placed? Were they likely to get through that all-important door? Here indeed was an insurance scheme they could ill afford to neglect, and many a simple soul was only too grateful to load up the plate. Dr. Stonhouse in his "friendly Letter to a Patient just admitted into an Infirmary"[42] bade his reader remember that he was both a sick man and a poor man, his twofold affliction coming from the Hand of God who nevertheless had been activated by considerations of mercy. Stonhouse, who at that time was not yet ordained, wished to see joined together the "happy purposes of a Reformatory with those of an Infirmary". The world, he thought, was from all practical points of view one great infirmary and it was sin that had forced the compassionate Father of men to have recourse to smarting rods, "to humble and reform his *thoughtless, foolish, rebellious* children". The patient, he said, must examine his conscience and confess his failings. Perhaps he had "forced a way through the fence of Sabbath breaking to a thousand other transgressions?" When he saw a corpse lying in the next bed he should, said Stonhouse, ponder on the awful lesson to be learnt; and then he added in a footnote that although it was customary to have dead houses in infirmaries, "so long as the spectacle is before their Eyes, it is so affecting that I would not but think fit to touch upon it".

It is perhaps understandable that certain diseases were regarded as the very embodiment of sin, and so we find those who were opposing the formation of the Lock Hospital being reminded that infants and children were the innocent victims

---

* The Act of 1744 (17 Geo. II, c. 5) recognized a class of "incorrigible rogue".

of venereal disease. However, it was the Samaritan's privilege "to restore to virtue and to religion those votaries whom pleasure has seduced, or villainy betrayed".[43] Richard Kidder had taken this view when he wrote in 1676 "when my poor Brother is falled into the Ditch, I do not think myself obliged to represent how many ways there are of falling in, but to do my utmost towards lifting him out".[6] Even lying-in charities had their critics because, it was argued, the knowledge that such places existed might encourage promiscuity. Most diseases in fact were thought to be due to "immoderate passions and vicious indulgence"[43] and who are we to say that this generalization does not hold even today? Nevertheless it was realized that the labourer was peculiarly liable to disease because of his frequent exposure to all weathers, his liability to injuries, his cold and crowded dwelling, his poverty and often his unhealthy and sedentary employment. Moreover, he had the anxiety of having at all times to maintain his wife and family, and so he was reluctant to admit that he was too ill to work. The poor man when sick had little to soften his lot save the comfort of knowing that he was exempt from the solicitudes attendant on the disposal of property.[43] Today we are perhaps more knowledgeable concerning the causation of poverty than we are of the aetiology of disease. As late as the year 1814 we find Anthony Highmore philosophizing as to the reason for existence in society of both rich and poor, and with that complete lack of economic insight which seems to have characterized all but the few in his day, concluding that it was due "to that infinite Wisdom which inscrutably disposes of all events".[44]

By the middle of the eighteenth century private charitable organizations abounded to the credit of the country and it was just as well because, as Thomas Smollett observed, "No Maecenas appeared among the ministers, and not the least ray of patronage glimmered from the throne".[45] The new hospitals and infirmaries established by the humanity of individuals, he wrote, would in any other country be honoured as national institutions. But he gave most praise to the legacy of Henry Paine to house and educate forty poor maidens, with a wedding dowry in addition for the best girl of the year, and also to the haven in Goodman's Fields for penitent prostitutes.[45] Although

Alcock[46] and Fielding[47] were two who believed that special provision was still needed for the sick and infirm, it is interesting that so humanitarian an individual as John Howard thought of hospitals and infirmaries along with prisons, lazarettos and houses of correction,[48] although it was his purpose to see that the inmates of all of them had sufficient fresh air, light and basic necessities.

Samuel Johnson was clearly concerned for the future of the voluntary hospitals because they subsisted not on funded capital but on gifts bestowed at pleasure. In 1758 he wrote "there is danger lest the blaze of charity which now bears with so much heat and splendour should die down for want of lasting fuel; lest fashion should suddenly withdraw her smile, and inconstancy transfer the publick attention to something which may appear more eligible because it will be new." He saw danger in the fact that hospitals were already competing among themselves for public favour and he felt that the frequent animosities between opposing patrons might prejudice weak minds against them all.[49]

In spite of these forebodings the voluntary hospitals maintained their hold on the public's sympathy and purse so that Aikin[50] was able to write "Never were the rights of humanity better understood nor the feelings of compassion more indulged than in our age and country". It was, he said, all due to the generous and disinterested zeal of individuals. There were still not enough hospitals. A writer in Garroway's Coffee House in 1761* rejoiced that there were moves afoot to provide an infirmary at Oxford. If they had one in Cambridge too, he said, few universities abroad would be able to vie with them. He believed that every market town needed an infirmary and then "we should not so frequently hear, as we do, of those unhappy disasters of broken limbs being attended with such calamitous circumstances as they commonly are".

The Infirmaries at Leeds and Norwich founded in 1767 and 1771 respectively seem to have excited much admiration. At Norwich John Howard had admired the Dutch heating stoves in the wards and the "little coppers for tea water".[48]

* *Gent. Mag.* (1761) 31, 305.

In his later years Samuel Johnson would have felt assured as
to the future success of the voluntary hospitals because by then
they had been long enough in existence to claim their share in
the nation's tradition, the love of which is the characteristic of
the Englishman. By the year 1780 they were already accepted as
a national heritage, a source of civic pride and at the same time
almost a religious obligation. The anniversary sermon and
annual meeting of the voluntary hospital had become a recognized social occasion when the subscriber learned of all that his
generosity had meant to the poor and found himself in a pew
commensurate with his largesse. It was in fact a step on the
British-built ladder of social preferment as well as one on the
way to Heaven. In Northampton the subscribers of four and
three guineas respectively, remarkably few in number, were
considered together between the very select but more numerous
groups of "5 guineas and over" and the more middle class
"2 guineas". At the end of the list came those who had given
one guinea. John Aikin need not therefore have been surprised
at the absence of intervention on the part of "the civil powers"
in the administration of hospitals,[50] for the government of this
country has never been wont to look round for worthy reci-
pients of its bounty. Some of the hospitals organized balls,
assemblies and bazaars. At Bristol disputants were obliged by
their attornies to pay "arbitration money" to the Infirmary in
the event of the case being settled out of court.* In Shrewsbury
they wisely arranged for their anniversary sermon and meeting
to take place on the Friday of race week, when some at any rate
could be expected to be "flush". Perhaps the most remarkable
way of providing money for the hospitals was the system of
licences imposed on private owners of sedan chairs in Dublin
(the order being granted in 1785). The trustees of the Lying-in
Hospital, for instance, proposed to enforce payments from the
refractory by "methods most coercive to a generous Mind—a
Sense of Shame", and by publishing a list specifying "the
Arrears of every Right Honourable or Honourable Tenant
. . ."[51]† This enterprising hospital also published copper-

---

* See *The Annual Account of the Bristol Infirmary for the year ending 21st December 1744*.
† The Charity received thirty-five shillings and the police (who were joint proprietors with the hospital) ten on each chair.

plate engravings of the coats of arms of the more generous of the annual subscribers, and legators of £300 or more were assured of the posthumous publication of their armorial bearings. There were plenty of free panels to serve as an encouragement to those who sought this inexpensive form of immortality.

From the middle of the eighteenth century until the time of the Crimean War the voluntary hospitals, apart from periods of cautious spending alternating with periods of rigid economy, seem to have been remarkably static. From time to time additional wards and even wings were added with improved amenities for the patients; an early fashion for electrotherapy gave way to one for balneotherapy, and tea was substituted for beer in the dietary of patients and nurses; but in general there was little change over these years. In 1748 for instance the income of the Salop Infirmary was £1,294 and in 1804 it was £1,683. Surgery was still a major hazard on account of erysipelas and gangrene, and so it was avoided if possible. Microscopes were still for the select few, as science had yet to invade these houses of healing. Only with the advent of roentgenology at the turn of the century did the bed costs begin to soar out of proportion to the increased costs of general living.

THE ROLE OF THE DOCTORS

In return for their free services the consultants on the staff of a voluntary hospital found themselves elevated in the eyes of the public and envied by those of their calling who were unsuccessful in what often proved to be quite spirited elections. It was of course nothing new for physicians to serve the poor free of charge, for the precedent had been set when the Dispensary of the Royal College of Physicians adumbrated in 1675 was eventually realized in Warwick Lane in 1696. Many of the voluntary hospital consultants succeeded in building up fashionable practices but in the provinces this was not always economically possible. These positions of prestige in the latter half of the nineteenth century tended in the smaller towns to go with partnerships thus adding to the value of the latter; and so for two or three generations representatives of rival practices might find themselves facing each other across the boardroom table.

Physicians claimed precedence over the surgeons because in the earlier days of the voluntary hospitals the physicians were educated men from Oxford and Cambridge or else illegitimate importees from the Scottish schools, illegitimate because until the Act of 1858 they were not legally entitled to practise in England. The surgeons by contrast lacked a university background but they were naturally always held in awe by their potential patients, and their stature gained with the rapid progress of their craft.

No doctor disdained to accept a hospital appointment although there were those who defaulted in their attendance once the post was secured. One way to obviate this abuse was to limit the duration of the post, so that at the end of five or seven years a man who deputed too much responsibility to his residents might find on seeking re-election that he had young and ambitious rivals competing with him.

Some doctors interested themselves in administration and others in hospital design, great efforts having been taken to ensure that the latest improvements were included in any new plans and in matters of hygiene. Edward Foster was one who wrote his Edinburgh M.D. thesis on the subject of hospital design and published it in Dublin in 1768. Like John Howard he was insistent on fresh air and good dry foundations. His recommendations for cleanliness are praiseworthy save for an unfortunate juxtaposition in his reference to the advantage of having a rivulet in the hospital grounds: besides its use for domestic purposes "it could", he wrote, "be extremely serviceable in keeping the cold bath always supplied and in carrying off the filth of the Necessary House, etc".[52] It is to be hoped that his recommendations were not adopted by a hospital downstream. He welcomed the provision of a garden for exercise and for the growing of herbs, preferring a quickset hedge or pales as a screen rather than a solid wall. He warned however that the desires of Nature were apt to return with health and so he recommended a division betwixt the men's and women's walk to prevent the possibility of any immodest behaviour.

The profession quickly recognized the use of hospitals for teaching and also the value of those intangible assets which went with a hospital appointment. The pupils paid fees and, when duly fledged, recommended to their chiefs patients who could afford a consultation. Except in the Scottish university cities, the importance of the facilities for research seems to have attracted less attention because time could more profitably be devoted to private consultations. Nevertheless, there must have been few hospitals towards the close of the eighteenth century that did not possess a basement back room for electrical experiments. John Aikin[50] was one who stressed the potentialities of the hospitals for clinical research. He called it "experimental practice" but he hastened to add that he had not in mind that which gave rise to great outcries from the public by reason of prejudices in their mind. The advantage of the hospital, he said, was that the physician was free to try out new treatments because there he was not restrained by the feelings of relatives and the presence of "prying and conceited bystanders". The commentator on Dr. Thomas Percival's aphorisms however lamented the singular fact that persons were generally appointed to public institutions who were least disposed to literary communication.[43] Almost every improvement had, he said, been promulgated by men who had only scant opportunities for private practice. He deplored the fact that public institutions were so often at the command of private influences and until they ceased to be used for private interests, science would be little benefited. Thus the circle had turned and the hospitals welcomed by Alured Clarke because they belonged to the public and were so free of private interests, were now often being charged with encouraging them.

THE CONTINUED SUCCESS OF THE VOLUNTARY HOSPITALS

Public charity may wax and wane but throughout the lifetime of our voluntary hospitals it showed no signs of extinction. Hospital charities in particular seem to have strengthened their position in the hearts of the people as they gradually came to realize that sickness was an inexplicable misfortune and not an avoidable sin. When times were not so good, on the threat of the Jacobite rising of 1745 for instance, and on those periodic occasions when unemployment was rising along with the price of corn, the public seems to have been stimulated to even greater charitable efforts. On such occasions municipal and state-supported institutions were apt to feel the pinch in the government purse, as is clear in reports from British visitors on the state of the Paris hospitals in the latter half of the eighteenth century and from Tenon's report prepared at the request of Louis XVI in 1788.* [53]

Nevertheless, in the preface to his unfavourable report Tenon, who was Professor Royal of Pathology at the College of Surgeons in Paris, was able to claim that the Hôtel Dieu was unique in the world in that without consideration of age, nationality or religion, the sick, the febrile, the wounded, the contagious, and the pregnant could be admitted at any hour. "Les portes, comme les bras de la Providence, sont toujours ouvertes à ceux qui viennent s'y refugier." In Britain we never had anything so comprehensive until 1947 and epidemiologists engaged on restrospective studies may think it just as well. London at the time when Tenon wrote was full of all sorts of specialized charities, independent, uncontrolled and unrelated. The victim of sickness must needs work out for himself with the aid of his family and acquaintances wherein lay his best chances of recovery. He had to find a governor with a reputation for sympathy, call on him and trust to luck that he would not be turned away at the door by a servant. The rules could be strict. As late as the year 1828 a man died outside St. Bartholomew's Hospital because he had neither of the alternatives necessary for admission, the fee nor the letter. [54] One man died of cold outside a hospital while waiting for the doors to open on admission day.† But the formality of a recommendation had been abandoned at the Rotunda as early as 1788 for they had learned that "the moment of extreme Agony is not calculated to enforce Repentance, or by the Refusal of Assistance add to the Miseries of Prostitution".

---

* Howard in 1789 was surprised to see how the Paris hospitals had deteriorated since his former visit, but he admitted that he was making his comparisons with the well-regulated hospitals of Spain and Italy. A quarter of a century earlier a British visitor to Paris had written "The Hôtel Dieu presents the most dreadful scene of human misery that can be imagined". The Paris hospitals, he said, compared most unfavourably with English hospitals which were notable for their neatness and conveniences. (*Gent. Mag.* [1763] **33**,293.)

† *Gent. Mag.* (1764) **34**, 612.

There were many complaints. At St. George's Hospital no visitors were admitted on Sundays and it was pointed out* that this precluded apprentices from visiting their relations, because if they lost time from work they would go hungry. At the Middlesex Hospital women after confinement were given every care but when discharged they were often too weak to work. One correspondent† called upon the governors to instruct the steward to issue tickets to allow the women to purchase a quartern wheat loaf, 3 lbs of mutton, 4d. of sugar or spices, 6d of greens and herbs. There were many abuses in voluntary hospitals, some of which disappeared as a result of the enlightened policy pursued at the Royal Free Hospital founded in 1828 by Dr. Marsden.[55]

With the coming of the nineteenth century the voluntary hospitals were firmly established and before long every small township called for its cottage hospital. Both for the community and for the doctors the voluntary hospital had become a social distinction as well as a necessity, and often it was a major factor in bringing the rival administrations of town and country together. All that Dr. Alured Clarke had said in support of the Winchester Infirmary turned out to be true, and a succession of parsimonious governments kept their distance, being thankful that the public continued to be charitably minded. They encouraged local authorities, however, to improve their workhouse infirmaries which, while they sometimes vied with the voluntary hospitals in matters of statistics and expenditure, never acquired that intangible cachet of respectability and never succeeded in displacing the voluntary hospitals from the hearts of the people. The great voluntary hospitals became centres of research and universities in the real meaning of the word, so that, in course of time, wealthy patients in need of the best found it expedient to seek entrance by a modest but exclusive side door to what was originally the pauper's hospital rather than entrust themselves to the care of a private nursing home.

A trend towards egalitarianism with a decreasing tolerance of the public to patronage, combined with the mounting costs of modern hospitals and finally the mobilization of resources

* *Gent. Mag.* (1764) **34,** 611.   † *Gent. Mag.* (1765) **35,** 183.

necessitated by total war, caused the Government to inter-
vene. The voluntary tradition may have been shaken by events
of the last twenty years but it has not been broken.

REFERENCES

1. STANLEY, "MASTER" (1646). *Stanley's Remedy, or the Way how to Reform
   Wandring Beggars, Theeves, Highway Robbers and Pick-pockets, or an
   abstract of his Discoveries, wherein is showed that Sodome's Sin of Idleness is
   the Poverty and Misery of this Kingdom*, London.
2. CHAMBERLEN, PETER (c. 1649). *The Poore Man's Advocate, or England's
   Samaritan, powring Oyle and Wyne into the Wounds of the Nation*, London.
3. CORNELISSON (CORNELIUS), PETER (1659). *A Way Propounded to Make the
   Poor in These and Other Nations Happy*, London.
4. HAINES, R. (1676). *Proposals for Building in every County an Working-
   Almshouse or Hospital as the Best Expedient to Perfect the Trade and Manu-
   factory of Linen Cloth.*
5. BURNET, GILBERT (1823). *Burnet's History of His Own Time*, vol. vi, p. 213,
   Oxford.
6. KIDDER, RICHARD (1676). *Charity Directed, or the Way to Give Alms to
   Greatest Advantage*, London.
7. PERAN, L'ABBÉ (1756). *Description historique de l'hotel Royal des Invalides*,
   Paris.
8. ADDISON, J. (1713). On the uses of a Foundling Hospital, *Guardian*,
   no. 105.
9. BELLERS, JOHN (1714). *An Essay towards the Improvement of Physick in 12
   Proposals*, London.
10. Hospital for French Protestants (1892). *Charter and Bylaws of the Corpor-
    ation of the Hospital in Bath Street, St. Lukes for Poor French Protestants and
    their Descendants residing in Great Britain*, London.
11. LANGDON-DAVIES, J. (1952). *Westminster Hospital, 1719–1948.* p. 14,
    London.
12. HUME, D. & SMOLLETT, T. (1825) in *The History of England*, vol. x. p. 453.
13. Westminster Hospital. *An Account of the Proceedings of the Trustees of the
    Public Infirmary in James Street, Westminster near St. James Park 1719–1736.*
14. Westminster Hospital (1733). *A Defence of the Majority of the Infirmary of
    Westminster against a small minority of it*, London.
15. St. George's Hospital (1733). *An Account of the Occasion and Manner of
    erecting the Hospital at Lanesborough House near Hyde Park Corner*, London.
16. Winchester. *An Account of the Establishment of the County Hospital at
    Winchester from 18th October 1736, to Michaelmas 1737.*
17. CLARKE, ALURED. *Correspondence with Mrs. Clayton, 1730–1738.* B.M.,
    W.Mss. 20102, ff. 28–132.
18. CLARKE, ALURED (1737). *A Sermon preached in the Cathedral Church of
    Winchester before the Governors of the County Hospital at the opening on
    October 18th 1736*, Winchester.

19. CLARKE, ALURED (1741). *A Sermon preached before the Trustees of the Charity Schools at the Cathedral Church of Exeter on 13th October 1741*, Exeter.
20. MILLER, JEREMIAH (1748). *A Sermon preached at the Cathedral Church of St. Peter's Exon before the Rt. Rev. the Lord Bishop of Exeter and the rest of the Governors of the Devon and Exeter Hospital for the Sick and Lame Poor, at their Anniversary Meeting on 27th August 1748*, London.
21. CLELAND, ARCHIBALD (1743). *An appeal to the Publick, or a Plain Narrative of Facts Relating to the Proceedings of a Party against Mr. Archibald Cleland (one of the Surgeons of the said Hospitals)*, Bath.
22. Bath (1744). *A Short Vindication of the Proceedings of the Government of the New General Hospital at Bath in Relation to Mr. Archibald Cleland*, Bath.
23. Bath Chronicle (1857). The Bath General or Hot Water Hospital, Bath, 1857. Reprinted from *Bath Chronicle*, 21st May 1857.
24. RUSHWORTH, JOHN (1731). *To the Masters and Governors of the Mystery and Commonalty of Barbers and Chirurgeons of London*, Northampton.
25. DODDRIDGE, PHILIP (1804). Compassion to the sick recommended and urged, in *The Works of Philip Doddridge, D.D.*, Job Orton (Ed), vol. iv, p. 359, London.
26. GREY, RICHARD (1744). *A Sermon Preached in the Parish Church of All Saints in Northampton before the President and Governors of the County Infirmary for the Sick and Lame Poor*, Northampton.
27. STANFORD, CHARLES (1880). *Philip Doddridge, D.D.*, London.
28. ORTON, JOB (1804). *The Works of Philip Doddridge, D.D*, London.
29. COURTNEY, W. P. (1898). Sir James Stonhouse, in *Dict. Nat. Biog.*, **54**, 417.
30. Anon. (1844). *Life of the Rev. Sir James Stonhouse, Bart., M.D.*, Oxford.
31. York (1809). *An Account of the Public Hospital for the Diseased Poor in the County of York*, York.
32. MADDOX, I. (1743). *The Duty and Advantages of Encouraging Public Infirmaries*, London.
33. MADDOX, I. (1744). *The Duty and Advantages of Encouraging Public Infirmaries further considered*, London.
34. MADDOX, I. (1752). *On Inoculation*, London.
35. SMITH, G. MUNRO (1917). *A History of the Bristol Royal Infirmary*, Bristol.
36. HALLIFAX, SAMUEL (1771). *A Sermon for the Governors of Addenbrooke's Hospital*, Cambridge.
37. SECKER, THOMAS (1771). Sermon preached before Governors of London Hospital at St. Lawrence Jury, 20th February 1754 In *Collection of the late Archbishop Thomas Secker's Sermons on various subjects*, B. Porteus & G. Stinton (Ed.), London.
38. ADAMS, WILLIAM (1777). *Sermons and Tracts*, Shrewsbury.
39. TURNER, A. LOGAN (1937). *The Story of a Great Hospital. The Royal Infirmary of Edinburgh (1729–1929)*, Edinburgh.
40. FLEETWOOD, JOHN (1951). *A History of Medicine in Ireland*, Dublin.
41. KIRKPATRICK, T. PERCY C. (1924). *The History of Dr. Steevens' Hospital, Dublin (1720–1920)*, Dublin.

70   *The Evolution of Hospitals in Britain*

42. STONHOUSE, JAMES (1748). *A Friendly Letter to a Patient Just Admitted into an Infirmary*, London.
43. PERCIVAL, THOMAS (1827). *Medical Ethics*, London.
44. HIGHMORE, ANTHONY (1814). *Pietas Londiniensis*, London.
45. SMOLLETT, T. & HUME, D. (1825) in *The History of England*, vol. xiii, p. 5, London.
46. ALCOCK, THOMAS (1752). *Observations on the defects of the Poor Laws, and on the Causes and Consequences of the Great Increase and Burden of the Poor*, London.
47. FIELDING, H. (1753). *A Proposal for Making an Effectual Provision for the Poor*, London.
48. HOWARD, JOHN (1789). *An Account of the Principal Lazarettos in Europe*, Warrington.
49. JOHNSON, SAMUEL (1758). *The Idler*, no. 4, Saturday, May 6th.
50. AIKIN, JOHN (1771). *Thoughts on Hospitals*, London.
51. Dublin (1788). *A List of the Proprietors of Licenses for Private Sedan Chairs at 25th March 1788 Alphabetically Arranged*. Lying-in Hospital, Dublin.
52. FOSTER, EDWARD (1768). *An Essay on Hospitals*, Dublin.
53. TENON, J. R. (1788). *Mémoirs sur les Hôpitaux de Paris*, Paris.
54. EVANS, A. D. & HOWARD, L. G. R. (1931). *The Romance of the British Hospital Movement*, p. 93, London.
55. POWER, SIR D'ARCY (1933). Medicine, in *Johnson's England*, G. A. S. Turbeville (Ed.), vol. ii, p. 284, Oxford.

BIBLIOGRAPHY

BAYLY, EDWARD (1749). *A Sermon Preached at the Abbey Church, Bath, on Sunday 23rd April 1749*, Bath.
BURDETT, HENRY C. (1893). *Hospitals and Asylums of the World*; vol. iii, History and Administration, London.
GRAY, B. K. (1905). *The History of English Philanthropy*, London.
HUMPHREY, J. D. (1829). *Correspondence and Diary of Philip Doddridge, D.D.*, 5 vols.
IMBERT, JEAN (1958). *Les Hôpitaux en France*, Paris.
LAYNG, HENRY (1746). *A Sermon preached in the Parish Church of All Saints in Northampton on 22nd September 1746 in aid of the County Infirmary for the Sick and Lame Poor*, Northampton.
LEVY-VALENSI, J. (1933). *La Médecine et les Médecins Français au XVII Siècle*, Paris.
London Hospital. *An Account of the Rise, Progress and State of the London Hospital, or Infirmary for Relief of all Sick and Diseased Persons and in particular Manufacturers, Seamen in Merchant Service and their Wives and Children from the first institution on 3rd November 1740 to 17th March 1747-8.*
LE MAQUET, P. E. (1900). *Le Monde Médical Parisien sous le Grand Roi*, Paris.
MORRIS, F. W. (1906). *The London Hospital*, London.

NICHOLLS, R. H. & WRAY, F. A. (1935). *The History of the Foundling Hospital*, London.

SPENCER, W. G. (1924). *Westminster Hospital: an Outline of its History.* p. 31 et seq., London.

WARBURTON, WILLIAM (1742). *A Sermon preached at the Abbey Church at Bath for Promoting the Charity and subscription towards the General Hospital or Infirmary, on Sunday 24th October 1742*, London.

WILKS, S. & BETTANY, S. T. (1892). *Biographical History of Guy's Hospital*, London.

The History of the Dispensary Movement

SIR ZACHARY COPE

IN THE HISTORY of the development of the medical services of Britain there is no part which has been so neglected as that played by the dispensaries. Yet for more than a hundred years they filled a gap which neither the hospitals nor the poor law service could fill, and even fifty years ago were bidding fair to become a permanent sub-division of the Health Service.

During the seventeenth century the apothecaries were growing in number but the number of physicians remained about the same and soon, with the increase in population, the apothecaries were called upon to give advice to patients who could not afford to pay the fees demanded by physicians. In spite of opposition the services of the apothecaries became necessary and began to trespass on the prerogatives of the physicians. In an attempt to stop this habit, the College of Physicians, in 1697, opened three dispensaries, one at the College in Warwick Lane, another in Gracechurch Street, and a third near St. Martin's Lane, where they would give advice free to any who cared to consult them. The apothecaries would not help them by making up medicines at reduced prices, so the physicians engaged dispensers to dispense at low rates. This attempt to keep the apothecaries in check was not very successful and these dispensaries closed in 1725. Meanwhile the apothecaries, by a decision of the House of Lords in 1703, had been granted permission to give advice to patients, though they could only charge for medicines. However they could now practise, and undoubtedly their number and importance grew. From 1700 to 1750 the population of England did not rise much but from 1750 to 1800 it increased rapidly, and as a consequence there was much overcrowding, and a great deal of sickness and poverty. Many could not afford to pay for advice or medicine, and, though

73

there were a number of new hospitals in London, there was not room enough for the many who needed medical attention, and at first there was no regular out-patient department in these hospitals. There seemed therefore scope for a place where the poor could go for advice and medicine without having to pay for it. The example of the Royal College of Physicians was still in memory and in 1769 a Scots doctor called George Armstrong started a small dispensary for children in Red Lion Square. This was followed the next year by the foundation of the first general medical dispensary in Aldersgate Street, largely on the initiative of John Coakley Lettsom, an ambitious, generous and clever physician, a graduate of Edinburgh and a friend of John Fothergill. The Aldersgate Street Dispensary was near St. Bartholomew's Hospital and the Royal College of Physicians, at that time still in Warwick Lane. Patients were seen daily at the Dispensary and those who were too ill to attend were seen at their own homes, a new departure. The first physician was Dr. Hulme but soon Lettsom was put on the staff. The Dispensary was very successful and was soon followed by the foundation of similar institutions in other parts of London and Westminster. By 1800 there were fourteen dispensaries in the metropolis and by 1830 as many as thirty-five. They did a great service, were managed economically because they were dependent on the subscriptions of the charitable, and were free for those who brought a subscriber's letter, except that in some cases a charge was made for medicine. Subscribers of a guinea a year became governors and were able to give letters of recommendation to those who wished to attend the dispensary.

Similar dispensaries were soon established in provincial towns, in Newcastle-upon-Tyne, Liverpool, Manchester and Birmingham, and in all of them the organization was along similar lines with free treatment and home visiting.

After about 1830, however, though there was still much poverty, the general condition of the working classes had slightly improved and some doctors complained that the dispensaries treated some who might well afford a small sum for treatment. This led to the founding of the *provident* dispensaries in which the members paid a small sum each week—a penny or two-pence—and in return were entitled to medical attendance either as out-patients or at home when necessary. There was a reduction for children and for families. In some instances a dispensary had free patients as well as provident members. The provident system was started by a Dr. Henry Lilley Smith of Southam in Warwickshire and his example was soon followed in many parts of the country. The provident dispensary was often handicapped for it had to compete with the free dispensaries, the free out-patient department of the hospitals, the various benefit societies, and the medical "clubs" which provided medical attendance at very low rates.

In 1878 Sir Charles Trevelyan took a great interest in furthering the cause of provident dispensaries. In London an association was formed to help their extension but it was uphill work because of the rivalry of the other institutions and by 1900 the position of the dispensaries, though well established, was stationary. In some places they were very prosperous; in others they did not exist. Their future was difficult to forecast.

In 1905 the Government appointed a Royal Commission to enquire into the condition of the Poor Laws and the relief of distress and in their investigations they had to consider the position of the dispensaries. They received evidence from many dispensaries but there was no organization which could furnish accurate information as to their exact number and influence, and the evidence was very scrappy. However, the majority of the commission—fourteen out of eighteen—recommended that the dispensary system should be widely extended. The minority —four members—including Mrs. Beatrice Webb, opposed any extension of the dispensary system. It was probably partly due to the adverse opinion of the minority report that the National Health Insurance Act did not make any special mention of dispensaries, and almost immediately their importance diminished. They continued to treat women and children, for workers' families were not covered by the Insurance Scheme, but when the National Health Service was established the need for dispensaries almost vanished. Some, however, continue their benevolent function as centres for special treatments not included in the National Health Service, e.g. centres for chiropody or for the treatment of chronic rheumatism.

A function of the early dispensaries should be mentioned—they served as centres for medical education. Clinical work could be done and signed up for at the dispensaries, and many students from all over the country were in the 1830s able to get their clinical instruction there. For a time there was a private medical school conducted at the Westminster Dispensary, Gerrard Street, and clinical instruction was available at the Aldersgate Street School attached to the dispensary there.

The best example of early post-graduate education was the instruction given at the Carey Street Dispensary from 1793 to 1820 by Robert Willan and Thomas Bateman, the founders of British dermatology. These Yorkshiremen were Edinburgh graduates who had little chance of getting on the staff of a London hospital, but at Carey Street they did great work. Their clinics were the training ground of many of the younger physicians of that time. Richard Bright worked there for more than a year before he got on the staff of Guy's. Thomas Addison was on the staff of the Carey Street Dispensary before he was elected to Guy's, and many other well-known physicians attended the clinics there. From the middle of the nineteenth century the educational function of dispensaries rapidly diminished, but it may not be without interest to know that the writer of this brief sketch first took medical responsibility as resident at the Western Dispensary, Rochester Row in 1905.

Maternity Hospitals

ALISTAIR GUNN

ONE OF THE nobler characteristics of the eighteenth century was the growth of voluntary organizations for the treatment of the sick. If we consider the great general hospitals of London we see that two only, St. Bartholomew's and St. Thomas's, were established before 1700 and that of the remainder Guy's, the London, St. George's, Middlesex and Westminster were all founded in the eighteenth century. Special hospitals, too, appeared at this time and among the first were the lying-in hospitals, all of which were founded between 1749 and 1765, a surprisingly short period of seventeen years. Aveling reminds us that in England until the eighteenth century midwives were women of inferior education who learnt by experience, undoubtedly at the expense of their patients. They were however licensed by the bishops, who were concerned that weakly or dying children should be baptised at least by the midwife.[1]

The advent of printed books on midwifery in the vernacular started a new era because through text books knowledge and new ideas became widely disseminated and standards of practice improved. The first printed text book on midwifery, Rosslin's *Schwangern Frawen Rosengarten* published in 1513, was translated into English in 1540 by Richard Jonas who called it *The Byrth of Mankynde*. Medical practitioners had not intruded into the lying-in room unless called upon when the mother's death was impending. The fact was that they knew nothing of midwifery nor were they expected to.

Medicine in the seventeenth century shared in the beginnings of science as we know it. Pioneer works on midwifery were the translations of Ambroise Paré in 1634 and William Harvey's *De Generatione* with its chapter on *De Partu* in 1653; and these were soon followed by many more. At the same time surgeons

77

and apothecaries took up the study of anatomy, so that many of them soon had the desire and ability to go to the aid of midwives when labours became abnormal. There was also the Chamberlen family who invented the midwifery forceps and kept their secret for nearly a century. The revelation of the secret and the general use of forceps from 1720 onwards did more than anything else to transfer the control of midwifery into the hands of the man-midwives.[2] In *The Female Physician*, 1724, John Maubray says, "In England, Scotland, etc., men are stiled 'extraordinary midwives', being seldom or never called but in extraordinary cases of difficult or preternatural births".[3] But only thirty years later, in 1754, Benjamin Pugh of Chelmsford was writing in his *Treatise of Midwifery* "every young surgeon now intends practising midwifery".[4]

By now surgeons and apothecaries, but not physicians, were seeking instruction, and private schools were springing up in London and other centres, notably those run by John Maubray, Sir Richard Manningham and William Smellie. These teachers had been to Paris and had seen there the clinical material for teaching midwifery. Maubray in 1725 called attention to the value of the Hôtel Dieu where lying-in women were admitted and midwives were trained. He made a plea for the foundation of a lying-in hospital as a "Christian Charity, provision for poor miserable women in the time of their natural affliction". In 1736 John Douglas, who opposed man-midwives, appealed for the establishment "at the publick expence" of a lying-in hospital as a school for midwives.[5] In 1739 Sir Richard Manningham was instrumental in getting a ward of the parochial infirmary of St. James's, Westminster, set apart for lying-in women and there he taught his students.[6] In 1747 five beds were reserved for lying-in patients at the Middlesex Hospital, founded two years previously, and these were increased to a separate maternity department when the new hospital was opened in 1757, a mere ten years later.

Dublin Lying-in Hospital

It was in 1745 in Dublin that the first separate hospital for maternity patients in Great Britain and Ireland was established. This was the Dublin Lying-in Hospital now known as The

Rotunda, and its founder and first Master was Bartholomew Mosse.

This Irish surgeon saw the obstetric need of the poor in Dublin, and by his inspiration and energy provided the hospital which stands to this day. He had no private fortune, he was without affluent friends, he had no experience of hospital construction or management, and yet he embarked on an unprecedented scheme with vision and vigour, opening in a disused theatre in George's Lane on 15th March 1745 a hospital with twenty-eight beds.[7] It was very soon apparent that a much larger building was required. He not only governed the hospital and made ambitious plans for the new one, but he also had to enlist the support of subscribers and benefactors. When this was not sufficient Mosse proved resourceful, even organizing lotteries. In 1748 he obtained a lease of land on which the Rotunda still stands, now in the centre of the city which has grown round it. He laid out the grounds as pleasure gardens for banquets, breakfasts, and concerts to raise funds. He had to appeal for money to the Lord Mayor and City Corporation, and to the Irish Parliament, before the new hospital was opened in 1757, and they gave him strong support. Mosse obtained a Royal Charter in 1756 the terms of which were so far-seeing that they are substantially those under which the hospital is governed to this day. The building is impressive, well designed and includes the beautiful chapel, though this was not completed when Mosse died in 1759. The first Masters, Fielding Ould, Collum, Jebb, Rock, Clarke and Evory, were outstanding obstetricians and it was on their merits that the subsequent fame of the Rotunda was founded. The hospital was always seeking funds; in 1767 it opened elegant round rooms as public entertainment rooms, and it was these that gave the hospital its name Rotunda. Another source of income was the grant by the first Parliament of a tax levied on all sedan chairs hired within a mile of the hospital, and a royalty on coaches licensed within the area. The story of the Rotunda is indeed a romantic one, covering as it does two centuries of solid achievement.[8,9]

The British Hospital for Mothers and Babies

Within five years of the foundation of the Rotunda, lying-in hospitals were being established in London. It is traditionally accepted that the first of all was The Lying-in Hospital in Brownlow Street, Long Acre, which opened with twenty beds in 1749. The hospital still has the complete minutes of all the Board and Committee meetings from that day to the present. They make fascinating reading and tell their own story.[10] In the early minutes we see that the four members of the staff included William Hunter and two of the staff of the Middlesex Hospital, Francis Sandys and Daniel P. Layard, all famous man-midwives.

In the first year of its existence the hospital recorded an embarrassing truth which has bedevilled maternity departments ever since. The minutes of a meeting held on 23rd November 1749 read "that some of the Governors of the Middlesex Hospital for Sick and Lame and Lying-in Women were dissatisfied with the way in which monies subscribed were allocated . . . they point out that a lying-in woman costs twice as much as the sick and lame".

Its name was The Lying-in Hospital until 1756. The suggestion that the General Lying-in Hospital (later to be called Qoeen Charlotte's) had been founded before 1749 lends interest to a minute of the Committee of the Governors dated April 1756 which reads " . . . when this hospital was first established it was the only one in Great Britain solely employed for the Reception of Lying-in Women but other hospitals of the kind having been since instituted, a title of fuller distinction becomes . . . necessary . . . and . . . recommend that this hospital be for the future called . . . The British Lying-in Hospital for Married Women." The Governors resolved not only to adopt the new name but also that the resolution with its preamble that the Lying-in Hospital was the first established in Great Britain be "forthwith advertised in the public papers".

A further insight into contemporary opinion is afforded by the minutes in October 1757 which give a copy of a letter written from Bartholomew Mosse requesting that he be sent "the established Rules and Orders of your hospital in regard to the admitting and discharging of patients and the manner of treating them whilst they are in the House and in return we shall take care to send you any New Orders that we may make

The Righteous considereth the cause of the poor. PROV. 29.

EXPLANATION.

The British Lying-in Hospital, Brownlow Street, Long Acre
A picture taken from the topographical collection of King George III, purchased
by the British Museum in 1823
Reproduced by permission of the Keeper of Prints and Drawings, British Museum

Dublin Hodges & Smith

Bartholomew Mosse and his signature
*Reproduced by permission of the Royal College of Physicians
of Ireland*

on the opening of the New House, or at any other time, and beg the same from you and that a constant correspondence may be kept up between the Two Houses which I hope will be a mutual advantage to both."

On 11th November 1768, the minutes record Dr. Hunter "having been desired by the Committee to put Mr. Garrick in mind of a benefit play for this hospital". On many occasions there were charity performances in aid of the hospital, at Drury Lane and other theatres.

The British Hospital moved to Endell Street in 1845, and in 1914 when it encountered financial difficulties it moved again, this time to Woolwich to amalgamate with the Home for Mothers and Babies, under the name British Hospital for Mthhers and Babies. Many distinguished obstetricians have followed William Hunter, Sandys and Layard, and in our own times J. S. Fairbairn, President of the Royal College of Obstetricians and Gynaecologists from 1933 to 1935, and the paediatrician who has added much to our knowledge of lactation, Harold Waller.

The City of London Maternity Hospital

On 30th March 1750 there gathered in the Black Swan tavern in Bartholomew Lane ten benevolent gentlemen who were to found the Lying-in Hospital for Married Women in the City of London, also for Sick and Lame Out-patients. Of these ten, Thomas Craddock became Treasurer, Richard Ball surgeon and accoucheur, and William Ball apothecary, the last named to continue on the staff for forty-six years. On 13th June 1750 the hospital opened at London House, Aldersgate Street. In the following year it moved across the road to Thanet or Shaftesbury House, and giving up the out-patient work for the sick and lame, it dropped these words from the title. There were thirty beds in large wards.

In 1773 a new hospital was opened at the junction of City Road and Old Street, the site it occupied until the bombing of 1940 and 1941 made it necessary to transfer in-patient work to north London where the new building in Hanley Road, Highgate, was opened in 1949.

The 1773 building was principally of wood except the outside walls and it accommodated forty-two patients in three wards. Above the entrance to the hospital was the chapel and it had a garden at the back. It was surrounded by the residences of well-to-do merchants, and nearby were pleasure grounds and a bathing pool. Extending northwards between the hospital and the village of Islington was open country, Finsbury Fields, and White Conduit Fields.

After a hundred and thirty years this building became unsafe, allegedly because the Underground Railway was constructed beneath it, and so in 1907 the building known to many of us replaced it.

The City of London Maternity Hospital has always been closely connected with the Corporation of the City, and Lord Mayors have supported the hospital, many of them being either Patron or President.

Pupil midwives were first accepted in 1771 but male students were not admitted until the hospital was rebuilt in 1907.

The history of the hospital, published in 1922, was written by R. B. Cannings who was secretary for twenty-four years.[11] In it he gives a list of all the officers and staff from 1750 onwards and we notice among them the names of Dr. John C. Lettsom, the Quaker physician (1785–1815), Sir Comyns Berkeley (appointed 1908) and Sir Eardley Holland, a former president of the Royal College (appointed 1909).

Queen Charlotte's Maternity Hospital

An earlier name for Queen Charlotte's was The General Lying-in Hospital which was founded in 1752, according to Thomas Ryan, the secretary, who published its history in 1875.[12] It certainly existed in 1752 in Duke Street, Grosvenor Square. We know from the Sloane manuscripts in the British Museum that Sir Richard Manningham wrote to Sir Hans Sloane saying that he would open a lying-in apartment in Jermyn Street, and Peachey quotes an advertisement from Sir Richard dated 20th September 1739 for lectures and classes to teach young physicians and women (on different days) at the Lying-in Apartment in Jermyn Street.[13]

The Sloane papers also contain an account of "Mony Expended" which includes "Paid Rent for the Apartment for a

year, quarter in full to Mich'mas 1740, for beds, bedding, linnen
etc. as per Acc't, £75. 12. 0.", which suggests that the beds and
bedding belonged to the landlord.

Peachey's idea is that Felix Macdonough succeeded to the
management of an establishment in Jermyn Street started by
Manningham in 1739 and was also participating in the work of
the Lying-in Hospital in Duke Street, Grosvenor Square, in
1753; this corroborates Maitland's statement of 1756 in his
History of London that the Duke Street Lying-in Hospital was
formerly in Jermyn Street.[14] It certainly makes the association
possible; but whether Queen Charlotte's Hospital and its pre-
decessor the General Lying-in Hospital can on this evidence be
accepted as *founded* in 1739 is another matter. It could well be
that new evidence will decide this question.

Compare the legal form of the establishment of the Rotunda
in Dublin and of the British Hospital in London. They regarded
each other as the first in their respective cities and there are no
recorded contradictions. The Lying-in Hospital was started in
1749 and changed its name to the "British" Hospital after
others had sprung up; and at this time it advertised in the
public papers its declaration that it was the first established in
Britain. We can find no evidence of this claim being contested.
All the authorities for over a hundred years seemed to regard the
British Hospital as the first[15,16,17] and any dispute belongs
entirely to the twentieth century.

The General Lying-in Hospital made several moves and in
1782 it was in St. George's Row near Oxford Street Turnpike,
facing Hyde Park a short distance from Marble Arch and in
those days very near to Tyburn, where the last public execution
took place in 1783. In 1791 it removed to Bayswater and indeed
was called Bayswater Lying-in Hospital, probably just by the
present Queensway station on the Central London line.

To quote Ryan,

"from 1791 to 1809, or at any rate for a considerable part of
the time, certainly from 1800, the Charity was extremely badly
managed. Highmore, in 1810, says: 'It had lately fallen almost
into disuse.' Not much is known of the cause of this trouble,
but something has come down to us. From the Report of a
Special Committee, which was appointed in July 1809 'To make

Enquiry into the nature of the establishment of the General Lying-in Hospital, the manner in which it had been conducted, and its present state', which I have now before me, it appears that for some reason the Hospital had got to be considered as the private property of the owner of the house, that hence all the money raised by subscriptions, legacies, or otherwise, for the benefit of the Charity, was considered as disposable by him; that two doctors actually purchased the goodwill of the house, with all the supposed privileges, and by a special agreement stipulated to pay to the former proprietor one-third of a legacy bequeathed to the Hospital by the late Admiral Dennis, when it should be received, and did actually so pay it afterwards; that the Hospital was purchased by one of these doctors, and directions were given in his will to sell it again by private bargain or by public auction. It also appears that the purchaser of the house assumed the power of nominating himself Physician to the Hospital, without an election, and without the consent, or even the knowledge, of the subscribers by whom the Hospital was supported; that one of the doctors laid out considerable sums of money for the purpose of keeping the house in habitable repair; that the part of the house then allotted to patients was two small rooms in the attic storey only, the matron living in the basement, and the principal floor having been reserved for the owner of the house, and in no case for the patients; that by these proceedings the pecuniary and medical management of the Hospital fell under the control of the person who owned the house, and that the subscriptions to the Hospital had for several years so much declined, that they were not adequate to the necessary expenditure of the Charity. No wonder the subscriptions had declined, when things were in the state described in this Report. Indeed, it is evident that the affairs of the Institution had been grossly mismanaged, and that its condition had become serious."

In 1809 after the special committee had reported most unfavourably on the hospital, it was reconstituted and from this date the history of the hospital is one of leadership and preeminence in the practice and teaching of obstetrics in England. The Duke of Sussex became interested and not only accepted the Presidency but also became Chairman of the committee. A code of laws was drawn up by a special commission of which His Royal Highness was the head. Later in the year Queen Charlotte became patron of the hospital and by the efforts of the

Duke of Sussex numerous members of the nobility became subscribers, including ten royal princes and princesses, and nearly a hundred titled people.

In 1813 the hospital transferred to Lisson Green Manor House, Marylebone Road, where it was rebuilt in 1856, the building being now occupied by St. Dunstans.

The year 1874 saw the foundation of the midwifery school at Queen Charlotte's Hospital, to provide preliminary obstetric training for students of medicine, the second school in the British Isles, preceded only by the Rotunda.

Queen Charlotte's Hospital moved to Goldhawk Road, Hammersmith, in 1940, and under the National Health Service Act in 1948 it became closely associated with the Chelsea Hospital for Women. Queen Charlotte's has had many famous obstetricians on the staff, too numerous to name. Early writers of obstetric text books were William Osborn, Sir Charles Mansfield Clarke, David D. Davis (of University College) and Thomas Denman. The doctor who did more than any other to found the Central Midwives Board, Sir Francis Champneys, a former president of the Royal College of Obstetricians Sir William Gilliatt, and the present president, Sir Arthur Bell, are names which spring to mind, with Dr. Leonard Colebrook, a leader in scientific research, who has added lustre to the name of Queen Charlotte's Hospital.

The General Lying-in Hospital, York Road, London

In 1765 Dr. John Leake founded the New Westminster Lying-in Hospital, which, unlike the British Hospital and the City of London, admitted unmarried women from the day of opening. He was a well-known teacher who lectured and wrote a number of text books on midwifery. Spencer gives a list of ten works which went into many editions.[18] A. R. Simpson (1893) quotes Pennant's words in his *London* (3rd edition 1793, p. 36),

"On approaching St. George's Fields from Westminster Bridge are two charities of uncommon delicacy and utility. The first is the Westminster Lying-in Hospital. This is not instituted merely for the honest matron, who can depose her burthen with the consciousness of lawful love, but also for the unhappy wretches whom some villain, in the unguarded moment, hath seduced, and then left a prey to desertion of friends, poverty, want and guile. Lest such may be driven to despair by such complicated misery and be tempted to destroy themselves, and murder their infants, here was founded in 1765 this humane preventative, the Westminster Lying-in Hospital. To obviate all objections to its being an encouragement of vice, no one is taken in a second time; but this most excellent charity is open to the worthy distressed matron as often as necessity requires. None are rejected who have friends to recommend."[19]

The minute books have been preserved and give an almost continuous record from 1765. The hospital changed its name to the General Lying-in Hospital in the year 1818. It started training pupil midwives in 1769 but male students were not admitted until more recent times.

In the years from 1800 to 1875 this hospital, like other lying-in institutions, and to a still greater degree general hospitals, suffered from the ravages of puerperal fever so that in 1878 it had to close its wards for a time. A common maternal mortality rate for lying-in hospitals at that time was 25 per 1,000 and some general hospitals had very much higher maternal death rates.[20]

And so, in 1878 they appointed Surgeon Major de Chaumont, Professor of Hygiene at Netley Hospital, to enquire into and report on the hospital. He criticized ventilation, methods of dealing with soiled linen, disinfection and spacing of patients. Accordingly the staff was reorganized and Joseph Lister, F.R.S., was appointed consultant surgeon. New rules and methods of antisepsis were laid down with the encouraging result that in 1882 it was recorded that maternal mortality for the previous two years was 1 in 166 for in-patients compared with 1 in 120 for home midwifery. In 1886 it had fallen to 1 in 383 for in-patients.

Dr. W. S. Playfair and Dr. R. S. Fancourt Barnes were appointed to the staff in 1878 with the future Lord Lister; and two years later Dr. John Williams and Dr. Champneys joined the staff. A strong alliance has grown between the General Lying-in Hospital and the staffs of St. George's and St. Thomas's hospitals. The present building was opened in 1828.

Princess Mary Maternity Hospital, Newcastle-on-Tyne

This was an early foundation dating from 1760, but for some years it provided only a district midwifery service. Records go back to its earliest days and continue throughout the nineteenth century. They show that patients, in addition to being married and possessing a subscriber's recommendation, had to be Newcastle residents. Itinerant women, whom they referred to as Scots women, were barred. Some 140 years after its foundation, Professor Ranken Lyle reorganized and strengthened the hospital. but had great difficulty in abolishing the exclusion of the unmarried. His leadership resulted in an industrial school being converted into a hospital which was opened in 1901 by Princess Mary, and named after her. One of its distinctions is that in 1935 under Professor Farquhar Murray it was the first to form an Obstetric Flying Squad to stand ready to go to the aid of women who were in danger from obstetric complications.

St. Mary's Hospitals, Manchester

In 1790 Charles White, who forty years earlier had assisted in founding Manchester Infirmary, with his son Thomas White and Edward and Richard Hall, resigned from the staff of Manchester Infirmary and founded the Lying-in Charity in a private house in Old Bridge Street, Salford, now known as Victoria Bridge. Five years later they took over the Bath Inn, so called because it was built on the site of a small public house, the Spaw House, which contained a bath filled by a spring. The inn also owned the ferry across the Irwell, and the half-penny fee to cross to the Manchester side was remitted to anyone who bought a drink at the inn.

Charles White, F.R.S. was one of the most distinguished of the pioneers of obstetrics in Britain. He not only introduced enlightened methods of hygiene, dietetics, and non-interference in normal labours, but also wrote convincingly on these and also other quite unrelated scientific subjects. His works on phlegmasia alba dolens and his *Treatise on the Management of Lying-in Women* are classics. [21]

The hospital moved to North Parade, St. Mary's, in 1821, and in 1856 to Quay Street. There were amalgamations with

Manchester Southern and Maternity hospitals in 1904 and the Whitworth Street building is now the maternity department.

The many famous men who have been on the staff of the hospitals include Charles Clay, the early ovariotomist, Archibald Donald, pioneer gynaecological surgeon, and Sir William Fletcher Shaw, one of the founders of the Royal College of Obstetricians and Gynaecologists. One of the staff, Dr. J. W. Bride, is our authority on the history of the hospitals;[22] and H. R. Spencer has written very fully on Charles White in his *History of British Midwifery from 1650 to 1800.*[18]

Edinburgh Royal Maternity and Simpson Memorial Hospital (Simpson Memorial Maternity Pavilion)

Edinburgh had the distinction of having the first professor of midwifery when in 1726 the Town Council appointed Joseph Gibson to be the City Professor of Midwifery for the proper education of midwives. The third holder of the office, Thomas Young, as soon as he was appointed in 1756 began to teach medical students as well as midwives, and obtained beds for lying-in women in the Edinburgh Royal Infirmary. The demand for instruction in midwifery from both midwives and students was heavy and eventually in 1793 Young's successor, Alexander Hamilton, obtained a separate foundation with a board of its own in Park House (or Ross House) in Park Place near the site of the present University Union.

The next professor was Alexander Hamilton's son James, and when James Hamilton died his executors sold the hospital which he had been supporting at his own expense. This left James Young Simpson to find new premises to continue the work. The hospital occupied various buildings described by Sturrock until it came in 1879 to 79 Lauriston Place as the Royal Maternity and Simpson Memorial Hospital.[23] At that time it was the first building in Edinburgh to be set up with maternity wards and the design shows the views of the day on the planning of lying-in hospitals. It had a separate labour ward but several patients were delivered within sound, if not in sight, of each other.

In March 1939 the hospital moved to the new Simpson Memorial Maternity Pavilion adjoining the Royal Infirmary.

Throughout the years of its existence the emphasis has been on teaching both for midwives and doctors, and many leaders of the profession have been trained there, including some of the founders of the great American schools and many teachers who have staffed the universities of the world.

The Royal Maternity Hospital, Belfast

The foundation of this hospital in 1794 appears to be unique in that the prime mover was not a medical practitioner but a young clergyman, the Rev. John Clark, who, seeing the deplorable home conditions in which confinements took place among the very poor, enlisted the help of a certain Mrs. McTier. Her brother was Dr. William Drennan, a well-known Irish practitioner and man of letters who had been trained in midwifery by Professor Thomas Young, of Edinburgh, whom I have already mentioned.

In 1793 they formed the Humane Female Society for the Relief of Lying-in Women and rented a house in Donegall Street which provided six beds. Unmarried mothers were nursed in a separate ward and were not admitted a second time. Conditions were insanitary and the medical care does not appear to have been of a high order even for those days, but there was a great improvement when a lying-in hospital was built on land granted by the Charitable Society on condition that the hospital could not be used for any other purpose. It opened in 1830 in Clifton Street, and provided eighteen beds. In 1837 Dr. William Burden, the pioneer of Belfast midwifery, was appointed as medical officer. He succeeded Dr. Little, the first Professor of Midwifery in the Royal Belfast Academical Institution, in 1840, and became the first professor in Queen's College in 1849. After overcoming much opposition he introduced the training of medical students at the hospital about 1853 and the training of midwives which, after failure many years earlier, was regularly instituted in 1879. He organized the teaching as professor and continued at the Lying-in Hospital until 1867. In its centenary year, 1893, its name was changed to the Belfast Maternity Hospital. Professor R. F. Dill followed Burden and he was succeeded by Sir John W. Byers; but until 1902 the professor was not on the staff of the hospital. Professor C. G. Lowry, appointed in 1920, was only the fourth holder of the Belfast chair from 1840 to 1945 when Professor Macafee took over. His energy equalled Burden's because within five years he had reorganized the hospital on modern lines, inaugurating an ante-natal department, appointing consultant staff, clinical assistants and a University tutor, opening a residence for students and obtaining seats for two of the medical staff on the Board of Governors. In 1933, after amalgamating with the Royal Victoria Hospital, the Royal Maternity Hospital opened its new building of 100 beds in Grosvenor Road. This has now been enlarged to 153 beds.[24]

The Nineteenth Century and After

The south of Ireland produced its second lying-in hospital in the year 1798 when the County and City of Cork Lying-in Hospital (Erinville) started with six beds. The third was the Coombe Lying-in Hospital, Dublin, founded in 1826 and the fourth did not appear until 1885, when the National Maternity Hospital, Holles Street, Dublin, was established. The first three hospitals in Ireland, the Rotunda, Belfast and Cork, were all Protestant foundations, while the Coombe and the National were predominantly Roman Catholic. The four in Southern Ireland since 1930 have benefited from the Irish Sweepstake but their new incomes from private benevolence and voluntary efforts have diminished considerably.[25]

From their records between 1790 and 1810 we gather that many lying-in hospitals deteriorated in their management, with committees failing to meet and staff not attending, while at the same time financial support was diminishing. This may have been part of a general malaise as the country was at war until Waterloo (1815). It is hardly surprising that no new maternity hospital was opened until 1830 when the Sussex Maternity and Women's Hospital at Brighton again began the combination of charity with midwifery training. Five hospitals were founded in centres where medical schools already existed, although they were not actually connected at that time. The Glasgow Royal Maternity and Women's Hospital made a small beginning in 1834 and moved to Rottenrow in 1860. It early showed the benefit of Listerian teaching because in the year 1872, when the mortality rate in London was very high, out of 323 indoor patients only one died.[26]

In 1841 the forerunner of the Liverpool Maternity Hospital was established in Horatio Street, and moved later to Pembroke Place, and in 1862 to Myrtle Street. Its subsequent development was strongly influenced by the danger of sepsis so that its new building in Brownlow Hill, opened in 1885, had twenty-eight beds all in single rooms, and these were divided into two blocks separated by the administrative offices.[27]

Many notable contributions to obstetrics have been made by the staff. Professor Henry Briggs was an early Caesarean sectionist, while J. St. George Wilson and C. McIntosh Marshall popularized the lower segment Caesarean operation. Robert J. Minnitt's work on gas-air analgesia, and the breech delivery method of J. W. Burns and Marshall, brought fame to the hospital. Its new building was opened in Oxford Street in 1926. The names of Professor W. Blair Bell, founder and first president of the College of Obstetricians and Gynaecologists, and of Sir Arthur Gemmell, a past president of the College, are honoured ones in obstetrics.

In the same year, 1841, the Birkenhead Maternity Hospital was established.

Birmingham Lying-in Hospital opened in St. Mary's Square off Broad Street in 1842; but because of the danger of infection the in-patient work was discontinued from 1868, although for some of that time the charity continued district midwifery with a few beds at 7 Newhall Street for cases requiring special treatment. In 1907 the Maternity Hospital was opened in Loveday Street as a training school for pupil midwives, and in 1911 it combined with the Women's Hospital. A new and larger hospital was opened in 1925. The present intention is to demolish the Loveday Street premises to make way for an inner ring road, and to rebuild within the hospital centre in two parts, one for undergraduate teaching and the other for a normal sample of patients from the immediate area.

After 1850 we find that although midwifery was still not required as a qualifying subject for medical practitioners, the new lying-in hospitals still appeared in what might be called medical school centres. In Sheffield the precursor of the Jessop Hospital for Women was opened in 1864 in Figtree Lane. Two of the most active promoters were men of distinction. One, Dr. J. H. Aveling, who was later on the staff of Chelsea Hospital for Women, was an authority on midwives and the history of obstetrics. The other was Dr. James Hurd Keeling who was born in Malta, the son of a Methodist minister, and served as a medical officer with the Turkish army in the Crimean War; on his return he was lecturer in medical jurisprudence for a time before taking up obstetrics and gynaecology. He survived until 1909, and so there are still people who remember him, perhaps as an amusing character who wrote verses about the tubercle bacillus.[28] In 1878 Mr. Thomas Jessop's liberality enabled the hospital in Gall Street to be built.

At Bristol 1865 saw the beginnings of the future Bristol Maternity Hospital which started as the Temporary Home for Young Girls who had Gone Astray; but it was not until 1894 that it became a lying-in hospital. After this it gradually turned over to admitting married women.[29] The Hospice in Bruntsfield, Edinburgh, later to become the Elsie Inglis Maternity Hospital, began as a hospital and dispensary for women and children in 1878.

Although the Aberdeen Maternity Hospital was preceded by the Aberdeen Dispensary, Vaccine and Lying-in Institution founded in 1781, it did not have qualified midwives until the year 1892 and only began admitting patients in 1893 "to a rented house in Barnett's Close for the lying-in patients whose homes are too wretched". Dr. Stephenson, the Professor of Midwifery at the University, was put in charge.[30] Dundee Maternity Hospital followed in 1900 and Leeds in 1905.

All these hospitals were supported by subscriptions and organized charity funds, so that even in populous centres the need had to be sufficient to stimulate and sustain the voluntary efforts required to build and to maintain these expensive hospitals. Two non-teaching centres in the Midlands illustrate this. Nottingham Hospital for Women started as two hospitals in 1875 and 1885, and in 1926 they combined to build the sixty-bed unit in Peel Street. The Leicester and Leicestershire

Maternity Hospital, on the other hand, was not founded until 1911.

In another category we find, particularly in London, that the plight of the very poor has evoked a charitable response from well-to-do people far removed from those they help. The East End Maternity Hospital founded in Glamis Road, Shadwell, in 1884 is an example. The minutes often refer to mothers in an advanced stage of starvation. It was created "to maintain in the East of London a home for the treatment of poor married women in child-birth free of any charge, and for the training of midwives". It was the only maternity hospital in the densely populated East End. Its wonderful record of normal midwifery is associated with a very strong personality, Miss Margaret Anderson, who was matron (Lady Superintendent) from 1905 to 1938.

The Clapham Maternity Hospital, staffed by medical women, was founded in 1889, and the Mother's Hospital of the Salvation Army at Clapton in 1913.

As far as my researches go, the first municipal hospital supported by the local authority was Springfield Maternity Hospital, Rochdale, Lancashire, founded in 1918.

Even as late as 1921 we find the need for teaching material to train medical students provided the immediate incentive for the establishment of maternity wards. In that year the Nuffield Maternity Home was opened at Oxford and developed into the maternity hospital associated with clinical training, and at Glossop Terrace the maternity hospital at Cardiff for the newly founded Welsh National School of Medicine.

The scope of this paper makes it impossible for me to do justice to British maternity hospitals outside Great Britain and Ireland. I can only touch briefly on one or two.

In Canada, two very early hospitals were founded in Montreal in the 1840s, and they survive attached to the two universities of that city. The Montreal Catholic Maternity Hospital is the lineal descendant of the Montreal Lying-in Hospital founded by William Macnider in 1842. From the beginning it had worked with the old Ecole de Médecine which has now become the University of Montreal. Similarly the Royal Victoria Montreal Maternity Hospital was derived from the amalgamation of the Royal Victoria Hospital with the original University Lying-in Hospital, established in 1843 by the McGill Faculty.[31]

In Australia the Royal Women's Hospital, Melbourne, was founded in 1856 as the Lying-in Hospital. In the six years between 1851 and 1857, following the discovery of gold, the population of Victoria rose from 97,000 to 457,000 and many pregnant women were homeless and destitute. Mrs. Perry, the wife of the Bishop of Melbourne, and two doctors Richard Tracy and John Mound organized the first temporary premises, now become a hospital of 468 beds in which 8,000 deliveries take place each year.

At Sydney in 1866 the Lying-in Hospital of New South Wales was formed as a new wing of the Benevolent Asylum founded by Governor Macquarie in 1820 for the blind, aged and infirm. It stood near the Turnpike House on the site now occupied by the Central Railway Station, and it was used partly as a hospital even as early as 1820 when a committee of ladies was formed to care "for the poor married women during their confinement".[32] Another early Australian foundation was the Rockhampton Queensland Maternity Hospital in 1895 and it is noteworthy that the first ante-natal clinic in the world was conducted in Adelaide from about the year 1911.

Although ten separate maternity hospitals were founded between 1745 and 1800 only fifteen more, which still survive, were added to the list in the next hundred years, in spite of the enormous growth of population. There were, however, good reasons for this, particularly the fear of puerperal fever. Many lying-in hospitals were founded but did not last long; and it is noticeable that in the nineteenth century some of the established hospitals had greatly reduced numbers of deliveries. The twenty-five maternity hospitals existing in 1900 had increased to thirty-six by 1921, four being in Southern Ireland. At this time there were probably smaller ones not recorded in Burdett's annual guide.[33] Many general hospitals had small maternity departments and some of the Poor Law infirmaries had quite large obstetric wards.

From 1921 onwards numbers rose rapidly so that the *Hospitals Year Book* for 1962 names 172 maternity hospitals and 152 maternity nursing homes in Great Britain and Northern Ireland.[34]

The voluntary hospital system applied to all these maternity hospitals until 1918 and it gave subscribers and donors the right to nominate for treatment. Although the State did not support them, Parliament did nct ignore their existence, for lying-in hospitals had to obtain a licence from the Justices of the Peace at Quarter Sessions and the law insisted on an inscription over the entrance to the hospital with the words "Licensed for the Publick Reception of Pregnant Women Pursuant to an Act of Parliament Passed in the 13th year of the reign of George the Third". Subsequent hospital legislation has overruled this.

At the present time private maternity hospitals and nursing homes cannot be opened in England and Wales without planning permission from the local authority, and without being registered with the Public Health Department, which has been designated as the Local Supervising Authority under the Maternity and Child Welfare Acts of 1936.

The early hospitals had to make their own standards and then compare notes, as Mosse arranged to do between the British Hospital and the Rotunda.

The Duration of Stay in Hospital

In the eighteenth century, women were admitted to some hospitals up to four weeks before term and remained in hospital for three weeks after delivery (British Hospital minutes). At the Rotunda, however, patients were not admitted until labour had commenced or symptoms indicative of its approach were present.[35] If they wished, they were allowed to go home on the eighth day after their delivery. This was still the case in 1904 when Queen Alexandra intimated her desire that women should remain in residence for fourteen days after delivery as was customary at Queen Charlotte's Hospital. It came at a time when the Rotunda was admitting so many patients that there was overcrowding. The request was met by building an annexe for nurses' quarters, thus setting free many beds to enable patients to stay longer. The City of London Hospital started by admitting women when they presented themselves.

The Committee soon found it necessary to guard against imposition on the part of their patients, for it was resolved "That such pregnant women who shall come into the house to lie in, shall be liable to be turned out at the discretion of the House Committee, if not brought to bed within a month". Subsequently it was decided to impose in that contingency a fine of twenty shillings.[36]

Separate Labour Wards

At first it was usual to deliver women in general wards. The Rotunda admitted patients until an empty ward was filled, then stopped admissions until the ward was cleared eight days later; but they conducted all deliveries in the ward. In 1890, Master Smyly altered this by creating a special labour ward which contained six or more labour beds and served all the other wards. This continued until recent years. In the same way at the City of London Hospital there was no privacy for labours, which took place in the general wards. In 1791 the Matron was asked at an enquiry whether she advised a separate room for labours but she replied that it would "create dissatisfaction, experiments would be suggested and suspected". It was not until after 1860 that separate labour rooms were provided.[37]

The move for special labour wards, through which all the women would pass, coincided with the increase in puerperal fever and in the light of modern knowledge this is understandable.

The Unmarried

The exclusion of unmarried women from lying-in hospitals was a symptom of a common attitude of those days that the erring must pay the price. There was also a fear that by admitting single women, particularly for second or third pregnancies, the hospital might be branded as a resort of sinners which respectable married women would not wish to enter. The Rotunda did not publish any ban on the unmarried. Queen Charlotte's Hospital's predecessors in Duke Street and Bayswater accepted a deserving unmarried woman in her first pregnancy, and the General Lying-in Hospital, York Road, had the same rule. But the British Hospital and the City of London were strict in excluding the unmarried until over a hundred years had elapsed. It is noteworthy that Liverpool Maternity Hospital refused to accept unmarried mothers at all until the National Health Service in 1948 abolished the individual book of rules.

The boot was on the other foot at Bristol where the Maternity Hospital, after starting as a refuge for girls who had gone astray, gradually turned over to the normal working of a maternity hospital.

Medical Education

This important feature of the history of maternity hospitals has been covered by Holland in the *Historical Review of British Obstetrics, 1800–1950.*[38] There is no doubt that lying-in hospitals were started to provide practice for the teaching of midwifery and this could only be done at the bedside. The General Medical Council became operative in 1858 but at first did not insist on midwifery forming part of the medical curriculum. Although the four Scottish Universities and Dublin had included midwifery in the doctor's training for many years before that, in England it was possible for a doctor to qualify without answering any questions in midwifery until as late as 1886. After 1888 every medical student had to work in the lying-in wards for three months and this of course had one result, that schools which had no maternity wards were forced to create them. As the instruction of maternity nurses and midwives was another object in the founding of lying-in hospitals, this teaching took place at all such hospitals from the earliest times; and although it was not properly systematized the standards of midwifery steadily improved. Training was not followed by an examination until the second half of the nineteenth century when the Obstetrical Society of London in 1872 introduced examinations for their diploma. The Central Midwives Board became effective on 1st April 1903.[39]

Over the years the functions of maternity hospitals have changed. The original motive of the founders was to provide places where they could practice obstetrics and instruct midwives and doctors. Laymen responded readily because of the plight of the poor in populous centres, and instituted numerous charities, of which a number still survive.

There followed a difficult era lasting over a hundred and fifty years during which the benefits of hospital midwifery were threatened by the blight of puerperal infection and maternal deaths. Before the causes of puerperal fever were known it was recognized that it was contagious for patients in their own homes because the disease was carried by the doctor or midwife, as Alexander Gordon of Aberdeen described in 1795.[40] Semmelweiss in 1861 exposed the danger, in hospital work, of puerperal fever being conveyed from the post-mortem room and from patient to patient, and Florence Nightingale published horrifying figures from hospital reports.[20]

The discovery of streptococci and the introduction of antisepsis reduced the mortality considerably; but it was not brought down to its present low level until asepsis and a proper mask technique combined to lessen infection (1928–34) and eventually the introduction in this country of sulphonamides (1936) and penicillin (1944) reduced maternal deaths from sepsis to a minimum. The use of blood transfusion and the operation of Caesarean section completely changed the practice of obstetrics.

Nowadays a maternity hospital is no longer regarded merely as a place for a woman to be delivered. The ante-natal supervision is undoubtedly far more important than the actual delivery, when midwives and obstetricians stand by to support and relieve the normal mother while she delivers herself. In the words of Sir Dugald Baird, "The modern function of a maternity hospital is to be the central point of obstetrics for the area. It is expected to set a standard of midwifery, and must be prepared to treat serious emergency cases sent in by doctors for expert treatment. It must act as a training centre for midwives and doctors and by offering facilities for research work help to advance our knowledge of the subject".

REFERENCES

1. AVELING, J. H. (1872). *English Midwives: Their History and Prospects*, Churchill, London.
2. GRAHAM, H. [FLACK, I. H.] (1950). *Eternal Eve*, Heinemann, London.
3. MAUBRAY, J. (1724). *The Female Physician . . .* , Holland, London.

4. PUGH, B. (1754). *A Treatise of Midwifery* . . . , London, for J. Buckland.
5. DOUGLAS, JOHN (1736). *A Short Account of the State of Midwifery in London, Westminster* . . . , p. 73, London, for the author.
6. GLAISTER, J. (1894). *Dr. William Smellie and his Contemporaries*, p. 35, Maclehose, Glasgow.
7. FLEMING, J. B. (1962). The mysteries concerning the last illness, death and burial of Bartholomew Mosse, *Irish J. med. Sci.*, pp. 147–63.
8. KIRKPATRICK, T. P. C. (1913). *The Book of the Rotunda Hospital*, Adlard, London.
9. BROWNE, O'D. T. D. (1947). *The Rotunda Hospital, 1745–1945*, Livingstone, Edinburgh.
10. VARTAN, C. K. (1962). *The British Hospital for Mothers and Babies.* (Present address, West Kent Med. Chir. Soc.)
11. CANNINGS, R. B. (1922). *The City of London Maternity Hospitals: A Short History*, Forsaith, London.
12. RYAN, T. (1885). *History of Queen Charlotte's Hospital*, London.
13. PEACHEY, G. C. (1924). Note upon the provision for lying-in women in London up to the middle of the 18th century, *Proc. roy. Soc. Med.*, **17** (Epidem. Sect), 72.
14. MAITLAND (1756). *History of London*, quoted by Peachey.
15. VON SIEBOLD, E. C. J. (1839, 1845). *Versuch einer Geschichte der Geburtshülfe*, 2 vols., Enslin, Berlin.
16. LE FORT, L. C. (1866). *Des Maternités: Etude sur les Maternités et les Institutions Charitables d'Accouchement à Domicile* . . . , Masson, Paris.
17. FASBENDER, H. (1906). *Geschichte der Geburtshülfe*, Jena, pp. 85, 145, 208.
18. SPENCER, H. R. (1927). *The History of British Midwifery from 1650 to 1800*, Bale & Danielsson, London.
19. SIMPSON, A. R. (1893). Sketch of the history of the Royal Maternity and Simpson Memorial Hospital, *Edinb. Hosp. Rep.*, **1**, 42.
20. NIGHTINGALE, F. (1871). *Introductory Notes on Lying-in Institutions*, Longmans, Green & Co.
21. WHITE, C. (1773). *A Treatise on the Management of Pregnant and Lying-in Women*, London, for E. & C. Dilly.
22. BRIDE, J. W. (1922). *A Short History of St. Mary's Hospital, Manchester, 1792–1922*, Sherratt & Hughes, Manchester.
23. STURROCK, J. (1958). Early maternity hospitals in Edinburgh (1756–1879), *J. Obstet. Gynaec. Brit. Emp.*, **65**, 122.
24. MACAFEE, C. H. G. (1942). The history of the Belfast School of Obstetrics, 1793–1933, *Ulster med. J.*, **11**, 20.
25. CUMMINS, N. M. (1957). *Some Chapters of Cork Medical History*, Cork Univ. Press.
26. JARDINE, R. (1903). The Glasgow Maternity Hospitals, past and present, *Trans. Glasgow obstet. gynaec. Soc. (1900–2)*, **3**, 14–28.
27. FRANCIS, H. H. (1955). The history of obstetrics and gynaecology in Liverpool, *Sphincter* (Liverpool Univ.), **17**, 114.
28. FINCH, E. (1960). The song of the squirt, *Med. Hist.*, **4**, 59.

29. SMYTHE, H. J. D. and SHEPHERD, H. L. (1940). Midwifery in Bristol, *Bristol med. chir. J.*, **57**, 117.
30. BAIRD, D. (1939). *The Book of Aberdeen. B.M.A. Meeting*, p. 62.
31. ABBOTT, M. E. (1931). *History of Medicine in the Province of Quebec*, p. 83, Toronto.
32. *Australian Encyclopaedia*, Angus & Robertson, Sydney, London, vol. V., pp. 1–7.
33. BURDETT, H. C. (1925). *Hospital and Charities Annual*, Scientific Press, London.
34. MILNE, J. F. (Ed.) (1961). *Hospitals Year Book*, Institute of Hospital Administrators, London.
35. BROWNE, O'D. T. D., *op. cit.*, p. 45.
36. CANNINGS, R. B., *op. cit.*, pp. 5, 9.
37. *Ibid*, pp. 10, 24.
38. HOLLAND, E. (1954). The medical schools and the teaching of midwifery, in *Historical Review of British Obstetrics and Gynaecology, 1800–1950*, edited by Kerr, J. M., *et al.*, 294, Livingstone, Edinburgh and London.
39. ATKINSON, S. B. (1907). *The Office of Midwife*, London.
40. GORDON, A. (1795). *A Treatise on the Epidemic Puerperal Fever of Aberdeen*, London.

A CHRONOLOGICAL LIST

1745   THE ROTUNDA, Dublin Lying-in Hospital.
1749   BRITISH HOSPITAL FOR MOTHERS AND BABIES, The Lying-in Hospital.
1750   CITY OF LONDON MATERNITY HOSPITAL.
1752   QUEEN CHARLOTTE'S HOSPITAL, The General Lying-in Hospital.
1760   PRINCESS MARY MATERNITY HOSPITAL, Newcastle-upon-Tyne Lying-in Charity.
1765   THE GENERAL LYING-IN HOSPITAL, York Road. The New Westminster Lying-in Hospital.
1790   ST. MARY'S HOSPITALS, Manchester Lying-in Charity.
1793   THE SIMPSON MEMORIAL MATERNITY PAVILION, Edinburgh Lying-in Hospital.
1794   THE ROYAL MATERNITY HOSPITAL, BELFAST, The Humane Female Society for the Relief of Lying-in Women.
1798   CORK MATERNITY HOSPITAL (ERINVILLE).
1826   THE COOMBE LYING-IN HOSPITAL, Dublin.
1830   SUSSEX MATERNITY AND WOMEN'S HOSPITAL, Brighton.
1834   GLASGOW ROYAL MATERNITY HOSPITAL, Rottenrow.
1841   LIVERPOOL MATERNITY HOSPITAL.
1841   BIRKENHEAD MATERNITY HOSPITAL.
1842   BIRMINGHAM MATERNITY HOSPITAL, Loveday Street.
1856   ROYAL WOMEN'S HOSPITAL, Melbourne Lying-in Hospital.
1864   THE JESSOP HOSPITAL FOR WOMEN, Sheffield Lying-in Hospital.

1864 LADY BOWEN LYING-IN HOSPITAL, Brisbane.

1865 BRISTOL MATERNITY HOSPITAL, The Temporary Home for Young Girls who had Gone Astray.

1866 THE WOMEN'S HOSPITAL, Crown Street, Sydney. The Lying-in Hospital of New South Wales.

1878 ELSIE INGLIS HOSPITAL, The Edinburgh Hospital and Dispensary for Women and Children, Bruntsfield.

1875–85 NOTTINGHAM HOSPITAL FOR WOMEN, Nottingham Hospital and the Samaritan Hospital.

1884 EAST END MATERNITY HOSPITAL, East End Mothers' Lying-in Home, Glamis Road, London, E.1.

1885 THE NATIONAL MATERNITY HOSPITAL, Holles Street, Dublin.

1889 CLAPHAM MATERNITY HOSPITAL, London.

1893 ABERDEEN MATERNITY HOSPITAL.

1895 ROCKHAMPTON MATERNITY HOSPITAL, Queensland.

1900 DUNDEE MATERNITY HOSPITAL.

1905 LEEDS MATERNITY HOSPITAL.

1911 LEICESTER AND LEICESTERSHIRE MATERNITY HOSPITAL.

1913 MOTHERS' HOSPITAL OF THE SALVATION ARMY, Clapton.

1915 BROMLEY MATERNITY HOSPITAL.

1918 SPRINGFIELD MATERNITY HOSPITAL, Rochdale.

1921 PLAISTOW MATERNITY HOSPITAL.

1921 CARDIFF MATERNITY HOSPITAL, Glossop Terrace.

1921 OXFORD MATERNITY HOSPITAL, Nuffield Maternity Home.

Note on Continental Foundations

1589 MUNICH MATERNITY HOSPITAL.

1630 MATERNITY CASES admitted to HÔTEL-DIEU, Paris.

1712 ST. MERXER SPITAL, Vienna.

1728 STRASBURG MATERNITY HOSPITAL.

1751 BERLIN and GOTTINGEN.

Children's Hospitals

ALFRED WHITE FRANKLIN

THE BRITISH CHILDREN's hospitals are a product of the nine-teenth century. When that century began Britain contained not one. The first children's dispensary opened in 1816, the first children's hospital in 1852 and by 1888 there were thirty-eight hospitals for sick children. As far as can be learned today, when extinction, new foundations and loss of independence have done their work, forty-one children's hospitals remain.

"No new *ad hoc* children's hospitals have been built since the National Health Service Act came into operation" (Taylor, 1962). Paediatricians have multiplied, there has been a pro-liferation of professors of child health, who still play a part in the hospital care of the sick child, but no new children's hospital is, in official terms, even "envisaged". The twentieth-century trend is the development of paediatric units within the frame-work of the general hospital. Children's hospitals in isolation are in danger of being absorbed, diverted from their founding function, or destroyed. This is a study of the history of the rise of the children's hospitals that set the scene for today.

John Bunnell Davis founded the Universal Dispensary for Children in 1816. There were forerunners—there always are—notably Dr. George Armstrong who established in 1769 a dis-pensary for infant poor in Red Lion Square. Having thrice moved premises, this ended after sixteen years, sharing in the sad decline of its founder's fortunes but leaving as a legacy its good example. Sir Zachary Cope has already paid tribute at the conference to the value of Armstrong's dispensary in the dis-pensary movement. But Davis knew only the general dispen-saries, holding appointments at two, and was unaware of Armstrong's work.

He was aware, as all contemporaries must have been, of

another social experiment, Thomas Coram's Foundling Hospital, which influenced so many aspects of Georgian life. Coram, returning from the New World, where human labour was the greatest need, saw newly born children left deserted, to die, on the dunghills in and around London. The "Indefatigable Schemist" was as appalled by the wanton inhumanity as he was moved by the wanton waste. His charter was received after great efforts in 1739; the first babies were admitted in Hatton Garden on 25th March 1741, and building began in 1742 on a site in Bloomsbury Fields acquired from the Earl of Salisbury. This new building caught the imagination of the day. William Hogarth, himself a governor whose wife took on the care of some of the foundlings, suggested a scheme for adorning the walls with works of art. This inspired the offer of paintings from a group which included Francis Hayman, Allan Ramsay, Samuel Scott, Richard Wilson, and later Sir Joshua Reynolds himself.

The group dined and planned together, and some have seen in it the germ of the Royal Academy founded in 1768, although Hogarth, always something of a rebel, was against the teaching of the arts under regular Academy professors. Music also was laid under tribute. In the newly built chapel Handel himself opened the organ on 1st May 1750 with a performance of the *Messiah*. Concerts, held regularly in aid of the funds, attracted the rank and fashion of the town, and nothing was more popular in George II's day than a morning's lounge visiting the Foundling.

This strange juxtaposition—the highest creations of Hogarth, Handel and the Arts with the less elevated creation of illegitimate babies—attracted and impressed the ruling classes of an age that, ending in elegance, had begun coarse, callous and corrupt.

Government also took a hand, and when in 1756 the governors appealed to the House of Commons for financial help, the reaction was strong, favourable and dangerously ill-directed. Help was made conditional on a new principle, "that all children offered should be accepted". A public scandal followed in which all the Hogarthian vices of lust, greed and cruelty conspired to wreck the good intentions of a sentimental Parliament. The arrival of a multitude of debilitated, sick and dying unwanted babies from the length and breadth of England increased the hospital death rate until in 1760 a halt was called. During the forty-six months of indiscriminate admission 14,934 babies were received of whom 10,389 perished. The majority died under the age of six months, but it became clear that for those who survived their second birthday the outlook was very good.

The early experiences of the Foundling Hospital taught practical charity to a nation of laymen who had lost touch with the charitable practices of the mediaeval church, and played some part in what Sir John Simon has called the growth of a new humanity in British politics. These experiences also confirmed in doctors' minds the danger of separating babies from their mothers and of putting them in quantity and in contact with each other within the walls of a hospital. The twin dangers, separation and cross infection, are only now being mastered, two hundred years later.

The last quarter of the eighteenth century witnessed two disturbing events, first the American Declaration of Independence (1776) and second the French Revolution (1789). With the former came a challenge to think about the methods and the purposes of government, and particularly about the responsibility of governors for governed, so that it was easy to welcome the latter and to sing with Wordsworth

Bliss was it in that dawn to be alive.

All this helped to foster the humanitarian spirit, until the ways of the proletariat, seizing power, reversing the natural order of the state, and taking a public, cruel and bloody revenge upon its late governors, brought a sharp reaction. When the execution of the French King and Queen was followed by the seizure of power by Napoleon Buonaparte, a strong anti-Jacobin feeling revived. The war which Pitt waged against Buonaparte and which was to lead through Trafalgar to Waterloo, left England after 1815 to the aristocratic governments, paternal in intent, of Lord Liverpool followed by the Duke of Wellington.

It was in this atmosphere of *noblesse oblige* and of royal

patronage that John Bunnell Davis had to muster support for his Universal Dispensary.

Davis was born in 1780 in Clare, Suffolk, the son of Timothy Davis, one time surgeon and apothecary in Thetford, Norfolk, and later surgeon of the Honourable Board of Commissioners of His Majesty's Customs in London. He became an M.R.C.S. after three years in strict attendance on the lectures at Guy's and St. Thomas's and at St. Bartholomew's, but being unwell, accompanied a "family of distinction" to the South of France during the Peace of Amiens (1802). When the war broke out again (1804) he was made a prisoner and, unable to leave France, he pursued medical studies at Paris and Montpellier, graduating M.D. in the latter University. Leaving Paris for Verdun he published his *Observations on Precipitate Burial, and the Diagnosis of Death*. He sent a copy of the work to Corvisart with a petition addressed to Buonaparte, who granted him parole to return home early in 1806.

Davis must have been an industrious person with a fluent pen, for while in France he also published an *Ancient and Modern History of Nice* and *More Subjects than One concerning France and the French People*—in two volumes. In May 1806 he went to Edinburgh where he gained his M.D. in 1808 having published in 1807 *The Origin and Description of Bognor*. He next joined his father in the Customs, where he took charge of the medical department. In 1810 he was temporary physician to the Forces in Ipswich. His studies of the sick troops returning from Walcheren were published with numerous descriptions of cases and dissections.

In 1811 he became physician to the London Dispensary, and during the next few years pondered over the want of a dispensary for sick children. He made approaches to friends in 1812 but it was not until 1815, when the nation was tranquil after war, that he circulated a written address and put his mind to realizing his aim.

The main object was to reduce the number of infant deaths. Davis estimated that one third of all children born died before reaching five years, the majority under two years. Very few children were brought to the general dispensaries and infants under two years of age were hardly ever admitted to the general hospitals. After the first three months when the midwifery practitioners lost interest there was no special doctor. The children's dispensary would provide a central point of medical attention for investigation of the diseases of children and young persons. Lectures were to be given to doctors, and parents were to be instructed by leaflet. Because of the urgency of treatment the customary letter of recommendation would not be required and children would be accepted from birth until the age of twelve years. Children kept healthy until twelve, he claimed, were unlikely to become diseased later and so with healthier infants fewer workhouses and fewer hospitals would be needed, and the rates would be diminished.

The plan was to have a dispensary in London, in the centre of the metropolis, with stations in other areas, and to have an infirmary for convalescent care out of London. The dispensary system cost the least and children could "remain at home, however humble, surrounded and affectionately nursed by their dearest relations, and by those who feel a natural and earnest interest in their welfare". It was at the time considered too dangerous to separate any infant under the age of two years from its mother. The other danger was infection and Davis wrote that there would be "every precaution not to permit promiscuous intercourse of patients at the dispensary and to use every exertion to assist in exterminating that most infectious and fatal of all diseases, the *small-pox*, excluding such patients and promoting the cause of vaccination".

Waterloo had been fought on 18th June 1815, and on 30th November a meeting to launch the new dispensary was held in the committee rooms of the Royal Humane Society in St. Paul's Church Yard, at the invitation of Benjamin Hawes. It was estimated that 1,200 to 1,500 infant patients would cost £300 of which £40 would be for the actual purchase of medicines. By February 1816 the support of 107 Governors and the patronage of the Royal Dukes of Kent and of Sussex assured success and two gentlemen were authorized to look at a house on St. Andrew's Hill, Doctors' Commons. On 27th April Kent took the chair at an inaugural meeting and two days later the staff appointments began to be made—one physician, Davis, two surgeons, Gillham and Pettigrew, an apothecary, Field, who was to be resident at £50 a year with £25 expenses and the upper part of the house as a dwelling, and one collector who was to have five per cent poundage. Two weeks after the directions were issued for fitting up and repairing the house, the apothecary took possession and the first patients were received on 24th June, one week later.

During the first three and a half years 7,820 sick infants were admitted of whom 7,030 were cured and relieved, 300 vaccinated and 130 died, the remainder being still "on the books". "Papers of instruction as to the means to be employed for preserving health were gratuitously circulated among the poor." In one paper the early symptoms of influenza were described to help in early treatment during the epidemic in 1816, said to be similar to those of 1800, 1801, 1804, 1814 and 1815. In 1820 stations in Southwark and Lambeth had been opened, but the infirmary had not materialized nor had the parishes, as had been hoped, appointed poor houses a few miles out of town for the reception of convalescent children.

Davis published accounts of the dispensary practice in the current medical journals, following the lines of Sydenham's epidemic constitutions. He claimed too,' that the dispensary "had given birth to a school of medicine, in which the theory of disease is elucidated and confirmed by practice in that very imperfect department of science relating to children's diseases".'

By 1818 the care of patients and the lectures were in full swing and thirty-four pupils are listed by name.

All this is recounted with verbatim records of speeches at festival dinners, and correspondence with bishops about charity sermons in the large volume of *Annals Historical and Medical, during the first four years of the Universal Dispensary for Children*, published by Davis in 1821 and extending to 648 pages.

John Bunnell Davis died 28th September 1824 at the early age of forty-four, truly an enlightened and enlightening person, remarkable for his unwearied labours, and worthy to be remembered as one of the most important influences in British paediatrics.

In 1823 the Dispensary, now the Royal Universal Dispensary for Children, had moved to its present site in the Waterloo Road, where it continued to serve the neighbourhood, although two important functions, teaching and domiciliary visits, seem to have ceased. With the death of the founder in 1824 "the charity faded" in the words of a later Secretary, Edward Meymott.

In 1839 occurred an event of critical importance in the history of children's hospitals. Dr. Charles West, aged twenty-three, was allowed to attend the Dispensary by the kindness of Dr. Willis, whom he succeeded as physician in 1842.

West was born in 1816, son of a Baptist minister. After an apprenticeship to Mr. Gray of Amersham—learning to compound medicines and to know Shakespeare—he spent two years at St. Bartholomew's and then two years in Europe. From Bonn he went to Paris and then to Berlin, proceeding M.D. there in 1837. Midwifery in Dublin was followed by an unsuccessful partnership in the City of London, a turn of duty at St. Bartholomew's helping Latham with the typhus ward, and then the Royal Universal Dispensary for Children to whose services he gave himself and his youthful enthusiasm wholeheartedly for the next ten years. In 1844 domiciliary visits which had lapsed were recommenced in a well-defined triangle containing 70,000 inhabitants in just over half a square mile. In 1847 mothers were allowed treatment since a mother's illness could "communicate itself to the infant at the breast or protract and aggravate that of the child". In the dispensary's first thirty years over 175,000 children had been received at an estimated cost of less than one shilling each.

In 1846, and here West's influence can be seen, the Committee appealed for funds to open the wards to in-patients and for the delivery once more of clinical lectures on infantile diseases. The example was cited of the main cities of Europe each with its children's hospital.

The Committee claimed that the founders' plans included in-patient care, which was not strictly true. John Bunnell Davis wanted a convalescent infirmary but believed an acute hospital to be much too dangerous.

What had happened to change the minds of doctors, so that in the 1840s they favoured, indeed demanded, hospital beds for children? The prime object of the dispensary had been to lower the terrible toll of mortality in infants and children. The figures showed that the attempt had failed. Perhaps admission into hospitals might succeed. And almost certainly there was something else. Davis had spoken rather romantically of the home, however humble, and of the loving care within it. Two years' experience of domiciliary visits gave West some insight into those homes and must have convinced him and his contemporaries of the need to remove some of the sick children who were curable out of those overcrowded, ill-ventilated dwellings.

These were the hungry forties. The Reform Act of 1832 had opened Parliament to the middle classes. Railways had opened up the country to the movement of people. And yet with everything set for progress and prosperity, there was poverty and unemployment. Health, life itself, were threatened as typhus and cholera, recently arrived in Europe, burst forth from time to time out of the great conglomerations of the slum dwellings of the ill-fed, unwashed masses. Pointing the way out, for those with eyes to see, was Chadwick's momentous Report to Parliament on the Sanitary Conditions of the Labouring Population of Great Britain (1842). Davis in 1818, while London was expanding and new building going up to house a rapidly increasing population, could not have foreseen what would happen after these buildings had been standing inhabited for thirty or forty years, while families increased, children grew, married and begot more children, in an area without drains, refuse collection, proper water supplies or sufficient space in which to bury the dead.

As the forties advanced there seems to have been a slackening of spirit and a scarcity of money. The in-patient beds seemed as far away as ever and even Dr. Charles West began to lose heart —or was he over-working? He had collected teaching posts in midwifery at the Middlesex Hospital and at St. Bartholomew's. He had given lectures in paediatrics at the Middlesex, based on his clinical experience at the Royal Universal Dispensary, and had published them in book form in 1848 when he was elected F.R.C.P. During that year at the Dispensary he had improved the out-patients' waiting room, written a begging address and compared drug bills with those at the Middlesex. He attended the Committee on 29th December 1848, regular as ever, but this was to be his last and on 9th August 1849 he resigned.

Whatever the reason, this was a double tragedy for the Dispensary for not only was he lost but Dr. S. W. J. Merriman was gained. He lacked every qualification that West so notably displayed. Of West it was written "The fractious or frightened child could not long resist the magic of his smile or the winning gentleness of his manner.' And of Merriman: "He was sadly deficient in tact, child-like in manner, expressing himself awkwardly, undecided in opinion." West in his photograph looks serene, handsome, every inch the eminent Victorian. Merriman had a "round, unexpressive face, wore goggled spectacles, and had a peculiar white woolly hair". Promising in his youth, he seems to have failed to mature, retired early and nursed ill health on the Isle of Wight until his death in 1873 aged fifty-five.

In Merriman's hands the Infirmary rapidly sank. There was still some idea of in-patient beds and the cost of four beds was estimated in 1851 at £50 capital with an annual charge of £115. A boy had indeed been lodged in the hospital from 19th August to 17th October 1851 for lithotrity by the surgeon. But in 1852 a Committee of three members rejected the in-patient plan. Whereas in 1847 there had been 7,000 patients now, five years later, there were barely one thousand although this was then the only dispensary for children in London. The Infirmary did survive, flourished again, was rebuilt in 1902 as the Royal Waterloo Hospital for Children and Women. It is now a part of St. Thomas's Hospital.

Its last independent paediatrician*, saluting its founder, John Bunnell Davis, and paying tribute to its long years of service to the women and children of the South Bank, sadly reflects that when a time for greatness came in 1850, the hospital missed its historic opportunity.

On Charles West fortune continued to smile. In 1849 he surveyed the state of children in general hospitals, and what he found strengthened his resolve. He told later how a stroll one evening in June 1849, two months before his resignation from the Royal Universal Dispensary, had taken him through Lincoln's Inn Fields. Looking at Dr. Mead's house in Great Ormond Street the inspiration came that here he would found

* i.e. The present writer.

his children's hospital, here at last would be his in-patient beds. With the help and advice of Dr. Henry Bence Jones a Committee was formed which met at the latter's home on 30th January 1850 and resolved to establish in London a hospital for sick children. An advertisement duly appeared in *The Times* (16th February 1850) appealing on behalf of the Hospital, intended "to contain 100 beds for children between the ages of two and twelve years". Children under ten years occupied only three per cent of hospital beds although half the deaths in London were of children. West pointed out that this proportion had not changed in fifty years, despite the reduction in smallpox mortality since vaccination. After many enquiries and discussions No 49 Great Ormond Street was leased for twenty-one years at £200 per annum on 29th April 1851, in the Great Exhibition year.

During June and July, West studied the children's hospitals of France and Germany, experience useful for altering Mead's house for its new purpose. On 20th January 1852 Dr. Charles West and Dr. William Jenner were elected Physicians and Mr. G. D. Pollock, Surgeon. Mrs. Willey had been appointed Matron in December 1851. With Mr. Lynch as House Surgeon and Mr. Lunn as Dispenser, all was ready for the admission of patients on St. Valentine's Day, 14th February 1852. And so began the first British Hospital for Sick Children. Only eight patients were admitted into the ten available beds and twenty-four out-patients presented themselves. The hospital doubled its size in the first twelve years (sixty-two beds). The one hundred beds were achieved with the building of the new "hospital in the garden" completed by the twenty-fifth birthday (1877). Problems arose about the admission of fever cases, temperatures rising in the Committee so that Dr. Bence Jones resigned his place in March 1854 after quarrelling on this subject with Charles West. Scarlet fever was the main danger, with measles and whooping cough next. Diphtheria, described by Fothergill in 1748, had not assumed epidemic proportions, although it was destined to be a preoccupation of the infectious block later in the century.

Infants under two years of age were admitted grudgingly and to the great anxiety of the Board of Management, in 1878 only twenty, but in 1881 as many as eighty. They could be received into the Hospital with or without the mother. Convalescent beds were early provided in Brighton and later Mitcham, and for twenty years from 1869 in Cromwell House in Highgate.

Let us leave this prospering hospital and return to consider the aims of its founder as Charles West saw them, looking back in his retirement in 1877. First it was to provide hospital care for poor sick children and to advise the mothers of those who could not be admitted. Second it was to advance medical science and to improve student teaching in connexion with disease in children. Third it was to educate "all classes, but chiefly the poor" in the management of sick children, and to train women in the special duties of children's nursing.

The emphasis is now not so much upon decreasing mortality rates as upon learning and teaching, teaching both doctors and nurses. Although Davis's plan to instruct mothers remains, there is no record of leaflets to be distributed gratuitously as at the Universal Dispensary, and the calculation in 1880 that if a new case took as much as five minutes and an old one one and a half minutes, each medical officer's out-patients session would last five and a half hours, does not suggest much time for explanation to the mother, let alone instruction.

Charles West, the founder, was a difficult character. He had deserted the Royal Universal Dispensary, he resigned from St. Bartholomew's in pique, and in due course he fell out with Mr. Walter, the Chairman of the Committee of the Hospital for Sick Children. Born a Baptist, he had been converted to Roman Catholicism in middle age, and in the Chairman's view, had tried to bring into the practice of the Hospital the influence of the Roman Catholic priesthood. This West publicly denied. What cannot be denied is that he proved a difficult colleague.

At the Royal College of Physicians he had a good measure of success, being twice Censor, Croonian and Lumleian lecturer, and Harveian Orator in 1874. In 1880, because of London fogs he began to winter in Nice and died in Paris on 19th March 1898 aged eighty-two. Let his memorial be that great hospital and exemplar of other children's hospitals which his enthusiasm and his idealism brought into being.

The example of John Bunnell Davis was imitated in London

in The Royal Western Infirmary for Children, founded in 1820 with three stations, two in Marylebone and one in Westminster. There followed The National Children's Hospital, Dublin, founded in 1821 but not included in this survey. Davis tells us that on 7th July 1820 a professional gentleman from Manchester visited the Universal Dispensary in London "to gather information as to the mode of establishing a similar charity in that opulent and extensive town". But Manchester did not then add urgency to its opulence or its extent, and eight years passed before anything came of it. On 28th November 1828 "at a very respectable meeting held at the Exchange it was resolved to institute a Dispensary for the cure of diseases incident to children." The reasons recited at a later meeting are stated as: the multiplied diseases incident to infancy, their peculiar nature, the sources of epidemic disease which children constitute and the "fact" that general establishments cannot give immediate enough treatment. With the speed characteristic of those days, in just over two months from the first meeting, "The General Dispensary for Children" was open and receiving outpatients (2nd February 1829) at 25 Back King Street. Unlike the London Universal Dispensary and despite the plea for immediate treatment, a letter of recommendation from a subscriber was demanded.

The number of patients grew slowly, 1,105 in 1833, 1,388 in 1836 and 2,000 in 1842, but there was still a dreadful mortality rate in Manchester. The Dispensary, with all the work of Dr. Alexander and with the help of Dr. Stott and Dr. Hancock, did not provide the answer. In 1847, although only 76 out of 1,466 dispensary patients died, it was reported that one half of the children born in Manchester died before the age of five years.

In 1854 Dr. Alexander left the district and during the next year Daniel Grant, the founder, immortalized by Charles Dickens as one of the Cheeryble Brothers, disappeared from the scene. For these losses the dispensary was more than compensated by the arrival of Dr. Louis Borchardt, a specialist in children's diseases who would certainly have known the Children's Hospital in Berlin, and who had settled in Manchester in the early fifties. He succeeded Dr. Alexander as Physician in 1854, and at this time the need for in-patient beds is first mentioned. Since the name was changed to "The General Hospital and Dispensary for Sick Children" in 1855, it is likely that the hospital proper started in that year. In 1856 there were six beds in North Parade, but Dr. Borchardt was asking for at least twenty-five and these were provided in new premises in Bridge Street in 1860. Nine years later mounting work and the serious effects of epidemics among a population living in terrible conditions necessitated further enlargements. A new dispensary was opened in 1869 in Gartside Street, Manchester, and the next year the Hospital moved to Pendlebury.

Dr. Borchardt, who must be given much of the credit for stimulating these developments, was a German born in Silesia in East Prussia in 1816. He studied in Berlin where he graduated M.D. in 1838. He did good work as a Royal Commissioner in stemming a typhus epidemic in Upper Silesia, and settled in practice. This was the period when Frederick William was gingerly flirting with democratic forms of government for Prussia. When Frederick's patience was exhausted in 1848, Borchardt found himself in prison for anti-government agitation and after release in 1850 he was prevented by systematic persecution from once more succeeding in medical practice. He fled about 1852 to England, then as now the asylum for political refugees, and settling in Manchester practised largely among children, and established a twenty-five-year connection with the Children's Hospital. He died in 1883 having been on the Council of the section of diseases of children at the great London International Medical Congress of 1881. Clearly a man of courage who had known adversity, Borchardt well repaid Mancunian hospitality by his work for sick children and for their Hospital.

After London and Manchester, Liverpool was the next city in England to open a children's dispensary. This time a surgeon, Alfred Stephens, was the moving spirit, but alas, we have no details of "his views and intentions relative to the usefulness of the projected Institution which", needless to say, "were unanimously approved" by the two parsons and the one layman constituting the audience at the inaugural meeting on 22nd January 1851. The health of Liverpool and the mortality rates were then the worst in the kingdom. Following the Napoleonic Wars, from 1815 to 1835, eight new docks had been built, and trade, not now the slave trade but the cotton industry, flourished, holding out hopes of employment to many in less well-employed parts of Britain. The dock labour was unskilled and casual and with the failure of the potato crop in Ireland in 1846 conditions became appalling. For in the first half of 1847, 300,000 Irish pauper immigrants had landed in Liverpool, of whom 70,000 settled there. In 1801 the total population of Liverpool had been 77,653, but by 1846 it was four times as great, nearly half of them living in the narrow cul-de-sac courts and cellars which had been rapidly erected to give shelter from the weather but with little in the way of water supply, sewage or rubbish disposal.

There had been a cholera epidemic in 1832 during which a certain Dr. W. H. Duncan, Physician to the South Dispensary, had studied closely the living conditions of the poor. The mortality in Liverpool between 1839 and 1846 was two to three times as high as in what William Farr called the healthy areas. The year 1846 saw the passing of the Liverpool Sanitary Act giving the Council power to appoint a Medical Officer of Health and leading the way to the great Public Health Act of 1848.

Of the grand causes of death—war, famine and pestilence—the last has always been the concern of doctors. Infection, epidemic and sporadic, still provided the main cause of death and it was to reduce death rates among children that the founders of children's dispensaries and hospitals were pledged. They hoped to do this by learning more about disease in children and by perfecting methods of treatment.

To Dr. W. H. Duncan reporting on the sanitary state of the labouring classes in Liverpool in 1840, the causes of the 7,000 cases of fever treated each year were principally the condition of the dwellings of the labouring classes and some of their habits. The ill effects of overcrowding, want of cleanliness and disinclination to move to hospital when sick were exaggerated by imperfect ventilation, inadequate drains and sewers and the lack of refuse disposal or collection. The correction of these faults lay not in the hands of the dispensary and hospital doctors but in the exercise of powers to improve the public health by directly attacking the evil housing and sanitary conditions of the poor. So began the hundred years' war to improve hygiene and housing, waged through politics and economics and public enlightenment by the Medical Officers of Health. And when in later times prophylactic treatment was devised against acute specific fevers, it was the public health officer rather than the personal hospital physician who had largely to put it into effect.

Dr. W. H. Duncan, the first Medical Officer of Health to hold office in England, was appointed in Liverpool in January 1848, nine months before John Simon took office under the Corporation of the City of London. Gradually over the years improvement in public hygiene went hand in hand with improvement in personal health. In 1851 personal health still needed the establishment of more and bigger hospitals, and so on 3rd March 1851 the Liverpool Institution for the Diseases of Children opened as a dispensary in Upper Hill Street. In the first five months 308 children received advice and medicine from the three honorary medical officers. The most prevalent diseases were diarrhoea, bronchitis and scarlatina.

In 1853 new premises at 46 Great George Street were acquired and the name changed to the Infirmary for Children. On 14th January 1856 it was resolved to extend the benefits by admitting in-patients, and by appointing a resident house surgeon "and the requisite attendant nurses etc." Later in the year (6th June 1856) a five-year lease of No 58 Hope Street was offered and the rumour of the move at once provoked a storm from the prospective neighbours who feared serious loss and the deterioration of the property. Reduction in house rents and danger to the public health were instanced, the latter objection being quickly rebutted by the Medical Officer of Health, Dr. Duncan. In spite of everything the next quarterly meeting was held in Hope Street and nothing more is heard about nuisances.

Meanwhile subscriptions had been coming in well and Alfred Stephens had visited London to enquire into the details of the management and expenditure of the Children's Hospital there. The following April (14th April 1857) he reported "eight beds furnished and ready for occupation and that there are at present three patients".

The diet tables of the Children's Hospital in London were

adopted. A new Matron, Mrs. Ostler, was appointed in August, subject to her not succeeding in her candidacy for the situation of Matron at the Penitentiary. From 1864 various properties were examined to replace Hope Street since the landlord was asking an exorbitant price for that site. In 1865 (11th July 1865) the purchase of a new site was at last approved, 2,700 yards in Myrtle Street at 10/- per yard. The year 1866 is given over to plans for a new building and for the laying of the foundation stone on 3rd February 1869. And so was finally launched the Royal Liverpool Children's Hospital.

Liverpool cannot be left without mention of the Royal Liverpool Country Hospital for Children, which opened in 1899, and of its outstanding importance as a hospital for chronic cases requiring long periods of carefully supervised surgical treatment, the product of Robert Jones and Charles Macalister. Children's hospitals, like general hospitals, only admitted cases of acute disease or cases needing urgent treatment and likely to recover. The child with chronic bone and joint disease had to be rescued from the slums where he languished without treatment and without hope. It is to the credit of the founding fathers of British orthopaedics that they saw and met this need. And here may lie the origins in the practice of orthopaedics today of that mistrust both of paediatrics which would not care for the cripples of the Victorian age and of families then too ignorant and too poor properly to handle treatment at home.

During the decade after 1852 were founded the Jenny Lind Hospital, Norwich (1853), the Leeds Hospital for Women [and Children] (1857), the Edinburgh Royal Hospital for Children (1860) and Children's Hospitals in Birmingham and Newcastle (1862). But these are imitative creations whose place in history depends on the merit not of the founders but of the work done within them.

The last hospital to be included is the Infants' Hospital founded in 1903 through the energy and generosity of Mr. Robert Mond. Beginning in Hampstead it moved in 1907 to occupy fifty cots in Vincent Square, was extended with a new out-patients' department and research laboratories in 1911, and in 1918 was incorporated as the Westminster Children's Hospital in the Westminster Hospital. The objects of this foundation were primarily research and only babies were to be admitted who were ill but who had been healthy at birth. A particular interest was to be taken in the study of nutrition, a developing subject at the time. Every care was extended and no expense spared in the construction of what was planned as a laboratory for human study as much as a hospital for sick infants.

The first Senior Physician and Director of the Research Laboratory, Ralph Vincent, graduated M.D. Durham in 1901 and had served as R.M.O. at Queen Charlotte's Maternity Hospital and as Resident Obstetric Assistant at the Westminster Hospital.

In his view one of the most important instructions about feeding was that cow's "milk must be fresh. It must *not* be boiled, or pasteurized or sterilized". His name disappears from the Medical Directory in 1922 when he was succeeded as Director by Dr. Eric Pritchard.

Thus ends this survey of Children's Hospitals which have led to better treatment for, because of better understanding of, the diseases of the sick children of the poor. Mothers are more enlightened and so are doctors. To Davis's plan for domiciliary treatment as the ideal, with learning and teaching as important functions, West added the in-patient plan despite its recognized dangers, but forced by the low standards of housing and hygiene in the community. The in-patient brought the need for specially trained nurses, a need that still exists. In Liverpool can be seen the two strands, of personal medicine and of public health, beginning together but alas! growing apart. In the Infants' Hospital can be seen the beginning of the research hospital for the sake of research.

Children have been cared for in other kinds of hospital, especially in the long-stay chronic hospitals, now converted into Hospital Schools. The fever hospital, outside the general stream of paediatric thinking, has fortunately become redundant. The mental hospital, far from redundant, is still a thing apart.

The practising children's physician, seeming to be more and more occupied in the study of the incurable so as to defy the inevitable, and not affecting mortality rates even when he succeeds, sees in the maternity hospital the great opportunity for saving life and safeguarding health. Here he needs all the modern weapons of research. He also sees the need for re-integration of all these techniques that have developed apart, an integration only to be achieved in the University Departments of Child Health, and these require the continuance of the Children's Hospital, although whether in isolation or within the constellation of the General Hospital it is not for a historian to say.

Paediatrics has taught many lessons to general medicine from the day when George Armstrong's Dispensary inspired Lettsom. It highlighted the need to defeat infection in hospital wards. It has called, and not in vain, for the development of environmental medicine. And it is, I believe, with its insistence on the importance of lessening the emotional strain of illness and of hospital admission, playing no small part today in humanizing the hospital scene.

ACKNOWLEDGMENTS

I acknowledge with gratitude the help of Dr. Poynter and Mr. Gaskell of the Wellcome Library, and of Mr. Payne at the Royal College of Physicians of London. Sir Arthur Howard and Mr. B. S. Dobb have given me access to the records of the Royal Waterloo Hospital, and Professor John Hay to the Minute Book and other papers now belonging to the Alder Hey Children's Hospital, Liverpool. Many other colleagues have sent information about the early days of other children's hospitals not included in this short account.

BIBLIOGRAPHY

BROWNLOW, JOHN (1858). *The History and Design of the Foundling Hospital, with a Memoir of the Founder*, Warr, London.

DAINTON, COURTENAY (1961). *The Story of England's Hospitals: with a foreword by Lord Amulree*, Museum Press, London.

DAVIS, JOHN BUNNELL (1821). *Annals Historical and Medical During the First Four Years of the Universal Dispensary for Children*, Simpkin & Marshall, London

FRAZER, W. M. (1947). *Duncan of Liverpool*, Hamilton, London.

HARRALL, V. C. *Brief Notes on the History of the Manchester Children's Hospital*, unpublished Ms.

HIGGINS, THOMAS TWISTINGTON (1957). *"Great Ormond Street"*, *1852–1952*, Odhams Press, London, for the Hospital for Sick Children.

KERSHAW, RICHARD (1909). *Special Hospitals . . .* , Pulman, London.

Liverpool Institution for the Diseases of Children *Minute Book*, 1851–1874.

MACALISTER, CHARLES J. (1930). *The Origin and History of the Royal Liverpool Country Hospital for Children at Heswell*, privately printed at Campden, Glos.

NICHOLS, R. H., and WRAY, F. A. (1935). *The History of the Foundling Hospital*, Oxford Univ. Press, London.

Obituary, LOUIS BORCHARDT (1883). *Brit. med. J.*, **ii**, 1047.

Obituary, S. W. J. MERRIMAN (1873). *Med. Times & Gaz.*, **i**, 238.

Royal Waterloo Hospital for Women and Children, *Minute Book* of the Royal Infirmary for Children, 1843–1852.

SIMON, SIR JOHN (1890). *English Sanitary Institutions*, Cassell, London.

TAYLOR, DOROTHY (1962). Personal Communication.

VINCENT, R. (1910–11). The Infants' Hospital and its work, *Child, Lond.*, **1**, 723–31.

WOOD, C. J. (1898). Charles West (Letter), *Brit. med. J.*, **i**, 111.

Mental Hospitals

ALEXANDER WALK

THE ROYAL HOSPITALS, the voluntary hospitals which originated from the humanitarian movements of the eighteenth and nineteenth centuries, and the county and municipal hospitals which developed under the Poor Law, have all claimed your attention. The mental hospitals, with which I have to deal, belong historically to all three of these groups, and on this score alone would merit a fuller treatment; but one has to remember also how closely their existence has been bound up with the social and legal implications of mental ill-health, what diverse ideas have been and are held about their purpose and function, and how the whole subject is beset by legend, prejudice and misunderstanding. The task of condensation is truly daunting, and I can only offer an outline of trends and events which may perhaps serve for better orientation in this field. While doing this I hope to bring to your notice some of the less familiar aspects of the subject, and perhaps to correct some current misconceptions. May I say here that we owe a great deal to the scholarly work in this field in recent years of Drs. Kathleen Jones, Richard Hunter and Denis Leigh. They will forgive me if now and again I differ from their conclusions.

We are often asked to believe that medical psychology in the seventeenth century was dominated by false ideas concerning witchcraft and demoniacal possession. Nevertheless throughout the century many people all over the country were applying confidently and successfully to the county justices for some assistance to their frenzied, melancholy or distraught relatives, without any question of witchcraft arising from their applications.[1] These applications were dealt with for the most part by way of "community care"—such as a grant of money to enable the applicant to "hire an able person to stay and look to" the patient; or by lodging the patient with some person willing to keep him; in a minority of turbulent cases the justices would order admission to a workhouse or house of correction, or occasionally to the one existing hospital, the Royal Hospital of Bethlem. In the next century, with the opening of other public hospitals and privately owned lunatic-houses, these were used in addition.

Much has been made in some works of the terms of an Act of 1744, dealing with vagrancy and including a clause authorizing the justices to place a dangerous patient under control. Dr. Hunter and Mr. Payne have shown, however, that the clause was re-enacted from a previous Act of 1714, and as this latter was a consolidating Act, we may suppose that it merely recorded what had been the practice for many years previously.[2] The really significant feature of the 1744 version is that where the previous Act had referred to "removing, keeping and maintaining" the patient, on this occasion the word "curing" was added. Although far from mindful of their implied responsibilities, the Overseers did from time to time call in an experienced physician to advise on the treatment of their patients, at home or in the workhouse, as in the case recorded by Perfect in his *Annals of Insanity*.[3]

The removal of Bethlem in 1676 to its new site (facing what is now Finsbury Circus and backing on to London Wall), the erection of what was considered the finest public building in London, and the appointment of Edward Tyson as its physician, all showed a growing confidence in the benefits that medicine might have to offer in mental illness. Nor were mental patients entirely excluded from the general hospitals. When Thomas Guy founded his hospital in 1722 he directed that it should include twenty beds for lunatics, priority being given to those discharged from Bethlem or other hospitals. Bethlem, as is well known, failed to maintain Tyson's standards; more particularly, I would say, Bethlem and other hospitals failed to find means of coping with turbulent and refractory patients other than by repressive means. Other patients, of whom there must have been many, for depression was "the English disease" at that period, were, I think, treated with much more consideration. There is an article in *The Gentleman's Magazine* for 1763 which is constantly quoted for its denunciation of the evils of private madhouses; but the article contrasts these evils with the benefits of the public hospitals, where there are "no masters or keepers to be enriched, no one is admitted without the inspection of discerning and impartial governors, and the best means are used for a speedy recovery".[4] Nor need we disbelieve the report of a French visitor in 1788: "the doors are open, the rooms wainscoted, there are no bolts, no bars, and long airy corridors give a chance of exercise."[5] Conditions were indeed very different in the basement wards, but I believe the root of the evil lay in the utter inadequacy of the staff, both in numbers and in quality. As Dr. John Monro put it, in his *Remarks on Dr. Battie's Treatise*[6]: "They should be used with the greatest tenderness and affection, nor, were it possible to prevent it, should their attendants ever be suffered to behave otherwise to them"—evidently Dr. Monro, like many others in his position, did not find it possible to "prevent it".

During the eighteenth century the obvious need for accommodation elsewhere than at Bethlem led on the one hand to the growth of privately owned "madhouses" and on the other to the foundation of hospitals on a charitable basis. Both developments were slow at first and gathered momentum in the last decades.

As may be imagined, very little is known of the earliest madhouses; some no doubt had an ephemeral life, or at any rate went out of existence before records began to be kept. Thus the old Northampton Manor House in St. John Street, Clerkenwell, was opened by Dr. Newton about the year 1700; in the 1750s it was under the control of Dr. William Battie; it closed down about 1802.[7] Of those that survived into the nineteenth century, Hoxton House was by far the oldest, having been opened in 1695; it may well have been the successor to an even older establishment. In the provinces, Kingsdown House, near Bath, is said to date back to the reign of Charles II.

The Select Committee of 1763 is usually said to represent the first attempt to consider means of licensing and visiting these houses, but in fact a Bill had been drafted for this purpose nine years earlier, and the Royal College of Physicians had been asked to undertake these duties. At the time they felt unable to accept, but eventually, in 1774, a regulating Act was passed and five Fellows of the College were appointed Commissioners for licensing and visitation in London and the neighbourhood. With inadequate powers, and therefore quite ineffectively, they continued in these functions for over fifty years and neither their own representations nor the grim exposures of "neglect and ill-treatment" which were brought before the Select Committee of 1815-16 were successful in overcoming the stubborn opposition to any further reform.[8]

It is unfortunate that neither of the Select Committees attempted anything like a comprehensive survey of the madhouses in the country; consequently we know much about the nature of the abuses, but very little about their extent. William Pargeter, writing in 1792, invites the public to judge the merits of a madhouse according to whether or not it is "under the immediate inspection and management of medical men"—"such dwellings", he asserts, "are the seats of honour—courtesy—kindness—gentleness—mercy"—in contrast to those "under men who have just pecuniary powers sufficient to obtain a licence".[9] This is of course a naïve over-simplification. But William Cowper, in 1763, might have testified to the good treatment he received from Dr. Nathaniel Cotton at St. Albans;[10] and of Mary Lamb's stay at Islington her brother wrote that "the good lady of the madhouse and her daughter love her and are taken with her amazingly, and I know she loves them".[11] I have ventured to identify Mary's abode as Fisher House in what was then the Lower Road (now Essex Road) and the "good lady" as Mrs. Ann Holmes, who is recorded as the licensee from 1796 to 1807.

A number of these licensed houses established towards the end of the century by medical men played some part in the development of psychiatric ideas and practice. Such were William Perfect's house at West Malling, where his factual case-reports suggest skilled and assiduous treatment; Edward Long Fox's houses at Bristol, and Thomas Arnold's at Leicester, with a contemporary reputation as good as that of the York Retreat; and of course the one controlled by George III's Dr. Francis Willis at Greatford near Stamford, where there appears to have been an extensive system of "boarding out" or family care.[12]

During these same years a number of public hospitals on a charitable basis came into being. The earliest of these is exceptional in that it was founded by the benevolence of one person; this was Mrs. Mary Chapman of Norwich, who between 1713 and 1717 built and endowed a house for the purpose in the parish of St. Peter Mancroft, and by her will left the institution, under the name of Bethel Hospital, to a body of trustees. Bethel, which at its maximum housed about seventy-five patients, had a placid and blameless existence and is still serving as a geriatric annexe to one of the Regional mental hospitals.[13]

The great hospital movement of the second half of the eighteenth century very soon extended to the care and treatment of the mentally ill. In 1751 a committee of subscribers in London founded St. Luke's Hospital as a second Bethlem. A statement of "Reasons for the Establishment and Further Encouragement" of the hospital explains that Bethlem was "incapable of receiving all the unhappy Objects of this Sort" who applied, whereby "many useful members have been lost to Society by the Disorder gaining strength beyond the Reach of Physick"; it was also intended to "introduce more Gentlemen of the Faculty to the Study and Practice of one of the most important branches of Physick"—in other words to break the monopoly of the Monros at Bethlem. I cannot here touch on the famous controversy between its first physician, William Battie, and John Monro, in which I think the honours were even. George Dance the Younger's gloomy building, converted to other uses for the last fifty years, still stands in Old Street, though likely to disappear before long.[14]

The founders of St. Luke's did not think that it would have been proper or safe to join their hospital to one for the physically ill; but the same view was not taken in Manchester, where in 1766 the Lunatic Hospital was opened as an annexe to the Royal Infirmary on its site in Piccadilly;[15] similarly in Liverpool, the Infirmary and Lunatic Hospital were together on the site of the present St. George's Hall. At York, Newcastle and Exeter separate hospitals were provided, but both here

and at hospitals of later foundation the link with the local
general hospital was close. The York Hospital, now Bootham
Park, started with high hopes in its dignified home built by the
city's leading architect, John Carr, and was described by Sir
George Paul as a "truly noble institution"; it deteriorated to
such a scandalous extent that the exposure of its abuses—
though not its subsequent and rapid rehabilitation—forms one
of the best known chapters in the history of mental treatment
in England.[16]

The most famous of these voluntary hospitals is of course
the York Retreat. In assessing the importance of the influence
of the Retreat on subsequent developments one must, I think,
abandon the idea that anything really revolutionary was
intended by its founder, William Tuke; the stated intention
was rather to afford Quaker patients the comfort of treatment
by their own Community. Professions of humane principles
are common enough in medical writings of the period; and on
the other hand we read that harsher methods were at first
adopted at the Retreat "to an extent which we can now (1828)
hardly contemplate without surprise".[17] Its achievement
as a pioneer of "mild" treatment was made possible first by
its small size and even smaller admission rate, the paternal
supervision of the "family" by William Tuke, and the character
of the "superintendent" (or chief male nurse) and matron,
George and Katharine Jepson. By 1813 William Tuke's grand-
son, Samuel, was able in his *Description of the Retreat* to set out a
convincing case for the general adoption of Retreat methods.
I shall have further occasion to mention Samuel Tuke's
influence on mental hospital planning and practice.

Up to now I have referred to "madhouses" and "hospitals".
But in the 1770s a new word came into fashion to denote
institutions where any kind of relief or treatment was given;
this of course was "asylum". The early status of the word may
be judged from the fact that at Manchester it was applied to
the section of the Lunatic Hospital reserved for the "superior"
class of patient. New institutions founded after 1790, such as
those at Gloucester and Northampton and in Scotland, gladly
adopted the title, as did numerous orphanages and almshouses. As late as the 1870s we had in London the "Metro-

politan Asylums Board" and the "District Sick Asylums", and in 1875 Thornbury's *Old and New London* could still describe St. Thomas's as "one of the oldest hospitals as an *asylum* where all sick poor could be relieved.[18] But when the word was given the official sanction of the law, the rot set in and "asylum" suffered the same fate as "Union" and "panel" in later years. In 1841 the newly formed Medico-Psychological Association resolved in vain that "Hospital for the Insane" should be substituted for "Lunatic Asylum".[19] To this day this word's ephemeral vogue has left behind it one of the numerous stigmas which are so slow and painful to eradicate.

At last, early in the nineteenth century, it was realized that private enterprise and charity and the provisions of the Poor Law could not cover the needs of the insane for care and treatment. The credit for bringing these needs to public notice must certainly go to Sir George Paul, the Gloucestershire magistrate and disciple of John Howard. His memorandum and evidence, together with Sir Andrew Haliday's survey, form the basis of the report of the Select Committee of 1807.[20] Paul advocated a combined asylum "in each circuit or other large division" of the country, in which the expense of "maintaining and curing" the pauper patients would be borne by the Poor Law, while the public would be invited to participate by subscription, so that the asylum could be "suited to the different situations of the patients". The Committee recommended that the asylums should be built and controlled by the county justices of single counties or groups of counties, and that these might unite with a body of subscribers to provide a joint institution for paying, charity and pauper patients. They considered that asylums should be of optimum size—not too small, but not to exceed 300 beds, and therefore, underestimating the probable demand, thought that unions of counties would be the general rule. Like Paul they emphasized the need for "the best medical attendance" and agreed that "asylums should be near large towns, where physicians of eminence were to be found".

A permissive Act on these lines was passed in 1808. At Nottingham, where a subscription scheme was already well advanced, a union with the county was at once arranged, and a joint asylum was opened in 1811 at Sneinton, less than a mile from the town centre. The first purely county asylum was opened in the following year, in the town of Bedford.

I have mentioned these distances and locations in order to refute what has become almost a settled article of belief—namely that the asylums were built in remote places so that their inmates might be banished as far as possible from society. This is a mere projection of present-day attitudes. The earliest asylums, like the older hospitals, were within the cities or towns; Bethlem and St. Luke's in fact remained on urban sites until well into this century. But from about 1815 onwards the best authorities began to stress the importance of "healthy, airy sites", of a pure water supply, and of sufficient land to allow of exercise and outdoor occupations. The actual location of individual asylums was determined by such factors as proximity to the county town, road, canal and later railway communications, a central position making patients' transport expenses as near as possible equal for all parishes, sometimes by plain jobbery. Many years later, when asylums were commonly of a size far beyond what had been contemplated, and were thought to need estates of up to three hundred acres, the cost of land pushed their sites further away from the large towns; but later still others which had originally enjoyed country surroundings were engulfed in the spread of urbanization.

Like all permissive Acts, that of 1808 was not applied with universal zeal or promptness, and many counties took no steps to provide for their insane poor. Up to 1820 seven asylums had been opened, three of which were in union with subscribers, and only three more during the next decade. Neither Middlesex nor Surrey had taken any action, so that London still had to depend on the charities and on private enterprise. But meanwhile the great nineteenth-century growth of the urban populations had begun, and this for the next twenty years was met in the worst possible way—namely by a further multiplication of private licensed houses. Their number reached a peak of nearly a hundred and fifty in the 1830s, and about fifty of these received pauper patients under contract with the parishes. Thus in London there were several hundred pauper patients at Hoxton House and the Bethnal Green houses. With no effective inspection and with no incentive to anything but the cheapest and barest maintenance, conditions here became utterly degraded.[21] The exposure of this state of affairs, following on the equally scandalous revelations of 1815, led at last to the end of the perfunctory inspections of the College of Physicians and the setting up of the Metropolitan Commissioners in Lunacy with increased, though still far from sufficient, powers. More than another decade passed before the scope of the Commissioners was extended to the whole country, and when they issued their first comprehensive Report in 1844, the way was made clear for the passage of an Act making the provision of asylums mandatory on the counties and on certain boroughs. Already the effect of the new system of inspection had been such that the despised Bethnal House, for instance, was now praised for the comfort and cleanliness it offered its pauper patients.[22]

Locally, the events of 1827 at last shamed the Middlesex justices into action, and the result was the erection of the first of what were afterwards the London County Mental Hospitals—Hanwell Asylum, now St. Bernard's Hospital. As might be imagined, the construction of these early county asylums often suffered from insufficient consideration or understanding of their purpose. The general pattern was based on the gallery and the row of single rooms, in imitation of Bethlem and St. Luke's, and though distinguished architects were employed, such as John Nash, Daniel Alexander and later Gilbert Scott, there were often too many resemblances to the local prisons. A more enlightened procedure was, however, adopted at the West Riding Asylum at Wakefield, opened in 1818. Wakefield was founded by avowed admirers of the Retreat, and Samuel Tuke was accordingly consulted, and drafted a set of "Practical Hints" which are prefaced to the architect's drawings. A real attempt was made here to apply Retreat principles to a larger institution, and Tuke emphasized the need for comfort, variety and freedom, and for flexibility of classification, allowing patients in different phases to be treated in small separate groups within the overall unity of their ward. Small dayrooms opening into a central octagonal space in each ward were built with this in mind and can still be seen at what is now the Stanley Royd Hospital.[23]

At Wakefield there was also introduced the system of medical administration which eventually prevailed in all asylums, for here the justices appointed at the outset a resident Medical Director to whom the government of the asylum was entrusted. Elsewhere a lay officer of indifferent educational status was in charge, who might with good fortune develop into an efficient chief male nurse like George Jepson, but was more likely to function at the level of a mere workhouse master; visiting physicians attended frequently, but had little to do with the ordering of the patients' daily life. At Wakefield on the other hand the Director, Dr. (afterwards Sir) William Ellis, was able to pioneer innovations such as the employment of patients in industrial work and in individual occupations; he trusted his patients with tools, gave the more stable increased freedom, and was able to enlist the sympathy and help of local residents. He was the first to take practical steps for some kind of after-care of discharged patients, by means of a benevolent fund allocated for the purpose, and in his writings he urged the establishment of what were many years later called "after-care homes" or "half-way houses".[24]

The question of the government and medical staffing of asylums remained unsettled until the 1840s. Up till then various plans were tried: visiting physicians with a resident medical officer of junior status, or of equal status, or a lay master with or without a resident medical officer. But in the course of these years it became evident on the one hand that medical authority was necessary if the asylums were to make any progress as places of treatment, and on the other hand that with few exceptions the resident medical officers were becoming the real specialists in mental disorders. The position of the Medical Superintendent was assured almost everywhere by 1845, and Bethlem adopted the system in 1853 to its great advantage after further exposures of the evil of divided and confused authority.[25] Other problems of medical staffing remained, however, which I shall touch on later.

In 1830, Ellis was asked to take control at Hanwell, and so was able to bring his methods to London, where they received considerable publicity and approbation. But his achievements and those of some other progressive superintendents were soon forgotten in the turmoil and controversy which arose from the "no-restraint" movement in the years following Ellis's retirement in 1837.

Until then, no hospital or asylum—not excepting the Retreat, and certainly not excepting Pinel's hospitals in France —had thought it possible to do without mechanical restraint in some form, although much had been written about the conditions under which it might be possible to diminish its use. Hence, Gardiner Hill's manifesto proclaiming its total abolition at the Lincoln Asylum (a small subscription hospital, now The Lawn),[26] followed by John Conolly's announcement in the following year that restraint had been abolished at Hanwell within a few months of his succession to the superintendency,[27] aroused a natural incredulity and opposition. They, or rather their supporters, handled this unwisely by vehement and intolerant denunciation of all who differed from them.[28] It must be remembered that Gardiner Hill's substitute for restraint was "a sufficient number of tall attendants" and Conolly insisted that seclusion, padded rooms, special dress-locks and so forth were necessary "contrivances" in his system. If, however, we look on Conolly's system in the wider sense in which he himself conceived it, we can but admire the high ideals which he thought his staff could attain—"a watchful, preventive, almost parental superintendence" and the regulation of "every word, look and action of all who come in contact with the insane".[29] It is unlikely that such principles could have been fully established during the short time that Conolly held authority in Hanwell in the face of much opposition and many frustrations. The asylum Committee appears to have lost much of its initial enthusiasm, and after Conolly's departure refused to appoint a successor, so that for a further fifty years the Middlesex asylums were staffed by medical officers of inferior status. Most asylums accepted Conolly's ideas in principle, and settled down to an occasional use of restraint, which died out quietly in the early part of this century.

The Act of 1845 made the provision of asylums compulsory on counties and on the principal boroughs. A large number of asylums were therefore built during the years 1845–60, and in fact the majority of our mental hospitals date from the mid-Victorian period. Their design improved, and though Samuel Tuke's principles were generally forgotten, they usually included such features as larger and more comfortable day-rooms, moderate-sized dormitories, recreation halls and playing-fields and a chapel, workshops and large grounds for patients' occupation. However, all local authorities were not equally prompt to fulfil their duties: boroughs were especially backward, and a number failed either to build or to make use of another authority's asylum by union or contract. Many patients continued to be sent to poorly equipped licensed houses; since the pauper patients were liable to be withdrawn at any time the proprietors could not be expected to spend money on improving their premises, and it is to the credit of some of them that they nevertheless maintained a good standard of care.

The opening of County Asylums brought to the fore the question of providing for the mentally ill of the social classes above the poverty line. For it must be realized that the right of entry to the County Asylums was strictly limited to those who were "paupers" or who would be pauperized by their illness. The demand for care and treatment on a payment basis was partly met by an expansion of the subscription hospitals, now officially called "Registered Hospitals". In several instances the partnership with the county was dissolved; the Manchester Lunatic Asylum started on a new career as Cheadle Royal Hospital, and others, such as Barnwood House and The Coppice at Nottingham, came into existence in the same way. Bethlem itself took the same course after 1853 and settled down into a rather dull respectability for the next sixty years. Apart from the thorough reform of its administration, respectability was gained by the removal from Bethlem of the criminal patients, who had been concentrated there following the recommendations of the 1807 Committee. An Act of 1860 enabled Broadmoor to be opened for their reception in 1863.

In Scotland, progress had lagged after a promising start. The first subscription asylum was founded at Montrose in 1781, and between that date and 1827 five others were opened, including those at Edinburgh and Glasgow; they all obtained

Royal Charters and were known as the Royal Asylums.[30] Glasgow and Montrose were considered especially progressive; it was at Montrose that Samuel Tuke was impressed by the way in which deteriorated patients had been improved by good nursing and occupation. It was also from here that W. A. F. Browne, the father of Sir James Crichton-Browne, published his fighting book, *What Asylums Were, Are, and Ought to Be.* In 1839 another asylum, the Crichton Royal, was founded by a charitable endowment, with Browne as Superintendent, and this at once took its place as the finest institution of this kind anywhere in the British Isles.

However, these seven asylums were quite insufficient, and attempts to introduce the English system of asylums provided at the public expense met with determined opposition and were unsuccessful. Up to 1857 many patients lived in unspeakable conditions in gaols, poorhouses, or in licensed houses of the lowest grade, or remained quite uncared for. It was not until the agitation raised in 1855 by the "American invader", as she called herself, Dorothea Dix, that reform was achieved by the creation of a body of Commissioners and the building of District Asylums.[32]

In these middle years of the century the first institutions for the care of the mentally subnormal began their work. Samuel Gaskell, of the Lancaster Asylum, took a special interest in the idiot children admitted there, and in 1846 he drew attention to the work of Séguin in Paris.[33] Thereupon the Rev. Andrew Reed, already the founder of the Home for Incurables and of three large orphanages, took up the cause of "those who cannot plead for themselves", and in conjunction with John Conolly soon brought into being the Royal Earlswood and the Royal Eastern Counties institutions.[34] Others followed in Lancashire and Devon, and Baldovan in Scotland was founded by a charitable gift at about the same period. These early institutions started with high aims and too much was expected from the training given in them; some disappointment inevitably followed. Nor was this voluntary effort followed by official action; in the main the "imbecile class" continued to be regarded as the province of the Poor Law. Some asylums, however, provided special wards or blocks for the more severely subnormal patients who could be properly certified as "idiots" under the Lunacy Acts.

The administrative reforms of 1845, coinciding as they did with the spread of the "no-restraint" movement, led for a time to a spirit of optimism and even of complacency. Asylums were said to have reached a state as near as possible to perfection, and, as Lord Shaftesbury later testified, a recovery-rate of fifty to eighty per cent was confidently expected, if all recent cases were sent to them.[35] These hopes were disappointed, and for many years the asylums had to face frustrations arising from factors and problems some of which are still unresolved.

It must be remembered that there was no intention that all mental patients should be cared for in asylums. Just as today, a threefold division was envisaged: those needing asylum treatment, chronic incurables who might remain in the Union workhouses, and those fit to live in the community with the aid of medical and other Poor Law relief. But there was no adequate machinery for ensuring a reasonable classification; everything was left to the mercies of the Boards of Guardians and their officials, whose foremost care was always cheapness. Thus many patients were left to deteriorate under wretched home conditions; others were detained in the workhouses, indiscriminately mixed with the normal able-bodied inmates, underfed, and deprived of all medical and nursing care. Troublesomeness instead of curability became the criterion for transfer to the asylum, and so Conolly and other superintendents constantly complained of being overwhelmed with chronic cases for whom little could be done. Both they and the Commissioners stressed the importance of early treatment, but they were unable to make much impression on the Guardians or the Poor Law Board, and the situation showed little change until the 1870s or later.[36]

There was a vicious circle here, because with a low discharge rate the asylums were unable to convince the Guardians of their curative value, and they were criticized as unnecessarily costly to build and maintain. At the same time the rapid increase in the population of the country and the accumulation of chronic patients led to an expansion of individual asylums far beyond what had been originally envisaged. By

1860 asylums of between 500 and 800 beds were common, although only Hanwell and Colney Hatch exceeded 1,000 beds. Further, this expansion did not at first lead to better medical staffing—one superintendent, with perhaps a junior assistant, was expected to cover the medical needs of the patients, and much else as well. Nursing staff with the requisite qualities of heart and head could never be recruited in sufficient numbers— though as the Commissioners put it, they did achieve considerable success in "removing the bad habits of patients, suppressing their irritability or violence and guiding and improving their intellect".[37]

On the whole there was a strong feeling that the asylums were acquiring what are now called antitherapeutic features. As Arlidge, in his *State of Lunacy* (1859), put it, they had "grown into lunatic colonies" where the management had degenerated into routine, and individual study and treatment was impossible.[38]

This state of affairs led to much concern and discussion at all levels, and from the 1860s onwards a number of remedies were suggested, which I think can be considered under two headings:

1. Proposals involving other provision for chronic patients, so as to enable the asylums to do more for their acute cases.
2. Proposals bearing on the treatment of recent cases, with the object of warding off chronicity.

Under the first heading, the simplest was for a more intelligent and purposeful use of the workhouses, with special mental wards, in which patients of the "harmless chronic type" could be retained or to which they could be returned from the asylums. This implied at least an "infirmary" régime, with a medical officer having some knowledge of mental disorders. With the growth of the separate Poor Law infirmaries this became a practical possibility and was successfully carried out at Liverpool, Manchester and Birmingham.[39]

Another proposal, which in fact was envisaged as early as 1845, was the building of auxiliary asylums or annexes of a simpler construction, designed for nothing but the cheap housing of large numbers of inmates. When the reform of 1867 brought into being the confusingly named Metropolitan

Asylums Board, the supposed chronic patients scattered among the London workhouses were rounded up and two huge and dreary asylums—technically workhouses in the eyes of the law —were built for them at Leavesden and Caterham on sites selected entirely for their cheapness. This was hardly a success, for classification was haphazard and many of the patients were neither harmless nor chronic. Eventually these asylums gradually turned to the care of subnormal and senile patients. When Middlesex attempted to reserve its third asylum at Banstead for chronic patients the experiment had to be abandoned within five years.

The last device under this heading consisted in the "boarding out" of suitable patients on a small or large scale. At the Devon County Asylum and at Cheadle, villas in the neighbourhood of the asylum were built or rented for the purpose.[40] In Scotland, more extensive boarding out was practised for many years, patients being placed in the homes of cottagers, where they were supervised by a regular system of visiting. "Boarding out" still has a place in Scottish practice, though it is now mainly confined to the mentally subnormal.[41]

Passing now to proposals for the better treatment of recent and acute cases, we may first note the demand which persisted throughout what has been called the "legalistic" period—say from about 1830 to 1930—for permission to admit voluntary patients. It was felt that since certification requirements had been tightened up many early and curable cases who had previously been placed under care more or less informally were being excluded from treatment which might have saved them. This feeling was voiced by Matthew Allen as early as 1833, and later by Gaskell and Maudsley.[42] Voluntary admission was sanctioned on a small scale, for licensed houses only, in 1862, and for registered hospitals a little later; in Scotland for all private patients from 1866. But for the vast majority there was no opportunity for voluntary admission until 1930.

In the 1860s the success of the Dispensary movement led one or two asylum physicians to suggest the opening in London of similar dispensaries or out-patient departments for mental cases. The suggestion when put forward by Davey[34] of Colney Hatch in 1868 was not well received,[44] and it was not till after

1890 that the first out-patient clinics recorded were opened at Wakefield Asylum and at St. Thomas's Hospital.

Next there were proposals for the creation in London of "Reception Houses" for initial admission and classification before disposal to the county or M.A.B. asylums—they were in fact to be observation units, replacing the use of the workhouses for this purpose. The Metropolitan Asylums Board came within a short distance of building such a House on its site at Lawn Road, Hampstead, but the site was diverted to other uses. The proposal was revived by the London County Council after 1890, but was kept in suspense by the more ambitious plan of a special hospital for acute cases. The workhouses and Poor Law infirmaries retained their function as places of observation, but after they were taken over by the L.C.C. in 1930 the work was gradually concentrated in a small number of upgraded units corresponding to the intended Reception Houses.

The most controversial proposal was that for an acute hospital, separate from the asylums and situated nearer to the centre of London. This also, as far as I have been able to discover, was first suggested by Davey. The London County Council took up the idea with much vigour immediately after its formation in 1889, when the Middlesex and one of the Surrey asylums came under its control. It was in this context that the term "mental hospital" was first heard. The idea of a small hospital—one hundred beds were contemplated—intensively staffed, in which research and teaching could be carried out, was of course admirable; unfortunately the L.C.C. Committee joined to their zeal a strong animosity towards the asylums and indeed towards all mental specialists. They wished the proposed hospital to be staffed by visiting non-specialist physicians who, they were convinced, could produce cures by the application of medical remedies already available.[45] After needlessly causing much resentment the proposal was abandoned for want of funds, as it was found that to provide for the still rising population of London several large new asylums would be needed within a few years.

In 1909, however, a generous gift from Dr. Henry Maudsley (followed later by a legacy) stimulated the L.C.C. to take up the project afresh, and eventually the Maudsley Hospital was built and was opened just after the First World War. By this time the profession of psychiatry had acquired status, and the hospital was now staffed entirely by medical officers drawn from the Council's asylum service. Here also, by special legislation, voluntary patients were for the first time admitted to a mental institution controlled by a public authority.

Lastly, the possibility of making better provision for acute— or as we now say, "short-stay"—patients within the asylums themselves was not neglected. By the turn of the century the "acute hospital" or "admission hospital" began to make its appearance at some of the newly built asylums. At Hellingly in East Sussex, and at Napsbury near St. Albans, small self-contained units were built in the grounds in which short-stay patients might receive their entire treatment without entering the main building.[46] More commonly separate admission and convalescent villas were provided. In course of time the older asylums were also provided with such villas; there were very few without them by 1939. The age of the building as a whole ceased therefore to have much relation to the conditions which a patient might expect to find on his admission.

None of these expedients and developments served to stem the inordinate growth of the asylums; on the contrary, the previous tendency to retain too many patients in workhouses was largely reversed. By the 1890s asylums with 2,000 beds were normal around London and in Lancashire, and there was a corresponding growth elsewhere. In spite of this, many improvements are to be recorded during the period from 1888 onwards, when the asylums became the responsibility of the new County and County Borough Councils. Architecturally, they followed the prevailing trend in domestic building towards lightness and even gaiety. An open, spread-out plan, with wards stepped back to allow a south aspect everywhere, became almost standard. Besides the admission units, other detached villas were built in the cottage garden-suburb style of Edwardian days. Finally, in the 1920s and 30s, main buildings were dispensed with altogether, and the lay-out consisted of separate units designed on a functional basis, as at Shenley and Runwell.

Progress was also made in the staffing of the asylums. Between 1885 and 1891 a movement originating in Scotland for the more systematic training of asylum nurses led to the institution by the Medico-Psychological Association of their certificate in mental nursing, which was taken by many thousands until its discontinuance in 1948–51. The right of mental nurses to be included in any scheme for State registration was also success-fully established.[47] From 1911 onwards, Diplomas in Psycho-logical Medicine were established by several of the Universities and Royal Colleges, and soon became obligatory for asylum medical officers. The medical staffing of most asylums was, rather grudgingly, improved, though it remained far below Continental standards. Sporadic research work was carried on in many asylums, but a few enlightened authorities de-veloped research centres which were able to produce an impressive record of achievement. This was notably the case at Wakefield in the 1870s, under James Crichton-Browne, and later at the L.C.C.'s centre at Claybury, under Frederick Mott, and at Edinburgh, Glasgow, and Cardiff.[48]

Scotland made some remarkable contributions to progress in the care of the mentally ill. In the 1870s and 80s an "open-door" system was developed, first at the Fife and Kinross Asylum (now Stratheden Hospital) and later at others.[49] Its exact scope is hard to assess now, and it did not maintain itself fully, but it was not without its influence, and open-door wards and villas became common features until the further movement towards universal opening during the last twenty years. In Scotland, stress was also laid on the "hospitalization of the asylums", by the introduction of hospital-trained matrons and sisters and the copying of methods in use in the general hospitals.[50] Here also, at Barnhill Hospital in Glasgow there was opened, in 1894, the first psychiatric unit in a general hospital. This was not an observation or classification ward—the classification was done at domiciliary visits—but quite purposely intended for selected cases needing short, intensive treatment.[51]

With these developments, the long-standing claim of the asylums to discard their discredited title was justified, and from about 1920 onwards the term "mental hospital" came into general use, though it did not receive legal recognition until 1930. Of the historic hospitals which had never yielded to the "asylum" fashion, Bethlem removed to the outer suburbs in the same year, while the St. Luke's foundation was reincarnated as a kind of smaller Maudsley in North London, in association with the Middlesex Hospital.

With the passing in 1930 of the Mental Treatment Act, which sanctioned the admission of voluntary patients and gave local authorities powers to open out-patient clinics and to sponsor research projects, the mental hospitals were able to expand their activities and offer services which the public readily accepted. Since at the same time the Councils became responsible for what had previously been the Poor Law medical services, collaboration or even integration became possible; but financial stringency still hampered their upgrading to modern standards.

Finally, I must touch briefly on the parallel developments in the care of the subnormal—briefly because this part of the story has been so well covered by Dr. Jones in her *Mental Health and Social Policy*. At first, as we have seen, institutions for the subnormal were created by voluntary action. The first large-scale provision by a public authority was made by the Metropolitan Asylums Board in the 1870s, when, as part of the plan already described, the Darenth Training Schools were built near Dartford; later these were much expanded and other institutions belonging to the M.A.B. were taken over for the same purpose.[52] Further charitable foundations also came into being, and these and the older ones were regularly made use of by provincial Poor Law authorities. The passing of the Mental Deficiency Act in 1913 laid a duty on County and County Borough Councils to provide institutions for defectives. A number were built in the period between the wars, yet by 1939 there were still large areas in which no provision had been made. The movement which led to the passing of the Act had a fairly strong eugenic as well as a humanitarian purpose, and the stern word "segregation" was much to the fore; the institutions, usually named "colonies", but now "hospitals", were often more remotely sited than the mental hospitals, and the feeling that the patients were being "put away" appeared to be more justified. Nevertheless the original ideals of training with a view to return to community life were never lost sight of; as Douglas Turner, of the Royal Eastern Counties' Institution, used to say, "the aim is to make the institution a flowing lake, not a stagnant pool".

This is as far as I can take the history of mental hospitals, for their most recent developments are too much the subject of controversy, and their future uncertain. But I think that we shall be able to shape this future more confidently if we understand their past; and it is as a small contribution to such understanding that I have offered this paper.

REFERENCES

1. FESSLER, A. (1956). The management of lunacy in 17th century England: an investigation of quarter-sessions records, *Proc. roy. Soc. Med.*, **49**, 901.
2. Great Britain, Parliament (1714). *An Act for reducing the Laws relating to Rogues, Vagabonds, Sturdy Beggars and Vagrants into One Act of Parliament*, 13 Anne, c. 20.
3. PERFECT, WILLIAM (1791, 1801, 1805). *Annals of Insanity*, London, (previously published as *Select Cases in the Different Species of Insanity*, Rochester, 1787).
4. *Gentleman's Magazine*, January, 1763.
5. O'DONOGHUE, E. G. (1913). *The Story of Bethlehem Hospital*, p. 282 London.
6. MONRO, JOHN (1758). *Remarks on Dr. Battie's "Treatise on Madness"*, London.
7a. STORER, J. & H. S., and CROMWELL, T. (1828). *History and Description of the Parish of Clerkenwell*, London.
   b. Parish of Clerkenwell *Rate Books*.
8. Royal College of Physicians of London (1753–65). *Liber Annalium* (ms.).
9. PARGETER, WILLIAM (1792). *Observations on Maniacal Disorders*, Reading.
10a. COWPER, WILLIAM (1816). *Memoir of the Early Life of William Cowper, Esq.*, London.
   b. HUNTER, R. A. & WOOD, J. B. (1957). Nathaniel Cotton, poet, physician and psychiatrist, *King's Coll. Hosp. Gaz.*, **36**, 120.
11a. LAMB, CHARLES (1935). Letter to S. T. Coleridge, Oct. 3rd, 1796, in *The Letters of Charles and Mary Lamb*, E. V. Lucas (Ed.), vol. i, p. 45.
   b. NELSON, JOHN (1811). *History, Topography and Antiquities of the Parish of St. Mary, Islington*, London.
   c. Parish of St. Mary, Islington *Rate Books*.

12a. ARNOLD, T. (1809). *Observations on the Management of the Insane and Particularly on the Agency and Importance of Humane and Kind Treatment in Effecting their Cure*, London.

b. Anon. (1797). Détails sur l'Etablissement du Docteur Willis pour la Guérison des Aliénés. Letter to the *Bibliothèque Britannique*, Geneva.

13. BATEMAN, SIR F. & RYE, W. (1906). *The History of the Bethel Hospital at Norwich*, Norwich.

14. FRENCH, C. N. (1951). *The Story of St. Luke's Hospital*, London.

15a. RENAUD, F. (1898). *A Short History of the Rise and Progress of the Manchester Royal Infirmary*, Manchester.

b. BROCKBANK, E. M. (1934). *A Short History of Cheadle Royal*, Manchester.

16. GRAY, JONATHAN (1814). *A History of the York Lunatic Asylum*, York.

17a. TUKE, SAMUEL (1813). *Description of the Retreat*, York.

b. Anon. (1828). *A Sketch of the Origin, Progress and Present State of the Retreat*, York.

18. THORNBURY, W. & WALFORD, E. (1875). *Old and New London*, vol vi, p. 92, London.

19. WALK, A. & WALKER, W. L. (1961). Gloucester and the beginnings of the R.M.P.A., *J. ment. Sci.*, **107**, 618.

20. Great Britain, Parliament (1807). *Report of the Select Committee on the State of Criminal and Pauper Lunatics in England and Wales*.

21. GORDON, S. & COCKS, T. G. B. (1952). The case of the White House at Bethnal Green, in *A People's Conscience*, London.

22a. Metropolitan Commissioners in Lunacy (1844). *Report to the Lord Chancellor*.

b. Great Britain, Parliament (1845). *Lunatics Act*, 8 & 9 Vict., c. 100. *Lunatic Asylums and Pauper Lunatics Act*, 8 & 9 Vict., c. 126.

23. TUKE, SAMUEL (1819). Practical hints on the construction and economy of Pauper Lunatic Asylums, prefaced to Watson & Pritchett's *Plans etc. of the Pauper Lunatic Asylum lately erected at Wakefield*, York.

24a. ELLIS, SIR W. C. (1838). *A Treatise on the Nature, Symptoms, Causes and Treatment of Insanity*, London.

b. BOLTON, J. SHAW (1928). The evolution of a mental hospital: Wakefield 1818–1928 (Presidential Address). *J. ment. Sci.*, **74**, 588.

25. Bethlehem Hospital (1852). *Return to the House of Commons*.

26. GARDINER HILL, ROBERT (1839). *A Lecture on the Management of Lunatic Asylums*, London.

27. CONOLLY, JOHN (1856). Reports of the Resident Physician of the County Lunatic Asylum at Hanwell, 1839 to 1844. Summarized in *The Treatment of the Insane Without Mechanical Restraints*, London.

28. *The Lancet* 1839–40, **ii**; & 1840–41, **i**. Correspondence on nonrestraint. Drs. Blake, Browne, Button, Cookson, Corsellis, Gardiner-Hill, Hadwen, Stillwell, Miss Newell, Messrs. Adams, Harvey, Tulk; "A Looker-on", "A Peeper-in", "Pharmacopoeia", "Philalethes", "Philanthropos", also leading articles. (Many of these contributions omitted from volume indexes.)

29a. CONOLLY, JOHN (1847). *On the Construction and Government of Lunatic Asylums and Hospitals for the Insane*, London.

b. CONOLLY, JOHN (1856). *The Treatment of the Insane without Mechanical Restraints*, London.

30. CAMPBELL, R. B. (1932). The development of the care of the insane in Scotland (Presidential Address), *J. ment. Sci.*, **78**, 774.

31. BROWNE, W. A. F. (1837). *What Asylums Were, Are, and Ought to Be*, Edinburgh.

32. MACNIVEN, ANGUS (1960). The first commissioners: reform in Scotland in the mid-19th century (Presidential Address), *J. ment. Sci.*, **106**, 451.

33. GASKELL, SAMUEL (1847). Education of idiots at Bicêtre, *Chambers Edin. J.*, pp. 20, 71, 105.

34. REED, A. & REED, C. (1863). *Memoirs of the Life and Philanthropic Labours of Andrew Reed, D.D.*, London.

35. SHAFTESBURY, LORD (7th Earl, formerly Lord Ashley) (1859). *Evidence to Select Committee on Lunatics*, vol. i, p. 75, Q.664.

36. Commissioners in Lunacy (1859). *Twelfth Report*, Supplement: On the condition, character and treatment of lunatics in workhouses.

37. *Ibid*, p. 20.

38. ARLIDGE, J. T. (1859). *On the State of Lunacy and the Legal Provision for the Insane*, p. 102, London.

39a. ROBERTSON, C. LOCKHART (1867). The care and treatment of the insane poor (Presidential Address), *J. ment. Sci.*, **13**, 289.

b. TUKE, D. HACK (1889). *The Past and Present Provision for the Insane Poor in Yorkshire*, London; also in *J. ment. Sci.*, **36**, 319, 466.

40. Commissioners in Lunacy (1871 onwards). *Twenty-fifth and subsequent Reports*. Entries relating to the Metropolitan District Asylums.

41a. Devon County Asylum (1858–1874). *Reports*. Summaries in *J. ment. Sci.*, **4–22**.

b. MOULD, G. W. (1880). Presidential Address, *J. ment. Sci.*, **26**, 328.

c. TUKE, D. HACK (1889). The boarding-out of pauper lunatics in Scotland, *J. ment. Sci.*, **34**, 464.

42a. ALLEN, MATHEW (1833). *Essay on the Classification of the Insane*, London.

b. GASKELL, SAMUEL (1860). On the want of better provision for the labouring and middle classes when attacked or threatened with insanity, *J. ment. Sci.*, **6**, 321.

c. MAUDSLEY, HENRY (1862). Middle-class hospitals for the insane, *J. ment. Sci.*, **8**, 356.

43. DAVEY, J. G. (1867). On the insane poor in Middlesex and the asylums at Hanwell and Colney Hatch, *J. ment. Sci.*, **13**, 318, and Discussion.

44a. BULLEN, F. ST. J. (1893). The out-patient system in asylums, *J. ment. Sci.*, **39**, 491.

b. HARRIS, NOEL (1955). The contribution of psychological medicine to general medicine, *J. ment. Sci.*, **101**, 8.

45. London County Council (1891). Report of the Committee on a Hospital for the Insane. Reprinted in H. Burdett, *Hospitals and Asylums of the World* (1891), vol. ii, p. 159, London. Also Discussion before the Hospitals Association, *ibid*, 248.

46. NEWINGTON, H. HAYES (1900). The plans of a new asylum for East Sussex, *J. ment. Sci.*, **46**, 673.

47. WALK, ALEXANDER (1961). The history of mental nursing (Presidential Address), *J. ment. Sci.*, **107**, 1.

48a. BROWNE, SIR J. CRICHTON-(ed.) (1874–76). *West Riding Asylum Medical Reports*.

b. MOTT, SIR F. W. (Ed.) (1900–22). *London County Council Archives of Neurology and Psychiatry*.

49. Scotland, General Board of Commissioners in Lunacy (1881). *Report*. Summary in Tuke, D. Hack (1882). *Chapters in the History of the Insane*, pp. 373–92. See also references in *J. ment. Sci.*, **27**, **29**, **30**, **32**, **34**.

50. ROBERTSON, GEORGE M. (1922). The hospitalization of the Scottish asylum system (Presidential Address), *J. ment. Sci.*, **68**, 321.

51. CARSWELL, John (1894). An experiment in dealing with reported cases of insanity, *J. ment. Sci.*, **40**, 394, 469.

52a. BEACH, FLETCHER (1900). Presidential Address, *J. ment. Sci.*, **46**, 623.

b. TURNER, F. DOUGLAS (1933). Mental deficiency (Presidential Address), *J. ment. Sci.*, **79**, 563.

Note: Presidential Addresses were delivered before the (Royal) Medico-Psychological Association (before 1865 the Association of Medical Officers of Asylums and Hospitals for the Insane).

Naval Hospitals

CHRISTOPHER LLOYD

IF YOU LOOK in the journal of Edward Barlow, an ordinary seaman who was wounded in the Second Dutch War in 1666, you will find this entry:

> Sending our sick and wounded men ashore at Rochester, I went for one, for my leg that the shot hit was not well. We were sent some to one house and some to another, his Majesty paying 7/- a week for every man's diet and looking after, there being a kind of an hospital where they lay that were worst wounded and a doctor to dress them.

Such was the contract system, whereby the Admiralty in Tudor and Stuart times, and indeed up to the middle of the eighteenth century, hired temporary sick quarters at taverns and private houses for the accommodation of those wounded in the service of the Crown. At that date there was no difference between a merchant seaman and a naval rating. Since the nation would not maintain a standing navy, seamen like Barlow spent most of their days in what we would call the merchant service. No one bothered about the provision of medical facilities for merchant seamen until well into the nineteenth century, when the first merchant seamen's hospital ship was moored in the Thames near Greenwich.

Sick seamen were much better cared for in the Middle Ages. Almshouses, accommodation in the naves of churches and even small hospitals were provided by charity at most of the principal ports. What is described as "the first ordained for mariners diseased and hurt" was a hospital at Sandwich in 1244. But these charity foundations were swept away by Henry VIII and it is paradoxical that the king whom we call the father of the navy made no attempt to provide for the medical needs of his sailors. Such scandalous neglect continued for the next two hundred years. We know that a great many sick were landed after the Armada campaign, indeed the incidence of scurvy and typhus (as in so many other naval operations) brought the chase of the Armada to a halt; but we do not know what became of the diseased and destitute seamen who had saved England.

In this respect the naval powers of Venice, France and Spain were far ahead of this country. Hospital ships formed a regular part of their fleets, whereas in Britain the first of such ships appears in Cromwell's day, and then they were only old ships adapted for a temporary purpose. There were no permanent hospitals ashore. Since it soon became impossible even for the Navy Board to be blind to the sufferings of the men it employed, the Crown requisitioned a number of beds for them in the London hospitals. St. Bartholomew's had been under such an obligation since 1327, but in Stuart times the now defunct Savoy and Ely hospitals were most frequently used.

It is significant that the first practical step to provide a benevolent fund for the needs of disabled seamen was taken by serving admirals, and not by the Admiralty. This was the Chatham Chest, founded in 1590 by Drake and Hawkins and still preserved at Greenwich, with which hospital its funds were later amalgamated. The fund is of interest because it seems to have been the first attempt at a public health insurance scheme, each man contributing 6d a month out of his pay. It is true that the Treasurer of the Navy frequently raided the fund for his own purposes and that, since personal attendance at Chatham was necessary in order to benefit from it, it was of limited use to, say, men landed at Plymouth, where surgeons such as James Yonge were in charge. There was no permanent hospital because there was as yet no permanent service in the Navy; once a ship was paid off, the Admiralty took no further responsibility for her men.

The first man to press for such permanent accommodation on the French model was John Evelyn the diarist in the reign of Charles II, when he was a member of the Sick and Hurt Board, which supervised the medical department of the Navy. The Admiralty dismissed his appeals, partly because it was found cheaper to bilk the householder who was under contract than maintain the buildings and staff Evelyn envisaged. However, in 1694, as a thank-offering for the victory over the French fleet at La Hogue, William and Mary founded the Royal Hospital at Greenwich and Evelyn became its first Treasurer.

The splendid building which Wren designed for the accommodation of naval pensioners is now occupied by the Royal Naval College; but the infirmary—now the Dreadnought Seamen's Hospital—is today the largest building in the Seamen's Hospital group for the use of merchant seamen, and the Greenwich Hospital charity is still rich and active. Like the other "Royal Hospital", the Chelsea Hospital for soldiers founded by Charles II, the Greenwich Hospital was designed as an almshouse rather than a medical centre. Indeed, the separate building called the infirmary was only built fifty years after the first pensioners made their appearance in 1705. Before it was built the only laboratory was in a gardener's shed. The first record of a bath is in 1741 and there was only one tap and one lavatory for each block accommodating several hundred men.

The Royal Hospital was founded, to quote its charter, "for the relief and support of seamen serving on board the ships and vessels belonging to our Navy Royal, who by reason of age, wounds or other disabilities shall be incapable of further service at sea and be unable to maintain themselves". Although originally intended to cover both merchant seamen and naval pensioners, both of whom contributed 6d a month to its funds, it has always been a naval institution, with the First Lord of the Admiralty as chairman of the governing body. Nevertheless to this day the Charity owns the buildings, even if the Admiralty controls the funds. Greenwich Hospital was the largest institution of its kind in the world and housed 2,700 pensioners in the days of Nelson. It was regarded as a haven for the aged, and for the senior physician in the service, among whose duties was that of "viewing the drugs" supplied by the Apothecaries' Company, who held the monopoly of this for over a hundred years. Among the medical staff may be noted the Rat Catcher, the Bug Killer and a notable quack who was appointed Rupture Doctor until several years later it was discovered that he had not effected a single cure. His excuse was that sailors' hernias differed from those of soldiers, since he produced glowing testimonials of his success at Chelsea.

Greenwich, however, is not a port and an almshouse is not a hospital. The need for such accommodation at Portsmouth and Plymouth became increasingly apparent as the Navy developed in size during the French wars of the eighteenth century. The contract system simply ceased to work. In one year during the War of the Austrian Succession accommodation was found for 463 sick at Plymouth, but three times that number were landed there. More important from the Admiralty point of view was the fact that the system encouraged desertion, as did the futile attempts to transport men all the way to London. In 1744, therefore, Lord Sandwich as First Lord presented a memorial petitioning the Crown to build permanent naval hospitals at Portsmouth, Plymouth and Chatham. As he put it,

> "When the folly of the poor men is considered, intoxicating themselves with strong liquors in the height of their distempers, the great numbers that are swept away by such intemperance, and the desertion of great numbers who recover, both compassion to them and the interest of Your Majesty's service require putting a speedy stop to the evil of such pernicious consequences which can in no ways effectively be done but by building hospitals."

Even then consideration of expense nearly wrecked the scheme: no hospital was built at Chatham until 1828, and at Portsmouth vain efforts were made to convert a ruined castle into a modern hospital before a building was founded on an uninhabited marsh called Haslar Point. It took fifteen years to build Haslar Hospital, which opened in 1761, but only four years to build a similar hospital at Plymouth. These remain the principal naval hospitals to this day, and that they were built on such a generous scale may well be explained by the fact that the demand for naval hospitals coincided with the great civil hospital movement of the period.

We may consider the history of both hospitals together, because the regulations issued by the Sick and Hurt Board (which ultimately became the Medical Department of the

Navy) covered both. Haslar was the older and the larger. It was described by John Howard as the largest brick building in Europe. With its 2,000 cradles, as the beds were called, it remained the largest hospital in the kingdom until 1893, when 1,500 beds were in use and over 6,000 sailors treated in a year. It was designed by Jacobson, the architect of the London Foundling Hospital, on the lines of Greenwich Hospital, though in this case the ground plan was intended to form a square. The fourth side of the square was never built. Instead, a twelve foot wall, surmounted by a fearsome *chevaux de frise*, was erected to check large-scale desertion. After this had been done, deserters used the main drain and their numbers, sick and maimed as they were, reached formidable proportions, so unpopular was the naval service in those days.

Haslar had the advantage of having Dr. James Lind, the founder of naval medicine and the author of the famous treatise on scurvy, as its first senior physician. He and his son after him held the post for over fifty years and we are fortunate in possessing the very detailed instructions which he drew up for the use of his staff. From the point of view of hygiene, these are well in advance of his day, and since he was the first doctor in history to carry out a controlled dietetic experiment, particular attention is paid to diet. He describes the new hospital to the President of the Royal College of Physicians of Edinburgh in these words:

"We are remarkably clean. No patient is admitted until he is stripped of his clothes and well washed with warm water and soap in tubs always kept ready for the purpose; he is allowed the hospital dress during the time he continues in hospital, or until his clothes are returned to him quite clean, and he is regularly shifted and kept quite nice, clean and sweet at the government's expense. None of his clothes, bedding etc. is ever permitted to be brought into the hospital; we have large outhouses for the reception. In cases of fever, the patient's clothes are directly fumigated with brimstone in the smoke house and baked in an oven sprinkled with vinegar. The fever wards are cut off from all communication with the rest. We have 90 women nurses at a time; their pay is £12 per annum."

His instructions for routine in the eighty-four wards for which he was responsible stress the need for ventilation and for correct medication. Thus:

"To prevent the dangerous consequences of patients receiving wrong medicines from mistakes in dispensing them, every basket is to be inspected after the medicines are put up, and the medicines in it compared with the prescription ticket of each patient. The dispensing check, a line, to be drawn upon the ticket as the name of each medicine is called and put into the basket."

Possibly Lind's standards were too high. Possibly he was overwhelmed by his professional duties. In 1780, for example, 2,200 cases of scurvy were landed at Haslar after a mere six weeks' cruise of the Channel Fleet. Possibly the permission given to the medical staff to practise privately led to inefficient administration. Whatever the reason, it was decided in 1795 to make a naval captain Governor of the hospital, to be assisted by a medical council of physicians and senior surgeons.

The same thing happened at Plymouth and in the voluminous diaries left by the first two governors we can trace the consequences. Not until 1865 did the medical staff regain control of the hospitals and during that period there was continual conflict between the Governor and the Physician. When surveys were held to discharge patients, the exigencies of the service and the wisdom of medical opinion were frequently at loggerheads. Surgeons had no desire to see hospitals run on the lines of a man-of-war. Therapeutic bathing was turned into a military exercise and the nursing staff pressed into the local militia. The only period during which relations were not strained at Haslar was during the middle of the century when wars were few and the Governor and Physician were old friends as fellow Arctic explorers—Sir William Parry and Sir John Richardson.

The same sort of trouble occurred in the guard ships which served as overflow hospitals. In one case a certain Dr. Garlick complained that the officer in charge used to drink a bottle of gin at a meal and then "damned the nurses as bitches and threatened to tow them ashore". Women seldom served afloat. Ashore they were a constant problem because they were apt to drink too much, invite visitors to their rooms and even encourage dying patients to make out wills on their behalf. But men were too scarce a commodity to be wasted as nurses in shore establishments until the wars were over. After Florence Nightingale had demonstrated the value of female nurses, these were brought back into the naval hospitals in 1885 to become Queen Alexandra's Royal Naval Nursing Service in 1902.

At sea at that time all ships had a sick berth situated near the fo'c'sle and there was a complete hierarchy of sick berth staff, from Wardmasters down to loblolly boys. Hospital ships were never designed as such until the first *Maine* was presented to the Navy by a group of grateful American ladies during the Boer War. Since then there have been three *Maines*, and the present *Britannia* was designed in 1954 to serve the dual purpose of royal yacht and hospital ship. From the days of the Commonwealth onwards, temporary hospital ships had accompanied the great fleets. A singular lack of humour was shown in the choice of one which was called the *Charon*, after the character who ferried the dead across the Styx.

The Physician of the Fleet who had the misfortune to use this ship during the Napoleonic wars was Dr. Thomas Trotter, one of Lind's disciples who, with Sir Gilbert Blane, was responsible for the introduction of lemon juice into the Navy after a delay of forty years. This measure alone reduced by half the number of patients in the shore hospitals because scurvy, that ancient curse of the sea, was thereby eliminated. Trotter was also the first naval medical officer to suggest the use of the hospital as a postgraduate clinical school, and the installation of a library and a pathological museum. These additions to Haslar were not made until the days of Burnett and Richardson in 1827, but even then the London hospitals could offer few training facilities of a similar nature. However, in the middle of the nineteenth century, it is sad to say, there was no advanced training for naval surgeons. After 1871 they did their training at the new army hospital at Netley, where there was a Professor of Naval Hygiene, until the Royal Naval Medical School opened at Haslar ten years later. The curriculum at this school sounded so comprehensive that Sir Partick Manson declared that it was the only place in England where tropical medicine was taught. He was soon disabused by Inspector

General Turnbull, one of the officers there, who was put on the retired list for the outspoken comments he made on the deficiencies of naval medical training. However, Manson gave him a post at the new School of Tropical Diseases in London and in 1900 the subject was at last actually taught at Haslar. At the same time the Admiralty for the first time provided naval surgeons with instruments, instead of their having to buy their own.

It is pleasant to record that in the naval hospitals, if not in ships at sea, naval medical practice kept abreast of advances made in the profession—and there were not many before the bacteriological revolution towards the end of the century. Thus at Haslar the stethoscope was used in 1819 and in 1852 Richardson performed the first naval operation using chloroform. In 1868 antisepsis was introduced in the form of Lister's carbolic spray and it is interesting to note how the fear of operations thereafter diminished. In 1868 only fifteen operations were performed at Haslar, whereas in 1904 there were 1,172.

Apart from Plymouth and Portsmouth, the most important naval hospital was at Chatham, after the closing of Greenwich Hospital in 1869. Chatham Hospital had been recommended as early as 1744, but it was not built until 1828, when it was called the Melville Hospital. It was replaced by a larger institution in 1905. Overseas there were innumerable small hospitals which have disappeared in the course of time—at such places as Halifax, Antigua, Jamaica (a shocking one), Trincomalee, and Bermuda (which has only recently been closed). Of these the most important and the last surviving was Malta, where Nelson insisted that a hospital should be provided for the Mediterranean Fleet. His physician, Dr. Snipe, seized on the Bighi Palace, the home of one of the Knights Hospitaller. Many years later the present hospital at Valetta replaced it.

Although the naval medical service was for a very long time a despised branch of the profession, I should like to conclude this brief survey of naval hospitals with a tribute paid to them by a Royal Commission in 1869. In this Report they are described as representing "the perfection of intelligent construction and administration, which is unattainable in our London hospitals".

One peculiarity which they still share with military hospitals is the necessity for sudden expansion in the event of war. It is worth recalling that Wren solved this difficulty long ago at Greenwich, where the colonnades permit the building of new blocks without spoiling the architectural symmetry of the whole structure. Similarly at Haslar, Jacobson's cloisters or colonnades on the ground floor, which he built for the use of convalescents, proved exceedingly useful in the last war when they were bricked up for conversion into extra wards.

A final lesson which the past has to offer is the admission of an American naval doctor that a mistake was made in the last war in installing too many shore establishments during the island-hopping advance across the Pacific, thereby immobilizing too many medical officers. If the advice of Lind in his *Essay on the Most Effectual Means of Preserving the Health of Seamen*, published in 1757, had been taken, there would have been more hospital ships to keep up with the fleets in a truly maritime form of war.

Note—A more detailed account of this subject, with a comprehensive bibliography, will be found in *Medicine and the Navy; 1200–1900, vols. III–IV,* by Christopher Lloyd and Jack L. S. Coulter, Edinburgh and London, Livingstone, 1961–3.

Military Hospitals

MAJOR-GENERAL W. R. M. DREW

DURING THE LAST 300 years England has shown an increasing concern for the constant care of her sick and wounded. Many successful generals and other officers commanding have long appreciated that the outcome of a campaign can depend on the medical services. Broadly it can be said that the evolution of army hospitals has followed closely their civil and naval counterparts, and that following each war improvements have been accomplished in the organization of military hospitals and medical services.

It is probable that the first military hospital to be established in this country was that in Porchester Castle in 1563 which was required for the care of the casualties from the gallant garrison of Havre. The next was in Dublin where an army hospital was built and equipped in 1600, but this was closed when James I reduced the garrison in Ireland.

At the beginning of the sixteenth century there were still no proper arrangements for the collection and transportation of those wounded in war. Usually the victorious general arranged for the local country people to carry away and treat the wounded left behind on the battlefield. In this period there was no separate medical organization for either the Army or the Navy. Among the famous surgeons to serve in both of these armed services were William Clowes (1540–1604), John Woodall (1569–1643) and Richard Wiseman (1622–76), all of whom published works on the treatment of battle casualties. In 1598 surgeons were first appointed to companies of Essex's Army in Ireland, since these were often on detachment. These appointments were abolished in 1655 when surgeons were posted instead in infantry regiments.

When, during the reign of King James I, expeditions were sent in 1620 to Germany to aid the Protestant princes, and in

1624 to the Netherlands, they were accompanied by medical officers but had little or no provision for medicines or hospitals. In contrast the series of unsuccessful expeditions (1625–8) to aid the Huguenots of La Rochelle had better medical arrangements. In 1627 the commander, General Burroughs, wrote to the Duke of Buckingham: "If you expect men to fight, great care must be had in preserving them if they are hurt." There are no figures available for the numbers of killed and wounded in these engagements, but many casualties were brought back to the ports on the south coast of England. In 1627 practical help was sought from London and given by the College of Physicians and the Barber-Surgeons Company, and some of the wounded were sent for treatment to London hospitals. It is perhaps significant that for the final expedition to La Rochelle in 1628 Peter Thorney (d. 1628) was appointed Chirurgeon of the Army both by Sea and Land.

The Civil War of 1642–6 gave great opportunities for improving the medical care of the sick and wounded. Oliver Cromwell was most solicitous for his sick and wounded soldiers. Sometimes the casualties were sent to London; for example, after the siege of Reading. At other times, as in 1645 in Bristol, wounded were treated there in temporary hospitals. During this era the London hospitals, especially St. Bartholomew's and St. Thomas's, provided the only permanent arrangements for the treatment of sick and wounded soldiers. However, since these hospitals could admit only a limited number, and because with the need for a standing army, peacetime hospitals were required, Parliament decided to set up two military hospitals in London. The first was established in 1644 in the Savoy on the Strand and the second in 1648 in Ely House, off Holborn Hill. Together, these two hospitals, which could deal with all the sick of the garrison in London, had a total of 350 beds, with a staff of physicians, surgeons and thirty nurses. They were administered by the Commissioners of Hospitals.

During this period a military hospital, Heriot's Hospital, was established in Edinburgh, and another in Dublin in the Archbishop's House. All these were so costly to run that at the Restoration most of them were closed.

The Committee for Maimed Soldiers, which also controlled

the Commissioners of Hospitals at that time, did much of the work which now devolves on our Ministry of Pensions. But eventually at the Restoration the disabled soldiers were discharged, those on pension each receiving twelve weeks' pay and recommendations for assistance to the Justices of their counties.

In the reign of Charles II, two foundations for the care of aged and ailing soldiers were established—the Royal Hospitals at Kilmarnham, Dublin (1680), and at Chelsea, London (1681). At the outset these two institutions were a form of insurance for the Army since all officers and men contributed generously to their building and maintenance.

In 1670, during the first and second Dutch Wars, the Ely and Savoy hospitals were reopened under the Commissioners for sick and wounded seamen because the Navy was mainly involved.

DEVELOPMENTS IN THE EIGHTEENTH CENTURY

In Marlborough's Peninsular and Flanders campaigns (1702–11) casualties were treated on the battlefield or in tents, because hospital accommodation was generally unsatisfactory. Later, in 1742, as the result of the Battle of Dettingen, a considerable improvement took place in medical arrangements. There was a public outcry because so many British wounded were left on the battlefield in the care of the French surgeons. Soon afterwards a scale for marching and fixed hospitals was provided.

In Flanders, by 1748, Mr. David Middleton (d. 1785), Surgeon to the Forces under the Duke of Cumberland, had introduced a properly equipped hospital with separate beds, clean linen, and experienced nurses in attendance. For the first time, surgeons were placed in charge of all the administrative arrangements, including the hospital clerks and storekeepers.

We may contrast this state of affairs with those in North America and in the American War of Independence. In 1759, in Wolfe's battle for Quebec, there was neither transport for the wounded nor hospitals to receive them. At the Battle of

Lexington in Kentucky (1775), medical arrangements were so inadequate that many of the wounded were killed by Indians, into whose hands they had fallen.

Probably Sir John Pringle (1707–82) did as much as anyone to improve the health of the Army. As a result of his experience in Flanders he favoured the use of a number of regimental hospitals rather than one large one. For the campaigns of the War of the Austrian Succession he had flying (movable) hospitals set up near the camps and the stationary hospitals in the adjoining large towns. Pringle stressed the importance of proper disposal of the sick and wounded. He ordered medical officers not to send slightly ill soldiers to large hospitals, but to treat them in camp, or adjoining field hospitals. He said that "the more fresh air let into hospitals the less chance of spreading distempers".

During the Seven Years War (1756–63) for the first time, transport to bring the wounded to hospital was provided by contract. Dr. Richard Brocklesby (1722–97), who served in Germany during this time, did much to remedy the shortcomings of regimental and field hospitals. He favoured the use of special huts in which to treat the sick and wounded. He urged cleanliness, ventilation, good diet and exercise for the preservation of health. In his opinion the directors of military hospitals should be responsible for medical planning, and for the care of all the patients. Incidentally, Brocklesby, with the assistance of Pringle and Dr. Francis Home (1719–1813), first introduced regular post-mortem examinations before they became routine in civil hospitals.

About this time it was Dr. Donald Monro (1727–1802) who first emphasized the place of prevention. He said "the preservation of the lives of soldiers is a matter of the highest importance". Following his experience in military hospitals in Germany from 1761–3 he urged "that hospital marquees be provided, with a proportion of hospital mates to be kept ready in case of action".

Monro advised that regimental hospitals be employed, but also recommended the establishment of some general and convalescent hospitals. Among other things he advised the provision of water for drinking and ablution, more care with feeding and sanitation, and made plans for buildings to be kept dry and airy. He laid down a cubic capacity for each hospital bed and recommended that if, subsequently, fever appeared in a hospital, the number of beds should be still further reduced. It was his belief that hospitals should be neutral and protected by the parties waging war.

In 1787 Dr. Robert Hamilton (1749–1830) published his book on the duties of a regimental surgeon, in which he wrote that "more men perish in regimental practice for want of proper care than by the sword". And again he stated "among the causes of sickness and death in the Army are the hospitals themselves". He urged the keeping of proper patient records and said "when the hospitals were bad, the sick were better accommodated in tents".

Under the influence of John Hunter (1728–93) surgery gradually developed into a science. He served in the campaign in Portugal in 1762–63 in a general hospital, which had a "black hole" with irons in which a doctor could confine rebellious patients and keep them on bread and water. It also had a full complement of efficient experienced nurses. He preferred regimental to general hospitals and recommended that a medical officer should be responsible for not more than fifty beds, of which half should be convalescent.

Dr. John Bell (1763–1820) made many recommendations in advance of his time based on his experience at the Battle of Camperdown and his service in the West Indies. He urged improvement in rations and cooking; less general monotony in a soldier's life; changes of climate for regiments so that soldiers did not remain long in unhealthy places; that medical officers be taught to deal with the evacuation and treatment of wounded and how to improvise hospitals from public buildings and houses.

With a wide regimental experience in America and Europe Dr. Robert Jackson (1793–1843) was also able to make many changes for the better in army hospitals. He had a prolific pen and was a great sanitarian. Above all he urged the importance of an efficient medical staff. Dr. Theodore Gordon (d. 1845) decided that unless a man was fit for full duty he should be in hospital.

Dr. John Rollo (d. 1809) likewise improved hospital conditions. He took great interest in their siting, construction, ventilation, and size for convenience of administration. He believed that cleanliness, decency, and regularity were essential in the management of a hospital, whether military or civil, and urged that surgeons should be responsible for the nurses and servants working under them. Later he became Surgeon-General of the Ordnance and built the Royal Artillery Hospital, Woolwich.

MEDICAL CARE IN THE NINETEENTH CENTURY

From 1794 onwards Sir James McGrigor's autobiography is the source of much valuable information on hospitals. At Portsmouth he persuaded the Navy to allow him to take over a great part of Haslar Hospital to deal with the remnants of Sir John Moore's army evacuated from Corunna. One of the main problems with which he had to deal was epidemic typhus. At Walcheren he was closely associated with Sir Gilbert Blane (1749–1834) and Sir George Ballingall (1806–55). In 1812 he arrived in Portugal to join the Duke of Wellington and was highly esteemed because his estimate of casualties and numbers fit to rejoin their regiments was so often correct. It was McGrigor (1771–1858) who introduced the regimental aid post. The Duke favoured the general hospitals already established at home and abroad, but McGrigor persuaded him that the provision of regimental hospitals for every corps in the Army was much to be preferred.

Dr. G. J. Guthrie (1785–1856) who, in Brussels, treated numbers of the wounded from Waterloo and made many advances in military surgery, also favoured regimental hospitals, and Sir George Ballingall referred to his general hospitals as "his general but necessary evils", because they generated diseases and the patients got into slovenly and irregular habits. The standard of hospitals after the Battle of Waterloo as described by Drs. John Thompson (1765–1846) and John Hennan (1779–1828) was reasonably high.

By the time that Sir James McGrigor retired in 1851 the Medical Department of the Army was already organized on a sound footing; only specially selected and fit soldiers were allowed to proceed to overseas stations; hospitals were well equipped and staffed with properly qualified medical officers, and diseases like typhus, cholera and dysentery were under better control.

In 1854 the Crimean War broke out. During the first winter before Sevastopol there was complete absence of medical supplies and ambulance transport, and large numbers of soldiers were rendered ineffective or died from starvation. To those on the spot these happenings were not surprising. Apart from regimental and field hospitals of a sort, there was a general hospital at Balaclava, and two general hospitals at Scutari.

From the Royal Commission's Report we learn of appalling conditions in hospitals and of the inefficiency of the administrative staff. There was a total lack of trained attendants to deal with the sick and wounded. Apart from battle casualties, dysentery, frost-bite, cholera, scurvy and typhus took a heavy toll. The field hospitals were filthy and lacked mobility. There was no hospital clothing, no operating rooms and transportation of wounded was difficult. Accommodation, cooking and lighting were defective and there was a shortage of all kinds of stores, due in large measure to lack of transport for essential items.

It is beyond the scope of this paper to discuss the controversy between the principal medical officer, Sir John Hall (1795–1866), and the superintendent of the female nursing establishment, Miss Florence Nightingale (1820–1910). The story is already well known. However, this was a turning point in the history of army hospitals. Miss Nightingale certainly raised the whole status of the nursing profession, and henceforth military hospitals were to be models on which all hospitals should be built.

A series of Royal Commissions considered every aspect of hospital construction, the practical effect of which was "to purify the air in and around wards, with a resulting improvement in the health and efficiency of the Army". At that time the regimental hospital was often a dingy part of barracks or an adjoining house rented for the purpose. These could be discovered in many garrison towns and did little credit to the regiment or to its surgeon.

The regimental system of army hospitals lasted until 1859, after which it was gradually superseded by a series of larger permanent general hospitals built on the pavilion plan, in order to permit maximum fresh air and sunlight to reach the wards. Among them, the following hospitals were opened: 1863, Royal Victoria Hospital, Netley (1,000 beds); 1866, (Royal) Herbert Hospital, Woolwich (650 beds); 1879, Cambridge Hospital, Aldershot (268 beds); and in 1905, the Queen Alexandra Military Hospital, Millbank (200 beds).

TREATMENT OF WOUNDED IN THE FIELD

The campaigns of the last century have effected a gradual improvement in the hospital treatment of battle casualties.

The Zulu War of 1879 was notable in this respect. Each regiment was supplied with a medical officer and stretcher-bearers; bearer companies were provided to collect wounded and transfer them to hospital; the field hospitals employed were of both the movable and stationary types, where patients remained awaiting transfer to the base, and for the first time a contingent of nurses took part in a campaign. Finally, the hospital at Rorke's Drift gained fame because it put up a valiant defence when overrun by a savage and ruthless enemy. An important result of the campaign was that special medical transport was recommended for the sick and wounded.

It was therefore not surprising that in the Egyptian Campaign of 1882 the scale of field hospitals and bearer companies was satisfactory. A group of voluntary nurses formed part of the force and were awarded campaign medals for the first time. As a result the standard of nursing in the field was raised, and hospital cooking and dieting improved.

FIELD MEDICAL CARE SINCE 1900

The South African War tested the mobility of the Army. A number of bearer companies were provided, which moved with battalions. These collected casualties and transported them to field hospitals where they were retained and treated until they were sent to the base. Altogether, there were nineteen

Field Medical Arrangements in Three Major Wars.

bearer companies, twenty-eight field hospitals, sixty stationary hospitals (mostly tented) and twenty-two general hospitals, scattered over an area of more than 600,000 square miles of difficult terrain. Incidentally, during this war X-rays were used for diagnosis in a British field force hospital for the first time.

Dust, flies, shortage of water, poor roads and a lack of suitable transport added to the difficulties. Outbreaks of dysentery, typhoid and other epidemic diseases greatly extended the medical services, which were not equal to the task. The majority of wounds were caused by long-range small-bore bullets and this led to the belief that surgery should be undertaken only after evacuation to the base. Moreover, it was held that the surgeon's role in the field was to deal solely with complications of wounds such as haemorrhage and infection.

WORLD WAR I

By the time that World War I had broken out bearer companies and brigade field hospitals were combined to form mobile units called field ambulances. Next in the chain of evacuation was the casualty clearing station, really a small general hospital for the forward area. This was a static clearing and evacuation unit, in which it was not intended to retain casualties longer than was necessary. This type of organization was suitable for the trench warfare into which the war on the Continent developed.

Later, the casualty clearing stations, reinforced by surgical teams, carried out the early surgery of war wounds. However, in the rapid advance of 1918 these units were left far behind, and little surgery was then possible at a casualty clearing station. Fortunately, the war ended before any breakdown in the medical arrangements occurred. For the first time specialization and need for special hospitals was recognized. In this war, too, voluntary bodies like the British Red Cross Society and the Order of St. John rendered splendid service and have since formed an integral part of the medical services in war.

WORLD WAR II

As World War II progressed new factors affecting medical care confronted the Army, including new weapons, modern advances in medical sciences and circumstances of total war involving the deployment of mobile forces in a series of campaigns on many fronts.

It therefore became necessary to increase the mobility of field medical units in the forward areas generally. In addition, it was soon found that airborne and commando forces needed independent medical cover. Further, in order to supply good nursing, early surgical treatment, blood transfusion and chemotherapy, medical support had to be disposed as far forward as practicable. Then, with evacuation by land, air or sea to base and home hospitals, early definitive treatment gave the soldier the best chance of recovery in ideal conditions.

CONCLUSION

Finally, it might be said that the development of service hospitals and the comprehensive care of the soldier, and later of his family, may be seen as a forerunner of the civilian health services.

BIBLIOGRAPHY

GORDON, C. A. (1870). *Army Surgeons and Their Works*, H. K. Lewis, London,

GORE, A. A. (1879). *Our Services under the Crown*, Baillière, Tindall and Cox. London.

JOHNSTON, W. (1917). *Roll of Commissioned Officers in the Medical Service of the British Army*, Aberdeen University Press.

STEWART, D. (1950). Some early military hospitals, *J. Soc. Army hist. Res.*, **28**, 171.

WOOLFRYES, J. A. (1879). Medical history of the war in Zululand in 1879, *Army med. Dept. Rep.*, **31**, 277. H.M. Stationery Office, London.

The Rise of Specialism and
Special Hospitals

SIR FRANCIS R. FRASER

MEDICAL SPECIALISM APPEARS to be inherent in the human race, for we find evidence of it in the archaeological records of the civilizations that rose and fell thousands of years ago and we find it in the primitive societies of isolated tribes in North America, Australia, Siberia and Africa. To account for its rise would, therefore, be as difficult as to account for the ambitions, rivalries and enterprises of men. By linking, however, in the title of this contribution the rise of specialism with the rise of special hospitals the Committee must have had in mind particularly the specialties as we now know them, subdivisions of internal medicine and surgery which have arisen for the most part during the last hundred years or so. This specialism and its special hospitals differ from the earlier forms largely in the different extent of scientific knowledge and in the changed religious and social settings but, I think, the story of specialism throughout the ages leads to a better understanding of specialism as we now know it, and permits a glimpse into the future.

Herodotus visited Egypt in the fifth century B.C. and comments on the large number of specialists there for every organ and part of the body, each man dealing with one organ or region only. They were of the priestly class and learned in the relationship of the gods to the diseases—each disease and each organ being under the influence of a particular deity. Treatment consisted of placating the god concerned, usually by animal sacrifices, but also of administering concoctions of animal or vegetable origins of which they had considerable knowledge. It seems probable that so much theology, mythology and therapeutics had to be learned by apprenticeship to an elder member of the temple staff that this high degree of

169

specialism based largely on magico-religious practices was inevitable. Some of these priest-physicians were attached to the courts of the Kings and provincial governors and so were men of high standing and importance in the community. This close connexion between religious beliefs and medical practice, in spite of many changes in each, can be traced for the next two thousand years and largely influenced the character and extent of specialization in medicine. There is evidence that this specialism was present in Egypt as far back as the building of the great pyramids about five thousand years before Herodotus.

In Babylonia and Assyria the position appears to have differed only in detail from that in Egypt. In cases of obscure illness a priest skilled in the practice of divination was required to use his arts to decide how the patient had incurred the wrath of the gods, and of which god. A second priest skilled in incantations and the ways of placating the god then took charge, while a third, experienced in the use of herbs and other pharmaceutical substances or in surgery, seems to have been the really important member of the team and was a specialist for the particular organ or disease. The services of these members of the staffs of the temples and the Court must have been expensive, for treatment among the general population was apparently mainly carried out by laymen who had developed a reputation for success with a particular form of illness or injury.

Essentially the same mythological religious medicine is still to be seen in the primitive tribes now living in isolated parts of the world. The medicine-man of the American Indians, the shaman of the Siberian Eskimoes and the priest-healers of the Australian aborigine and of some of the Bantu peoples of Africa are trained in knowledge of the spirits that bring about disease and death, and have been instructed in the rites and procedures that must be carried out to induce the evil spirits to leave the patient. But there is a second type of healer who has acquired, usually from his father or other relative, a secret knowledge of herbs, as well as of animal and metallic substances that are of value in special conditions. These are more numerous than the religious medicine-men proper and may be highly specialized and skilled in the treatment of wounds as well as of diseases.

This specialism of the ancient civilizations of the Near East and of present primitive societies would appear to be necessitated by the large amount of experience and knowledge, even though irrational and based on myths and superstitions, that had to be acquired about any one disease or group of diseases, so that no man or woman could be competent to deal with all types of patients. The specialism of the last one or two centuries and of the present day is, as we shall see, the result of somewhat different conditions. They have, however, much in common, including the desire of patients and their families to get the most expert advice available, and of the physicians to take pride in their knowledge and acquire importance in their community.

During the centuries when Greece and Rome were at the height of their greatness and dominated the Eastern Mediterranean, their medical practices were similar in many ways to those of Mesopotamia and Egypt. Beliefs as to the reasons and causes of disease were largely the same—the gods and the stars controlled them, and the physicians were mostly priests and attached to temples. But there were also considerable numbers of lay physicians trained by apprenticeship and often in family groups. They were mostly Greek in origin but travelled widely, especially in Asia Minor where many of them settled. It was into a group such as this that Hippocrates was born in the year 460 B.C. Most justly is he called the Father of Medicine for he broke away from the beliefs in supernatural causes of disease, and rationalized medicine. He not only recorded his observations but his disciples and followers also wrote freely so that we know much about the medicine of his school from the voluminous Hippocratic Collection. This is not the place to discuss the details of the teaching of Hippocrates and his disciples, but their insistence on accurate observation of the patient's reaction to his illness, on his natural resistance which must be supported and aided by diet and rest and not interfered with, and that the whole individual takes part in the struggle was contrary to the idea of specialisms. There are many today who criticize specialisms for just this reason. We know that Hippocrates and his school practised surgery as well as medicine.

In many ways the medicine of Galen (A.D. 130–200) who practised five hundred years later, followed the general teaching of Hippocrates and he endeavoured to rationalize medicine still further. He studied anatomy on the skeleton of a mummy and in animals, but his physiology was fanciful and based on philosophy rather than observation. He wrote extensively and dogmatically and his writings formed the basis of medical practice in Europe for the next fifteen hundred years. He too practised surgery and held an appointment as medical attendant at gladiatorial shows, but when he later settled in Rome he found that surgery was regarded as a menial occupation only to be practised by slaves.

During the next few centuries, during which Europe suffered almost continuously from invasions by the less cultured races to the North and East, the educated and cultured classes in Europe almost disappeared, and learning and the ability to read and write were to be found only in the Christian monasteries and other religious foundations. The Christian Church forbade the shedding of blood as well as post-mortem examinations and the practice of medicine became dependent on the few who could read the writings of Galen and other ancient authorities, while the practice of surgery was left to uneducated itinerant bone setters, barbers, oculists, cutters for stone and so on.

By this separation of the specialties of internal medicine and surgery, and by the prohibition of dissection and of post-mortem examinations, internal medicine lost all stimulus and had no opportunity to check its clinical methods, diagnoses and the effects of treatment. It lost the capacity to advance and it was not until surgery and its specialties were again recognized as a proper activity for educated men, and surgeons obtained a social position equal to physicians, that medicine was able to take its share in the re-awakening of thought and of experiment, and to develop a renewed inquisitiveness as to the nature of disease and its proper treatment. Of the specialisms and special hospitals as we now know them in this country, the surgical specialisms were the first to be established, and modern clinical science owes much to the recent extension of surgery to such areas as the nervous system, the lungs, the heart and the blood vessels. For success in these new surgical fields the most accurate preoperative diagnosis is required and the physician has had to develop new diagnostic skills utilizing the methods of biophysics, biochemistry, microbiology, morbid anatomy and radiology, or developing his own.

The accurate observations on human anatomy, with which we associate especially the name of Vesalius in the sixteenth century, undoubtedly resulted in improved surgery at a time when military surgeons had ample opportunities of practice during the numerous religious wars of the time. The surgeon Ambroise Paré in particular improved the position of surgery and stimulated its acceptance as a learned profession of academic standing. He deprecated the usual practice of treating wounds with boiling oil or the cautery with consequent necrosis and suppuration, and pleaded for healing by first intention. From France this acceptance of surgery gained momentum and spread throughout Europe. The French Academy of Surgery was founded in 1731 and our Royal College of Surgeons in 1798, replacing the Guild of Barber-Surgeons founded in 1540. I need not remind you of the further development of surgery that resulted from the introduction of anaesthesia, antisepsis and asepsis in the middle of the nineteenth century, at a time when physiology was still in its adolescence and advances in internal medicine depended on bedside observations without much knowledge of pathology and of the reactions of the living body to disease. This may well account for the rise of surgical specialties and special hospitals in advance of the medical specialties.

At the beginning of the nineteenth century cases of eye disease in this country increased considerably. This was due apparently to the return of soldiers from the Napoleonic War and especially from Egypt, and the spread of "ophthalmia"—probably trachoma and its complications—to civilians. The treatment of diseases of the eye was still largely in the hands of itinerant quacks and it required foresight and courage on the part of Astley Cooper to advise a young pupil, John Cunningham

Saunders, to start a private practice in diseases of the eye and ear. Saunders had been apprenticed to a doctor in Barn-staple, joined the medical school of Guy's and St. Thomas's and became demonstrator in anatomy under Astley Cooper. He had not been articled at the College of Surgeons and so saw no hope of being appointed as a surgeon to the staff of any of the general teaching hospitals. He therefore accepted Cooper's advice and started in Holborn in 1800 not as a general surgeon but as a specialist in diseases of the eye and ear. As the teaching hospitals had no provisions for the treatment of such cases he realized that he must start an institution to deal with them, especially for poor patients. The staffs of Guy's and St. Thomas's supported him, a committee was formed to collect subscriptions, and the "London Dispensary for Curing Diseases of the Eyes and Ears" was opened in Charterhouse Street in 1805. Two years later at the request of Saunders the name was changed to "The London Infirmary for Curing Diseases of the Eye", as he found he could do little for diseases of the ear. At the end of four years over two thousand patients had been treated. Unfortunately Saunders died in 1810, but Astley Cooper took charge of the in-patient and out-patient work until the appointment of Benjamin Travers who later joined the staff of St. Thomas's Hospital as a general surgeon. This connexion was important as Travers was permitted to take undergraduate students to the special hospital and so initiate there a teaching school in ophthalmology. It also illustrates how many of the early members of the staffs of the special hospitals were also general physicians or surgeons on the staffs of the general teaching hospitals, a condition that existed well into this century and in the lifetime of many of us. In 1821 a new building for the hospital was erected in Moorfields and its name changed to the "London Ophthalmic Infirmary", and in 1827 when it enjoyed Royal Patronage, the Board of Governors again changed its name to "The Royal London Ophthalmic Hospital, Moorfields". Its reputation grew rapidly and graduates from all over the world attended the clinical practice, especially after the invention of the ophthalmoscope by Helmholtz in 1851. With the introduction of junior staff appointments in 1856 the hospital was training ophthalmologists who established special eye hospitals not only in many centres in this country, but in many countries overseas. In London several additional eye hospitals were founded to meet the needs of the public, notably the Royal Westminster Ophthalmic Hospital in 1816—it was rebuilt in 1928 in Holborn—and in 1843 the Central London Ophthalmic Hospital was erected in Bloomsbury. When in 1947, after World War II and the introduction of the National Health Service, Moorfields, the Royal Westminster and the Central were united as one Postgraduate Teaching Hospital, the clinical work was concentrated at Moorfields and the Royal Westminster, and the Central was converted into laboratories, library, lecture rooms, and so on, to accommodate the teaching and research activities of a postgraduate Institute within the University of London.

W. J. Little was born in 1810, trained at the London Hospital and looked forward to a career as a physician. He suffered from a club foot, the result of an attack of poliomyelitis. Learning of the successes of Stromeyer of Hanover in the treatment of club foot by tenotomy, he visited Hanover and spent a year with Stromeyer who operated on him and taught him the technique of subcutaneous tenotomy. At that time, antisepsis and modern anaesthesia were unknown and open operations for such deformities were out of the question. On Little's return to London the success of Stromeyer's operation impressed his colleagues and he was encouraged in his plans to establish a hospital for the treatment of the many crippled and deformed children in London who could not be admitted to general hospitals. Admission to the general voluntary hospitals was at this time limited by the necessity of obtaining a recommendation from a subscriber and by the regulations that did not permit the admission of chronic conditions for which the prospects of cure or improvement were negligible. An influential committee of interested laymen was formed and in 1840 "The Infirmary for the Cure of Club Foot and other Contractions" was opened in Bloomsbury Square with thirty-six beds and out-patient accommodation. The local residents objected to the name plate on the door of the house, but the objections died down when the name was changed at Dr. Little's suggestion to "Orthopaedic Institution".

The demands on this Institution were so great that in 1851 a second hospital was opened in Hatton Garden to deal with children resident in the City. At first it could deal with outpatients only, but in the following year six beds were provided and so arose the City Orthopaedic Hospital. The demands on its accommodation soon necessitated its enlargement and it was rebuilt and reopened in 1899 with fifty beds. It is interesting that so much could be done for crippling conditions of the spine and limbs by rest, splinting and the use of other apparatus before the introduction of antisepsis in 1869 and the development of open operations, tenotomies and osteotomies. Even the general hospitals awoke to the possibilities and an orthopaedic department was opened at St. Bartholomew's Hospital in 1864.

In the meantime Dr. Little's original foundation in Bloomsbury Square had been moved in 1856 to Hanover Square where fifty beds were provided and a Royal Charter was granted, the name being changed from Orthopaedic Institution to Royal Orthopaedic Hospital. Before long a larger building was required and in 1902 the hospital was negotiating for a site in Coram Street, Bloomsbury. Long before this yet a third special orthopaedic hospital had become necessary in London and in 1864 the National Orthopaedic Hospital with thirty-five beds was opened in the vacated premises of a private hospital in Bolsover Street. By 1881 it was decided to enlarge the accommodation and in 1891 a new wing was opened and the number of beds increased to sixty. By 1902 it became obvious that much more provision was required as the scope of orthopaedic surgery expanded. In that year, therefore, both the Royal and the National hospitals were planning expansion and the King Edward's Hospital Fund recommended that the three metropolitan hospitals should amalgamate. In 1904 the Royal closed its premises in Hanover Square and joined with the National in Bolsover Street. In 1905 a new Royal Charter was granted and the combination became the Royal National Orthopaedic Hospital. In 1906 the City Orthopaedic Hospital agreed to join and in 1909 the present hospital was opened with two hundred beds and good out-patient accommodation. In 1922 a most important step was taken by the acquisition of the estate of twenty-seven acres at Brockley Hill on which has been developed the country branch of Stanmore with more than two hundred beds at present and space for considerable expansion.

These brief histories of Moorfields and the Royal National Orthopaedic Hospital illustrate the origins and developments of many special hospitals not only in London but in other centres in this country. Members of the medical profession realized that methods of treatment had been devised that could improve the health, happiness and efficiency of many patients whom the general hospitals could not admit because of lack of accommodation or initial doubt of the value of the new methods. By enlisting the sympathy and help of influential laymen they obtained sufficient funds to start a special hospital in a small way. The results soon justified their initiative, expansion became necessary and in a large centre of population such as London additional special hospitals were founded to meet the needs of the population, for even when the general hospitals eventually made some accommodation available for the special cases, this could not meet the needs of the sick poor. For economy and efficiency two or three of the original foundations later amalgamated to form hospitals of national and international reputation where the considerable numbers of similar cases enabled surgeons to learn by experience the new methods of treatment, and study the natural histories of diseases.

Social conditions and charitable impulses on the part of laymen, rather than new medical knowledge, were the origins of other special hospitals, and their eventual influence on medical practice and the advance of knowledge has been the same as that of the hospitals founded by members of the medical profession who had new methods of treatment to offer. Philip Rose, a London solicitor, found it impossible to arrange for the admission to hospital of one of his clerks who had pulmonary tuberculosis. He collected a small committee of influential persons and raised enough money to open an out-patient department in 1842 in Great Marlborough Street. He regarded this as a preliminary step to a hospital with beds, and in the same year was able to convert the Manor House in Chelsea for hospital purposes and open it with accommodation for twenty in-patients. Rose was successful in obtaining the support of the Royal Family, and Prince Albert laid the foundation stone of a new building for sixty beds in 1844. Further buildings were added and in 1854 the Hospital for Consumption and Diseases of the Chest was completed for the admission of patients with heart disease, pleurisy, bronchitis, asthma and malignant disease of the chest, as well as pulmonary tuberculosis. The staff has included many famous physicians and the hospital soon established an international reputation. The First World War saw a rapid development of thoracic surgery which has continued since and although the Brompton was originally founded to provide for a medical specialty it illustrates the importance to medicine of the full collaboration of internal medicine and surgery.

The early history of the National Hospital for Nervous Diseases, Queen Square, is in some respects similar to that of the Brompton. Two sisters, Louisa and Johanna Chandler, and their brother Edward could not get any hospital to admit their grandmother paralysed by a stroke. They had no money but much perseverance. They sold home-made trinket boxes and eventually elicited the sympathy of Alderman David Wire, the Lord Mayor, in their endeavour to establish a hospital to care for such patients as their grandmother. A public meeting was held in the Mansion House in 1859 and an empty house—24 Queen Square—was acquired in 1860 to provide ten beds and an out-patient department. At first it was little more than a dormitory for paralysed and epileptic persons, but many famous physicians and later surgeons were appointed to the staff and seized their opportunities for the study of the anatomy and physiology of the nervous system. As in the case of the Brompton, wounds inflicted in the First World War stimulated the acquisition of new knowledge and led to advances in the surgical treatment of nervous disorders.

These four London hospitals illustrate the origins, development and reputation of special hospitals throughout the United Kingdom, as well as those in London. Including the hospitals for children, mental diseases and obstetrics and gynaecology which have been dealt with by other speakers there are thirteen special hospitals in London, the more recent histories and futures of which I now wish to consider briefly and as a group. In addition to the four considered above there are in this group The Hospital for Sick Children, The Maudsley Hospital, Queen Charlotte's Maternity Hospital and the Chelsea Hospital for Women, the Royal National Throat, Nose and Ear Hospital, the National Heart Hospital, St. John's Hospital for Diseases of the Skin, St. Peter's, St. Paul's and St. Philip's Hospital and the Eastman Dental Hospital.

It would be wrong if I left you with the impression that the medical profession has always approved of special hospitals and their multiplication. During the middle of last century when many of them had their origins, the Editor of the *Lancet* sounded a note of warning and in some instances expressed very strong disapproval, especially in the case of St. John's Hospital for Diseases of the Skin where the motives of the founder do not seem to have been as altruistic as those I have mentioned earlier. On 29th October 1864 the *Lancet* said: "Of all the abuses which afflict and injure the profession, we know of none more serious and requiring more steady repression than the rampant tendency to multiply special institutions, a practice which has the effect of interfering with medical education, of injuring the general practitioner, and of unnecessary expense to the public." There were many members of the medical profession and of the lay public then, and indeed now, who would support the plea of the *Lancet* that the general hospitals should provide sufficient accommodation in special departments to make special hospitals unnecessary. Some years later on the 19th July 1873 an editorial in the *Lancet* contained the following: "For there can be no doubt that the patient is greatly benefited by being in a general hospital although he is confined in a special department; for it not uncommonly happens that he has other ailments beyond those strictly called special, and may therefore readily be attended to by other members of the medical staff. The patient, moreover, escapes the risk of becoming a martyr to rank specialism . . ." and the article continued, "By affording to the student facilities for studying all the diseases to which flesh is heir we ultimately produce practitioners of greater skill and learning, and thus the gain is made universal, and patients eventually reap the benefit." All would agree with these arguments and the general teaching hospitals have, during this century, established special departments, but these have been limited in size relative to the departments of general medicine and general surgery in order to keep them suitable for the undergraduate education of students, most of whom will enter general practice.

There is little doubt that the special hospitals were welcomed and approved by the specialists, who had the opportunity of studying more examples of any single disease than were available in any general hospital, and of discussing with specialist colleagues the numerous problems of diagnosis and treatment. In early days many members of special hospital staffs were also on the staffs of the general hospitals as general physicians or general surgeons. This still pertains, though to a less extent, for nowadays most of them hold specialist appointments on the staff of a general hospital and by constant meetings and discussions with their general colleagues are able to avoid the "rank specialism" that the Editor of the *Lancet* justly feared. The specialist physicians and surgeons made good use of their opportunities to advance knowledge by painstaking and accurate clinical observations and the publication of numerous papers, both analytic and synthetic, and the reputations of their hospitals grew and spread, not only throughout this country, but also abroad.

But it was not only the patients and the staffs of the hospitals who gained greatly from the opportunities provided by the special hospitals of London, for postgraduates, not only from other centres throughout the United Kingdom but also from the British Dominions overseas and from foreign centres, attended the out-patient sessions and ward rounds in order to study and gain experience of the special methods of examination and the special forms of treatment employed. These postgraduates were often visitors seeking for a few days or weeks to fill gaps in the experience they had been able to obtain in their own centres before following careers as general physicians or general surgeons, but many were planning careers as specialists and spent considerable periods in London. During the early decades of this century the somewhat haphazard arrangements for these serious postgraduate visitors to London and the often casual opportunities provided for them to obtain the experience they were seeking had caused some concern, and numerous committees were formed and discussions held in an endeavour to improve matters. The special hospitals often originated in converted or improvised buildings on such sites as were available, without consideration for their subsequent growth and extension, and they depended on voluntary subscriptions for their running costs and for any new buildings or other developments. Their primary purpose was the care of the sick poor, and it was with this intention only that the hospital buildings had been constructed.

In 1911 a Royal Commission on University Education in London (the Haldane Commission) was appointed and its final report published in 1914 criticized the London Medical Schools and the clinical teaching in the undergraduate hospitals. The report pointed out that the students were being taught the art of medicine efficiently, but that this was not all that a University School should be doing. It recommended that professorial units should be established with salaried staffs, a University professor in control of wards, an out-patient department, assistants nominated by the professor to assist him in his researches on the problems presented by the patients and their diseases, and laboratory accommodation in close proximity to the wards. After the First World War these recommendations were accepted by the University and the University Grants Committee, and between the wars a number of such units were established in the undergraduate general hospitals, although considerable difficulty was experienced in providing the laboratory accommodation in close proximity to the wards. The year 1935 saw the establishment of the Postgraduate Medical School of London at Hammersmith Hospital with full-time professors in charge of the wards for medicine, surgery and obstetrics and of the department of pathology, to provide in these subjects for the increasing numbers of postgraduates coming to London. It proved possible to provide some accommodation for laboratories near to the wards, but, as a result of the financial difficulties at that time, this was much less than had been planned. The clinical training of postgraduates in the special hospitals was not affected at that time.

In 1942, towards the close of the Second World War, an Inter-Departmental Committee on Medical Schools (the Goodenough Committee) was appointed and reported in 1944. The war was drawing to a close, medical education had been disrupted, the voluntary hospital finances had been altered drastically and a National Health Service was being planned. The report of the Committee recommended not only the extension of the professorial units to all undergraduate medical schools in the country, but also that postgraduate institutes for education and research should be formed by the University of London in selected special hospitals, and that these and the Postgraduate Medical School at Hammersmith Hospital should be constituted as a federated organization to deal with the training and education of postgraduates. In 1948, in anticipation of the coming into force of the National Health Service Act, the Ministry of Health designated the London Special Hospitals, which I have considered earlier, as Teaching Hospitals under the Act, and the University of London delegated to the British Postgraduate Medical Federation the task of forming, in connexion with them, Institutes for postgraduate teaching and research of University standard in the special subjects.

Two initial difficulties had to be overcome. One was to find specialists with the training and experience necessary, and able and willing to give up time to guide and direct the formation and activities of the Institutes. The other was to provide the laboratory accommodation in the proximity of the wards, in these old buildings not designed for their new purpose and, in several instances, in cramped and adapted quarters. These difficulties have now been overcome sufficiently for the Senate of the University to recognize all the Institutes as having attained the necessary requirements as constituents of a Postgraduate School of the University.

These hospitals have been aware, I think, of the dangers of specialism to which the *Lancet* drew forcible attention a hundred years ago, but since the establishment in association with them of the University Institutes for teaching and research their staffs have been more conscious of their isolation. The hospitals are scattered throughout London and their positions do not make it easy for them to keep in touch with the new developments in methods of investigation and treatment being evolved in the other special hospitals, and in the departments of clinical medicine and clinical surgery, of anatomy, physiology, pathology, microbiology and biochemistry in the medical schools and general hospitals. The governing body of the Federation has always maintained that, ideally, the special postgraduate hospitals should be grouped around and with easy access to a postgraduate general teaching hospital, and to each other. For various reasons, especially financial, and the difficulty of finding a suitable site in London for such a centre, this ideal solution appears to be impracticable. But the University, the University Grants Committee and the Ministry of Health are well aware of the serious disabilities under which the postgraduate special hospitals are endeavouring to fulfil their purpose and their role in creating in London a postgraduate medical centre for Great Britan and the Commonwealth, of international repute and worthy of London. The Ministry is now considering plans for rebuilding many of London's special teaching hospitals and it is proposed to group them in two main centres, one in Bloomsbury and the other in Kensington, which will be, if far from ideal, at least a great improvement. It will enable these hospitals to be planned and built for research and teaching of University standard, and not merely for the care of the sick poor for which they were established a hundred years ago.

If I have ignored the special hospitals in other centres than London it has been because their origins were similar to those of the London hospitals. It is permissible perhaps to contemplate two kinds of special hospitals in the future.

For one reason or another there may still have to be special hospitals under the Regional Hospital Boards serving as overflows from the general hospitals in order to meet the needs of increasing or shifting populations. Some of the many special hospitals already in existence in smaller centres throughout the country may have to be retained for this purpose, but the more closely they can be associated with a general hospital, physically and administratively, the better for the specialisms, the specialists and the public. But those I have been especially considering today must be planned and rebuilt as University teaching hospitals with ample accommodation in close proximity to the wards for education and research on the problems presented by the patients and in the cognate basic sciences. Some of these may be constituents of undergraduate teaching hospitals taking the place of special departments within the main teaching hospital, but in London particularly there should be special postgraduate teaching hospitals, planned and built for this purpose and forming, as far as is practicable, a postgraduate centre for the education and training of specialists, not only for this country, but also for graduates from the Commonwealth and other countries overseas. In this way the unique conditions and opportunities that have arisen in London can be used for the advance of clinical science and the benefit of humanity. It is, I believe, inevitable that with the continual development of new methods of investigation and of treatment requiring training, experience and constant practice for their full utilization, further specialisms will arise with new special departments in general hospitals, and new and additional special teaching hospitals for postgraduate education and research.

BIBLIOGRAPHY

ACKERNECHT, E. H. (1955). *A Short History of Medicine*, New York.

COOK, C. (1961). The history of Moorfields Medical School, *Brit. J. Ophthal.*, **45**, 241.

CRITCHLEY, M. (1960). The beginnings of the National Hospital, Queen Square, *Brit. med. J.*, **i**, 1829.

DAVIDSON, M. & ROOVRAY, F. G. (1954). *The Brompton Hospital*, London.

GALEN (1921). *On the Natural Faculties*. English translation by A. J. Brock, Loeb Classical Library, London.

Great Britain, Ministry of Health (1944). *Report of Inter-departmental Committee on Medical Schools*, H.M.S.O., London.

Herodotus (1921). English translation by A. D. Godley, Book ii, para. 84. Loeb Classical Library, London.

Hippocrates (1923). English translation by W. H. S. Jones, vols. **i** & **iv**. Loeb Classical Library, London.

JONES, A. ROCYN. Personal communications on the origin of the Royal National Orthopaedic Hospital.

LYLE, T. KEITH (1961). Some of the great historical figures associated with Moorfields, *Brit. J. Ophthal.*, **45**, 251.

Report of the Royal Commission on University Education in London (1914), H.M.S.O., London.

SIGERIST, H. E. (1951–62). *A History of Medicine*, 2 vols., Oxford University Press, London.

The Hospital as a Teaching Centre

CHARLES NEWMAN

THE MAIN POINTS of interest in the subject of the hospital as a training centre are (1) why the hospital played no part for so long, (2) how the development of medical method finally diverted all medical education into hospitals, and (3) how hospitals then determined the course of medical theory.

Hospitals existed for a very long time before they were in any way concerned with teaching medicine; in fact the intention of their foundation and the general medical thought of the time were quite alien to any such idea, for they were a result of that complete change of attitude towards medicine which was produced by the general acceptance of Christianity. St. Jerome, writing in about A.D. 400, says that the first hospital was built by a friend of his, a Roman lady called Fabiola *et prima omnium* νοσοκομεῖον *institui.*[1] Jerome could find no Latin word for this new thing: but the Greeks had a word for it. Mediaeval Latin subsequently used the word "hospitium", but this also meant more what we would call an almshouse, or a "casual ward": the mediaeval hospitals on which the late Dr. Walter Godfrey was the authority were just that, and so, probably, were St. Bartholomew's and St. Thomas's originally. But there was certainly a relation between the two: the mediaeval hospitium, the long nave with the door at one end, rows of beds or cubicles on either side and the altar at the far end, was too like the modern hospital ward, the long room with the door at one end, the tightly packed rows of beds down either side, and the sterilizer at the far end, for the similarity to be accidental. The identity can still be seen unmistakably at Beaune, where the Hospice (which is literally the Hospitium) is in fact a νοσοκομεῖον. There was also the Hospital at Sandwich in 1244 to which Professor Lloyd refers (p. 147). At any rate, hospitals in the modern sense were certainly one of the effects of the Christian revolution, though whether these effects, which were quite fundamental to all medical thought, were beneficial or injurious, depends on one's ultimate beliefs. In the first place this revolution swept away all notion of material causation, substituting an equally deterministic system based on morality and theology. Such primitive notions of physical causation as were starting to develop were completely suppressed, and the belief in sickness as retribution for sin was substituted. The replacement of drug treatment by repentance and prayer, though official, was not in practice complete; like the pilgrim on his way to Lourdes, people asked for a Seidlitz powder to be going on with, or at least for the Dark Ages' equivalent of one. The Christian revolution meant the end of scientific medicine for a millennium. On the other hand, it introduced a new attitude to the sick, an attitude of pity and of desire to help which was quite new in that it extended to strangers and, still more remarkably, to the poor. This was the attitude which led to the foundation of hospitals, which in the end determined the nature of medical education and of all that was to follow from it.

During the thousand years from A.D. 400 to A.D. 1400 (and, to a slowly decreasing extent, for three hundred years more) the basis of medical theory and practice was the doctrine of the four humours and their four qualities, as elaborated by Aristotle and systematized by Galen. It was a logical system built on intellectual concepts, one remove from actual observation, but very complete and very satisfactory, if one could swallow the imaginary "facts" which made up its first principles. The details of this system, with its elements, temperaments, spirits and all the rest of it, were highly complex and were to be learned only from lectures and libraries. The essential thing was to study the classical authors, to whom all truth had been finally revealed, with some attendance at lectures, which explained exactly what the ancient authors meant. The practice of medicine consisted of fitting what the patient told the doctor into the framework of Galen's theory. What the doctor had to know was the theory in all its ramifications: the application was easy, simply the prescription of regimen, diet and drugs which would counteract the defects or excesses of humours and qualities which constituted "disease", so as to restore that perfect balance which was health. Hospitals, even the few which existed, had no part to play in the education of physicians. Nor were they used in the teaching of surgery, which was a despised and menial art, transmitted from father to son, or derived from the cruder forms of veterinary surgery, and of no interest to those who were concerned with professional teaching. Nor did the education of apothecaries concern the hospitals: it was not until the seventeenth century that apothecaries became of medical significance, and then, and for long enough afterwards, they were trained by apprenticeship, like the grocers from whom they had originated.

Surgery slowly improved in quality and status during and as a result of the wars of the later Middle Ages, which were incessant. The invention of gunpowder provided a greatly extended field for the exercise of the art. By the end of the Middle Ages there emerged a class of surgeons who were socially and intellectually of a much higher status than their more numerous inferior colleagues. This class consisted of such men as those who feature in Holbein's picture of Henry VIII founding the Barber-Surgeons Company. Thomas Vicary (d. 1561), the highly respectable London surgeon, for instance, and Edmund Harman (d. 1569), who was buried in a sumptuous (and unique) tomb in Burford church. Through the discipline of the new Company such men prospered and grew in number, and were typified by the Moulins family, who successively cut for the stone at St. Bartholomew's, and Thomas Hollyard, who was presentable enough to be a friend of Samuel Pepys and to own the site which the College of Physicians bought for the Warwick Lane College. The education of surgeons started in the form of anatomical teaching, which achieved a new importance and interest as a result of the advances made by the sixteenth-century anatomists on the Continent. As soon as the Barber-Surgeons Company had been chartered in 1540, the education of surgeons was organized, in the form of anatomical lectures and demonstrations of dissections. Dissection was restricted to the Corporations licensed for the purpose: the Royal College of Physicians, the Barber-Surgeons Company, and the two Universities. It is often forgotten that the College of Physicians trained in anatomy. The Lumleian Lectures (through which Harvey announced the theory of the circulation of the blood) were called "The anatomical lectures", and the Goulstonian lectures were delivered over a dissected body, which is why there were three of them; a body would not keep for longer.

The facilities of hospitals were applied to surgical education long before they contributed to education in medicine. It was not for the modern reason that proper operating theatres and teams of assistants were needed; they were not. Surgeons operated in the home, or in a home chosen by the patient as suitable. Samuel Pepys, for instance, was operated on for the stone by a St. Bartholomew's surgeon in the house of a distant cousin in Salisbury Court, and stayed there until he was healed. Surgical teaching started in hospitals because to teach students one must have numerous (and possibly varied) patients, and in private practice cases were few and, in the case of the best surgeons, restricted by the custom of the surgeon's living with patients in noble households and attending to the dressings and complications until all suppuration had ceased and the wound was healed, or as near these two desiderata as was attainable. This meant that, as Dr. Copeman said,[2] surgeons to the nobility (that is, the best surgeons) might be able to undertake only two or three cases a year. Even if surgeons to the merchant class could, by the end of the seventeenth century, deal with as many as four times that number of patients, and there is no evidence that they could, this experience would hardly have sufficed for educational purposes.

Students attended St. Bartholomew's Hospital for the first time, it is said, in 1662, and these were presumably surgical students. I can find no proof of this date, but it is certain that at St. Bartholomew's there were surgical students two years later, because on 1st February 1664 young men apprenticed to three surgeons were reported as having made a nuisance of themselves over the admission of patients.[3] It is from indirect references like this that the earliest existence of students is known: they appeared, rather than were attracted. Their education consisted less of clinical surgery than of anatomy, which was taught by lectures, with some demonstrations. How much dissection was, as a matter of fact, done in hospitals, on what subjects, whether on autopsy bodies, indeed what post-mortems were done before about 1780, are all matters needing investigation, and matters on which evidence is difficult to find.* Besides this, pupils probably had some teaching in the wards: the fact that at a later date the surgeon's pupils had no right to go into the medical wards, whereas the physician's pupils had the run of both medical and surgical wards, suggests that there may have been some ward-teaching from the first. But the revival of medical education in the latter half of the seventeenth century was fundamentally a revival of anatomical teaching, drawing its inspiration from the liberation of men's minds from slavery to Galen's authoritative doctrines. This took a long time to come about: it was originally the result of the work of the sixteenth-century anatomists, who showed that some of Galen's statements were quite simply wrong; it was intensified by Harvey, who showed that Galen's anatomy and physiology of the circulation, including the functions of the venous blood, of the natural and animal spirits and so on, were completely imaginary, and, as Dr. Copeman pointed out,[4] it was helped by the discovery of new drugs, which showed that the ancients did not know everything after all. The general atmosphere of seventeenth-century inductive science finally loosened the bonds of Galen.

The seventeenth-century revival of surgical teaching continued into the eighteenth century. In 1711 Cheselden started to lecture on anatomy and surgery at home, but in 1714 the Barber-Surgeons prevented this by enforcing the regulations against such dissections. He restarted his teaching at St. Thomas's when he was elected to the staff in 1718. In 1742 the London Hospital accepted students, again for surgical teaching only. But it was private teaching, outside as well as inside hospitals, which developed in the early eighteenth century, and led to the era of the private anatomy schools and the second revival of medical education.

The younger men not unnaturally took the lead. Apart from Cheselden, Edward Nourse (1701–61) was teaching in his

* Mrs. Gweneth Whitteridge is about to publish details about how autopsy bodies were studied anatomically, not in hospitals, but in private houses.

own house (London House, Aldersgate Street) in 1730, and in 1739 transferred his lectures on Anatomy, Chirurgical Operations and Bandages to St. Bartholomew's. At this point several things combined to bring about the second revival of anatomical and surgical teaching. In the first place there was a demand for it, and its provision promised financial rewards. For instance a Society of Naval Surgeons got Samuel Sharp (?1700–78) to give lectures on anatomy, surgical observations [*sic*] and the application of bandages in Covent Garden. Secondly, William Hunter (1718–83), who came to London in 1741 as assistant to Dr. James Douglas, to help him with his work on bones, brought with him from Edinburgh the teaching methods and enthusiasm of Monro Primus. Sharp transferred the lectures to the Naval Surgeons to William Hunter in 1746.[5] Thirdly, the Barber-Surgeons Company split in 1745, and the licence to dissect, instead of being transferred to the new Company of Surgeons, was abolished, and dissection became legal in hospitals and private establishments. Fourthly, great advances were made in Paris in the teaching of anatomy, which revolutionized the technique of education and reached new standards of excellence, by adopting the principle of allowing each student to dissect a whole body. In 1740 William Hewett was offering dissection "by the Paris method" in his house in Leicester Fields (though how he got round the restrictions or where he got his material are mysteries).[6] In 1746 William Hunter followed suit. He was already famous by reason of the eloquence, fullness and abundance of practical illustration in the anatomical teaching which he gave in Little Piazza, Covent Garden, with the help of his brother John, and later in the famous Windmill Street School.

The Hunters established the era of the private anatomy schools. In 1777 John Sheldon started his school in Great Queen Street; in 1786 Joshua Brooks followed with the Great Marlborough Street School; Joseph Carpue set up another in Dean Street in 1800. They continued down to the foundation of the school near Brunswick Square by Thomas Cook in 1870,[7] though their full tide was from about 1800 to 1835. But they had already affected the teaching in hospitals by their example and competition. During the eighteenth century the flow of students anxious to watch operations in hospitals had steadily increased: in 1760 there were disputes over their rights to attend operations both at Guy's and St. Thomas's. This was finally approved in 1768, and Guy's officially accepted students in 1769. Moreover, on 11th November 1768 the General Court of Guy's Hospital agreed that all surgeons appointed to the hospital should be allowed to give occasional lectures to the pupils, but Hector Cameron suspected that the Court of Committees did not confirm the decision, because the next surgeon appointed by the General Court was not told about being allowed to lecture.[8] Surgical teaching was then transferred to St. Thomas's, and for a time it was in medical teaching that Guy's took the lead.

To consider teaching in medicine it is necessary to go back to the general scientific revival. When the humoral theory began to collapse in the light of the genuine scientific discoveries of the seventeenth century, some physicians lost interest in the Galenic system and returned to the intellectual attitude associated with the name of Hippocrates. The interest was in observing disease as a phenomenon of nature, noting what actually happened to a sick person, studying the natural history of disease, how it originated and developed, what its outcomes were, how the phenomena of disease tended to fall into patterns which could be recognized as "diseases", and how they responded to treatments, rather than what treatments were theoretically indicated. To study the natural history of disease patients were needed, and nothing but patients, and more of them than might be available in the practice of a young and eager man. Then as now, the easiest and most convenient place in which to find them, to study them and to show them to students, was the hospital.

The originator of the scientific revival in medical teaching was Sydenham. He did not teach in hospitals, because he had not the opportunity: even a genius was lucky to be able to practise and teach at all during the Restoration, after having fought in Cromwell's army in the Civil War. The whole of Sydenham's life is most obscure, probably for that reason, and it is therefore impossible to trace the descent of modern medicine from him, through pupils, in the usual way. It is, however, fairly certain that he exerted his astonishing influence through his writings, which are indeed a first-class exposition of the Hippocratic observational method. His ideas were not by any means universally taken up; they were an enormous departure from the accepted basis of medicine, and would have been totally uninteresting to any Renaissance, mediaeval or classical physician.* What Sydenham was aiming at is admirably put in his own words, which might easily have been written by Hippocrates, "true practice consists in the observations of nature: these are finer than any speculations", and by his advocacy of "the investigation of the history of diseases, and of the efficacy of remedies, as shown by the only true teacher—experience". All this would have been the very opposite of the attitude of the classical Greeks, and of their spiritual successors for two thousand years, who believed wholeheartedly that speculation was the proper use of the mind and that observation and experiment were thoroughly banausic occupations, fit only for slaves and rude mechanicals.

Sydenham's doctrines fell at once, however, on a few patches of highly fertile soil, in particular Baglivi (1669–1707) and Franciscus Sylvius (1614–72). In the case of Baglivi there is no doubt of Sydenham's influence, because Baglivi called Sydenham "artis nostrae ornator et ornamentum".[9] Baglivi apparently lectured, but did not teach at the bedside. Sylvius, who came earlier, probably played Adams to Sydenham's Leverrier, and made the same discovery at the same time, because Sydenham started in practice in, or just before, 1661 (Munk) and published his first book in 1666, and Sylvius wrote in a letter in 1664 that he was teaching students "by a method unknown in Leyden, or perhaps elsewhere, i.e. taking his pupils daily to visit the sick at a public hospital".[10] Even if, as is certainly possible, Sylvius was first fired by the chance remark of a visitor who knew of Sydenham's work—a definite possibility, though one unlikely ever to have been recorded, and therefore unlikely to be capable of proof—Sylvius seems to deserve the credit for having invented bedside teaching, one of

---

*Hippocrates himself, or "the Hippocratic School" if one prefers not to believe in the one man, was a very early Greek, before the Classical era, and with a kind of mind very different from that of the classical Greek thinkers.

the greatest inventions in medical education, and the lasting glory of medical education as a new invention in the technique of education as a whole.

From that point onwards, the genealogy of clinical teaching is easy; it all went through Boerhaave (1668–1738), who was educated at Leyden. Sylvius had worked in Leyden, but Boerhaave was taught there in 1692, after the death of Sylvius, by Alexander Pitcairn, who had founded the Edinburgh Medical School in 1685 and had been called thence to Leyden as professor of medicine. Boerhaave himself taught Alexander Monro Primus (1697–1766), who really made the Edinburgh Medical School and introduced clinical teaching. Alexander Monro was, oddly enough, the son of an army surgeon, John Monro, who had been taught by Pitcairn. It was thus that clinical teaching in hospital was first practised and consolidated in Holland, and from there transmitted directly to Edinburgh, which became the premier school in the British Isles for a hundred years.

The use of hospitals for the teaching of medicine in England was delayed until much later in the eighteenth century. It is true that a claim for an earlier date has been put forward. Norman Moore[11] said that in 1584 the College of Physicians recognized the importance of St. Bartholomew's as a place of medical study on the strength of a letter from the then President, Roger Giffard, concerning the candidature of Dr. Wootton for a staff appointment. He wrote: "And in so far as that place hath oftentimes great and strange accidents and diverse cases of importance not elsewhere usual . . . we will be ready from time to time . . . to allow and impart to him our best advice and conference." It is more likely that the President was trying to persuade St. Bartholomew's to appoint a man who held the F.R.C.P. in preference to one (Dr. Timothy Bright) who did not (an interesting skirmish in the battle which, in the end, the College won so thoroughly). As an inducement to the hospital, the College was offering to come down and help Dr. Wootton with his difficult cases. This seems a simpler reading of the episode than an advocacy of the teaching of medicine in the hospital as such. Incidentally, St. Bartholomew's declined to appoint Dr. Wootton in spite of the College's kind offer, and the College, not long afterwards, committed Dr. Bright to the Fleet Prison, presumably for practising without the College's proper licence.

The generally accepted date for the beginning of regular medical teaching in a hospital in England is 1772, when Dr. George Fordyce (1736–1802) started courses of lectures on chemistry, materia medica and the practice of physic in St. Thomas's. But the psychiatrists forestalled their more organic colleagues in that William Battie, the physician to, and founder of, St. Luke's, the great lunatic asylum in Moorfields, wrote in 1758 that the worthy citizens of London who planned this foundation "very soon by an unanimous vote signified their inclination of admitting young Physicians well recommended to visit me in the Hospital and freely to observe the treatment of the patients there confined".[12] He confirmed this by saying that "Amongst the many good reasons offered to the Publick, for establishing another hospital for the reception of Lunatics, one, that was not the least considerable, was the introducing more Gentlemen of the Faculty to the Study and Practice of one of the most important branches of Physick" (p. V.). It is noteworthy that Dr. Battie's teaching was not only the earliest application of the facilities of a hospital to the teaching of medicine; it was also an application of these facilities in the form of clinical teaching in the wards, not by lecture. Even though the innovation faded away with Battie, he deserves to be remembered as its introducer. Psychiatry was not then a specialty: it was a part, and an important part, of the practice of many physicians.

The fact was that Boerhaave's simple clinical ward-rounds, vitally important though they were, had not developed in England, and English physicians had taken to going to Edinburgh, or abroad, for the teaching which was so completely lacking in Oxford and Cambridge. Clinical teaching even in the London hospitals was discouraged by the strong reversion to medical theorizing which was characteristic of the eighteenth century. The Age of Reason preferred to use its reason, and had a thoroughly classical belief in speculation as opposed to observation. The ancient system of noting what the patient said, without any attempt at examination by the doctor, became even more completely the whole of clinical medicine. In reading the recorded histories of patients before 1820 the most striking thing is the passivity of the physician: he let the patient say what he liked. The constant failure of the physician to ask the few questions which would have made the diagnosis retrospectively obvious is the most irritating feature of the clinical practice of the period. That failure was also damaging, as it encouraged the system of the consultants reading reports of cases from apothecaries and giving written opinions on them without ever seeing the patient at all, or listening to the apothecary's version of the history in a coffee-house and giving verbal opinions and instructions. Both systems were bad for the progress of medicine, even if they made little difference in those days to the progress of the patient. The medicine on which they were based was derived from books, whether they were by Galen or by the more modern but equally fanciful Stahl, Brown or Hahnemann. For that reason, practice could easily be carried on in this way, and practice of this kind offered no incentive to take medical teaching into the wards. There was reason for lectures, even if only to elaborate the conflicting theories of the contemporary intellectuals who offered substitutes for outmoded Galen. So that Dr. Fordyce's lectures on medicine were little improvement in themselves: he did not teach in the wards. But then, there was little more to teach in the wards than there had been fifty years before, and if the prophet Boerhaave had been ignored in England lesser men were not likely to be listened to.

Students in hospitals at this time were commonly called "pupils", because they were still largely the private pupils of members of the staff, attached to them as short-term consultant-apprentices. St. Thomas's allowed Assistant Physicians to take up to two pupils each in 1751. The starting of lectures in hospitals made it possible for medical students to take out tickets for lectures without incurring the great expense of becoming private pupils. So the kind of medical student with which we are familiar came into being, and by his demands for a more thorough, complete and systematic education ultimately induced the teachers to provide it. It cannot be too much stressed that it was in this way that medical education developed: it was not a system elaborated and inaugurated by the hospitals or their staffs, of which the students took advantage. Moreover, it must be remembered that the physicians had, until the 1830s, very few pupils. Christison found in 1820 that at St Bartholomew's there were only three physicians' pupils, all graduates, whereas there were several hundred surgical students. [13]

Private hospital pupils must have followed their teachers into the wards or out-patients' departments, must have seen something of practical clinical medicine and surgery, otherwise they would have got nothing more, at great expense, than the other students who attended lectures only. They ultimately had the privilege of preferential consideration for hospital appointments, but in so far as two pupils per "honorary" left many for whom no post would be available, they must have had advantages as pupils to induce them to pay large fees. Private pupillage if it did much to develop the characteristics of the individual hospitals, did nothing to develop medicine and surgery at large. Although the number of private pupils was originally very restricted, it became much larger in the second quarter of the nineteenth century, when hospital education suddenly developed, and the very high pupil fees became, for a short time, a considerable source of income to the younger members of hospital staffs. It would be very interesting to correlate the financial security that this contributed with the wonderful research effort of the young men of the time, and to see if they were related.

The period from 1740 to 1840 was the era of the private anatomy schools. Their prosperity started, it is interesting to note, before the Apothecaries Act of 1815 demanded higher standards of education. It is to the lasting credit of medical men that they were seeking a better education before the public thought of requiring it of them, and before the Universities had the least notion of providing any modern medical education, or, for matter of that, any medical education at all. The mediaeval kind that they had once provided had faded away a hundred years before, and nothing whatever had taken its place. Neither Addenbrookes nor the Radcliffe made any attempt to give the practical education they could easily have provided for the small number of medical students of the time, in preparation for the exclusive privileges enjoyed by the medical graduates of the two Universities. The private schools provided a far better standard of anatomical teaching than the outmoded, cramped, insanitary, understaffed conditions provided by the hospitals, where the staff were abusing their monopoly and thereby making it worth while for others to transcend it.

It must be remembered that anatomy in those days included physiology; indeed a study of the interesting collection of manuscript lectures and notes on lectures in the Library of the College of Physicians shows that they consisted more of physiology than of anatomy. Even the Scottish teachers in London, in the heyday of their influence, were completely free of the pedantry of anatomical detail which afflicted them (and their classes) in the period of their decline. This inclusion of physiology, and the direct contact with practical anatomy provided by the Paris Method, made the study valuable for all doctors; while for surgeons, in pre-anaesthetic days when speed was essential, anatomy, for all practical purposes, *was* surgery. The great increase in anatomical teaching had two side-effects: one was the exaggerated value attached to anatomy, as a result of its one-time importance, which afflicted medical education until quite recently, and the other was the necessity, as a result of laws regarding the provision of bodies for dissection, for the stealing of bodies for the purpose, and the scandals of the Resurrection Men and finally of murder as a means of procuring bodies. Nothing but an imperative need would have made possible the terrible things that happened.

The surgeon-anatomists who started the private schools later attracted medical colleagues who could lecture on medicine, materia medica, therapeutics and so on, who also brought with them diagrams, dried plants and other teaching material. In this way some of the private schools built up fairly complete curricula, details of which may be found on p. 26 of the *Lancet* for 1825. This made it all the easier to absorb them into hospital schools when the time came. In this way, for instance, Grainger's Webb Street School made a major contribution to the St. Thomas's School, and G. D.

Dermott's Little Windmill Street School to the Middlesex. Lane's Grosvenor Street School did more: it led to the founding of a hospital (St. Mary's) and its medical school. The private schools also did the bulk of the work of introducing and perfecting the teaching methods which the hospital schools ultimately followed. The reason the private schools could not continue was the development of clinical medicine. This happened when the technique of physical examination, popularized by Laënnec, was taken up by hospital physicians with patients in the wards to teach on, such as Peter Mere Latham at St. Bartholomew's, R. B. Todd at King's, Addison at Guy's and Elliotson at University College Hospital.

It was largely the private medical schools and their obvious success which stimulated the development of the hospital medical schools. These were, in any case, virtually private medical schools in hospitals, started by the medical staffs, with the not always enthusiastic permission of the hospital authorities. The distinction between a private school and a hospital school must have been very elusive: the distinction was only whether the teaching was done in a hospital or in a private house. The hospital schools did, in essence, belong to the hospital medical staffs, who in many instances actually paid for the buildings used for teaching in the hospitals, as in the case of Sir William Blizard, who in 1783 provided most of the money for the school at the London Hospital, the first complete medical school in London. In other words, it was enthusiasts among medical men who started medical schools in England, just as the same kind started special hospitals. That is why medical schools in England all came to be associated with, and were often started by, hospitals, whereas elsewhere it is more the rule that medical schools were started by universities and universities actually founded and maintained hospitals to provide facilities for medical teaching. In England it was more common for the medical men in a big town to start a medical school in the local infirmary, and for the medical school by its success to encourage, and by its presence to form the nucleus for, the starting of a university. Even where a university has started a medical school, as in the case of University College and King's College in London, the medical teachers, when they came to found a hospital for the express purpose of providing for the teaching of students, did it by invoking the aid of lay charity to start the hospital on the conventional voluntary system, so that the end-product was indistinguishable from the hospital which existed before its school. Occasionally, as in the case of St. Luke's and of the National Hospital, Queen Square, teaching was included as a primary object in the foundation of the hospital.

It should also be remembered that the hospital schools largely owed their existence to two factors; one the visible and competitive success of the private schools, and the other the powerful stimulus of discontented students, who, unable to get what they wanted from the official provision made by hospital staffs, formed student societies, such as the Abernethian Society at St. Bartholomew's, and the Guy's Society for Clinical Reports, which had an immense influence in improving the hospital education of students.

Thus it came about that in Great Britain medical schools were invariably attached to, and usually arose from, hospitals. The result of this was that medical education became what it was very far from being in the old days, essentially clinical, with bedside teaching the principal method. There is evidence, by comparing the British doctor with the product of other systems, that this works well, and has produced a kind of doctor who is both in practice and in ethical attitude better able to provide what patients want and what is professionally desirable than some of his Continental colleagues. It is well to temper self-satisfaction with the recollection that many Continental specialists have thrived in this country because they were better at providing magic and absolute authoritarianism than we are: it does not do to rely too much on self-satisfied high-mindedness and to refuse to learn the lessons offered by success. The claims of Continental teachers for their methods are not so important. They have always maintained that there is little need to teach bedside medicine, because a doctor is going to spend the rest of his life learning it in any case, but that he will never learn the basic sciences after his student days, which should therefore be devoted entirely to learning them. It is doubtful how much it matters teaching facts of any kind:

attitudes of mind, enthusiasm and the knowledge of how to find out are much more important, and a bedside clinical education can more certainly provide them than can an academic didactic education.

The rise of physical examination in the nineteenth century was not, historically, the cause of the transfer of medical education to hospitals: the cause was primarily the rise of surgery. Even if the work of Auenbrugger had been adopted at once, physical examination would still have been preceded, even on the medical side, by Boerhaave's clinical teaching half a century earlier. It was largely because of the use of hospitals for medical teaching that the examination of physical signs was taken up. Once physicians had started taking their students round the wards, one would think it was inevitable that they should begin to supplement the inspection of facies, urine and decubitus by looking at the lumps and other physical manifestations which the patients were trying to describe. It is extraordinary how long it was before they did. There is documentary evidence that in 1737 they did not (until compelled to do so by a King) and that in 1793 they did (but in both these instances it was to the credit of surgeons, not of physicians). Albertini's attention to palpation at the beginning of the eighteenth century[14] died with him: Auenbrugger had no influence until his "novum inventum" was taken up by the first physician who effectively examined patients: Corvisart. He was certainly doing so between 1789 and 1808[15] and started a line of succession. There may have been French physicians before him who did: it was in France that medical advance restarted after the stagnation of the eighteenth century. But it is inherently unlikely that many physicians ever examined a patient, because throughout the eighteenth century physicians had the greatest objection to doing anything with their hands except holding a cane or writing, and anyone who had done more would have aroused strong professional disapproval. What is odd is that surgeons, whose job was primarily to use their hands, were so reluctant to use them for diagnostic purposes.

Historically, hospitals began to be used for research when the Hippocratic physicians of the seventeenth century started to take a new interest in patients in the wards because they wanted to observe and record the features of disease. From this, much later, came the taking of students round the wards, and as part of the new clinical science the physical examination of patients was developed by isolated observers, Albertini in 1726,[16] Auenbrugger before 1761 and Corvisart around 1800. His pupil Laënnec, by inventing the instrumental method of listening to the chest, started to make physical examination popular. The movement was taken up by the young, including independent medical students, and drew into itself all methods of physical examination, including looking and feeling, methods which might have been used ages before, but which became popular only after the invention of the stethoscope. The efforts of the first enthusiasts did not advance medicine very much, except for some improvement in the diagnosis of phthisis and the recognition that palpitations were not so significant of heart disease as had been supposed. Many of the students who took up physical examination in the early days fell by the wayside, and it was only the persistence of a few physicians, such as Peter Mere Latham, Sir John Forbes and John Elliotson, that kept the science alive in this country until the next generation showed, by the work of Bright and Addison, how diagnoses made in life by physical examination, as Laënnec had taught, could be compared with post-mortem appearances on the principles laid down long before by Morgagni, revealing not only the seats of disease, but the appearances of recognizable "diseases".

All this development was the result of research and teaching settling in hospitals, and the importance of the hospital as a teaching centre lies in that fact. Because it was practised in hospitals, physical examination led directly to two things which form the basis of modern medicine: the theory of "named diseases", and laboratory investigation. No one is happy about the theory of named diseases, as it is so difficult to believe that "diseases" can really exist at all, but we get round that difficulty by not facing it: it is a great convenience if not taken too seriously. The physical basis on which it developed had, however, the unfortunate effect of making non-organic disease seem imaginary, unnecessary, wilful nonsense on the part of the patient. Even today, when we are all psychologists, it has led to a reversion in the treatment of insanity to physical methods which may be thought by our descendants to be not much better in nature than those of the eighteenth century.

Medicine might have developed very differently, and would have done if students had been educated in the practices of physicians and surgeons and in dispensaries. It would have become a medicine of patients and disordered physiology, with disordered psychology thrown in. There would have been much more prevention, little or no interest in rare diseases, but a great deal of research on common colds, summer diarrhoea, bronchitis, typhoid fever, diphtheria, cancer, chlorosis, and all the diseases which mattered from the patients' point of view. That research and advance on this front would have been possible has been shown by the work of Sir James Mackenzie, Clement Dukes, Dr. Pickles, and the recent band of investigators working under the inspiration of the College of General Practitioners. Whether it would have been an advantage in the long run will probably be known in a hundred years from now; in the short run it would certainly have been acceptable to patients. But in the present context that does not matter in the least: the important point is that medicine would today have been completely different, and that medicine as it is is the result of the hospital as the teaching centre.

Hospitals have not only determined the nature of medicine and of medical education, they have, like the machine in modern civilization, got partly out of control, and become master rather than servant. It would now be impossible to divert medical education into a different milieu and retrieve the opportunity lost when University College abandoned the dispensary and converted it into a hospital. This was done, not because a dispensary education had been tried and found wanting, but because surgery was still the important aspect of medical education, and needed a hospital, and because the dispensary was unfashionable and did not provide the status due to a highly academic institution: it was necessary to keep up with the other schools.

The teacher-research workers forming the staffs of the hospitals have developed the concept of a strictly physical, materialistic basis, which has led through the medicine of physical signs to the medicine of laboratory investigation, binding its practice still more firmly to the hospital. The teacher-researchers have taught this attitude to students, thereby indoctrinating them with the belief that materialist medicine is real medicine, and the same men have, as examiners, unwittingly seen to it that this is a medicine which must be learned in order to become a doctor. This circular cause-and-effect system has converted the hospital, and hospital teaching, from a servant to a master. Only recently has a new movement appeared, towards a consideration of the whole patient, including his emotional troubles, and towards disordered physiology as opposed to hypostatized "diseases". It is remarkable that at the same time there is a drift away from the doctor's surgery towards the hospital clinic. Does this foreshadow a new sort of hospital becoming a new sort of teaching centre?

REFERENCES

1. *Hieronymi Epistolae* (1606). Lugdun., Pillehotte, p. 393.
2. COPEMAN, W. S. C. (1960). *Doctors and Diseases in Tudor Times,* Dawson's, London.
3. MOORE, NORMAN (1918). *History of St. Bartholomew's Hospital,* vol. ii, p. 321, Pearson, London.
4. COPEMAN, W. S. C., *op. cit.,* p. 99.
5. ROLLESTON, H. D. (1939). The early teaching of: I, Human anatomy in London, II, Morbid anatomy and pathology in Great Britain, *Ann. med. Hist.,* 3rd S., **1**, 210.
6. PEACHEY, G. C. (1924). *A Memoir of William and John Hunter,* p. 97, Brendon, Plymouth.
7. ROLLESTON, H. D., *op. cit.,* p. 215.
8. CAMERON, HECTOR (1954). *Mr. Guy's Hospital,* p. 89, Longmans, London.
9. WITHINGTON, E. T. (1894). *Medical History from the Earliest Times,* p. 323, Scientific Press, London.
10. *Ibid,* p. 312.
11. MOORE, N., *op. cit.,* vol. ii, p. 431.
12. BATTIE, W. (1758). *Treatise on Madness,* p. v, London, for Whiston & White.
13. CHRISTISON, SIR ROBERT (1885). *Life of Sir Robert Christison,* edited by his sons, p. 193, Blackwood, Edinburgh.
14. EAST, C. F. T. (1958). *Story of Heart Disease,* p. 30, Dawson's, London.
15. GANIERE, P. (1951). *Corvisart: Médecin de Napoléon,* Flammarion, Paris.
16. HAESER, H. (1929). *Hirsch, Biographisches Lexicon,* vol. i, p. 66, Berlin.

The Development of Hospital Design and Planning

BARBARA DUNCUM

WHEN A NEW kind of hospital system began with the establishment of the Publick Infirmary in Westminster, in the winter of 1719–20, the preamble to the subscription-roll already attached some importance to the effect of buildings on people. It said:

> "Amongst those who . . . receive relief from their respective parishes, many suffer extremely, and are sometimes lost, partly from want of accommodations and proper medicine in their own houses or lodgings (the closeness and unwholesomeness of which is too often one great cause of their sickness). . . . We, whose names are underwritten . . . desiring so far as in us lies to find some remedy for this great misery of our neighbours, do subscribe the following sums of money . . . for the procuring, furnishing, and defraying the necessary expenses of an infirmary, or place of entertainment."

An account of the Infirmary's first eighteen months recorded that "it was some time before the Society could find a house in all respects convenient for an infirmary. . . . About the beginning of April 1720 a house was taken in Petty-France, Westminster, and fitted up with all the necessary accommodations for an infirmary."

Four years later the Infirmary was moved to a larger and still more convenient house, in Chapel Street, Westminster. Eight years after that the trustees of the Infirmary ordered that "an advertizer, for six days successively, should invite persons who had any large house to let or sell to bring their proposals to the trustees". The advertising seems to have been successful for the Infirmary removed to James Street, Westminster.[1]

Meanwhile a minority of the subscribers who had wished the Infirmary to remove to Lanesborough House near Hyde Park

Corner removed there themselves, soon after Michaelmas 1733, and founded St. George's Hospital.[2]

The first hospital established by subscription in the provinces opened its doors in Winchester on St. Luke's Day 1736. The Bishop preaching in the cathedral on that occasion said:

> "One advantage to the publick from an hospital, too material to be omitted here, is, that the expense of relieving a great number of sick persons who shall attend for that purpose in the *same* place, bears no proportion to the charge of assisting them at their separate homes."[3]

A month after the Winchester hospital opened, a subscription was started in Bristol for establishing an infirmary there; but when a suitable house was found alterations still had to be made. The Bristol Infirmary opened in December 1737 with "34 beds for patients, 17 in the men's ward and the like number in the women's". It expanded rapidly and in 1739 "the Society having a considerable balance in the treasurer's hands . . . thought proper to enlarge the buildings: as well for providing a wash-house, laundry, and other accommodations of that kind for the family, which were absolutely necessary, and for rendering the charity to in-patients more extensive." By 1743 new wards had been added and the bed complement was seventy: thirty-nine in the men's ward and thirty-one in the women's.[4]

Between the 1740s and the end of the century the chief towns of England and Scotland established voluntary hospitals. Most of those hospitals, from beginnings in ordinary houses, were soon being partly or wholly rebuilt to accommodate an increasing number of patients. In an age when large private mansions were a commonplace, the voluntary hospitals managed to keep much of the domestic quality of their origins. Staff and patients still formed a kind of family. The matron had the title of Housekeeper. Nevertheless hospital buildings were already different from ordinary houses. One of the important differences was the attention paid to ventilation because of the empirical association in people's minds between foul air and sickness.

Stephen Hales adapted the ventilators he had designed for ships for use in hospital wards. In his *Treatise on Ventilators* published in 1758 Hales recorded:

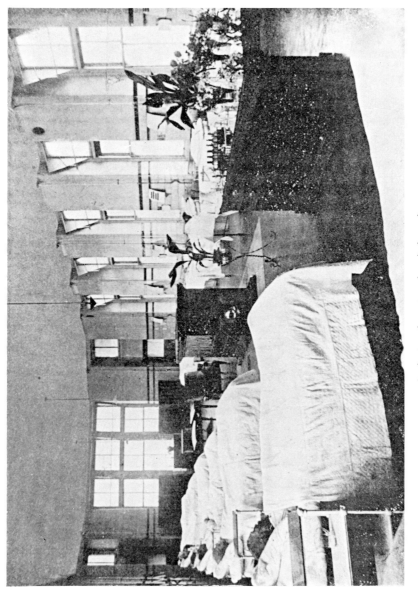

A nineteenth-century hospital ward

Reproduced by permission of the Medical Superintendent, Western Infirmary, Glasgow

A twentieth-century hospital ward

"The first trial of ventilators in a hospital, was made in the County Hospital at Winchester, where they were fixed under the floor, at the farther end of the ward from the entrance, yet so as to be worked with great ease by those in the ward, by means of a lever fixed across the ward between the beds. The air is drawn out of the ward through a large trunk, which reaches near up to the ceiling that it may not incommode the patients with the velocity with which it rushes into the trunk."

A trial was made also in St. George's Hospital where fresh air was drawn in through "midriffs", as Hales described them, fixed on the top of the building and worked by a windmill. Fresh air flowed down a wide trunk into the wards displacing the used air into a little trunk running the whole length of the ward near the ceiling. "Fresh air must by no means enter at the windows in cold weather", Hales said, "because such cool air will fall precipitately down thro' the warmer air of the ward, and thereby greatly incommode the patients."[5]

Hales's contemporary, the military physician Sir John Pringle, advised that:

"The wards are to be warmed by chimneys, and never by stoves. . . . A fire kept up in a chimney, acts like a constant ventilator.

"It is incredible [Pringle said] in how few days the air will be corrupted in thronged and close wards: and what makes it harder to remedy the evil, is the impossibility of convincing either the nurses, or the sick themselves of the necessity of opening the doors or windows, at any time, for air. I have always found those wards the most healthful when by broken windows and other wants of repair, the air could not be excluded."

An especially notable saying of Pringle's was:

"The best rule is, to admit so few patients into each ward, that a person unacquainted with the danger of bad air might imagine there was room to take in double or triple the number."[6]

During the last quarter of the eighteenth century John Howard visited hospitals as well as prisons at home and abroad, and made some general comments on hospital construction and management:

"The situation of an Infirmary or Hospital should be on elevated ground, near a stream of water, and out of town. . . . The building to consist of only two stories beside the cellars. . . . The first floor raised four or five steps from the ground, and the ascent made easy to the entrance. The wards fifteen feet high to the ceilings, and distinct ones for medical and chirurgical patients. . . . Staircase of stone, spacious, convenient and easy. . . . No room to contain more than eight beds. The windows lofty and opposite. . . . The fire-places in the middle of the longer side of the wards: the beds in spacious recesses . . . or to each bed a recess with curtains. . . . The bedsteads iron, painted, and with a screw, that the backs may be easily raised or lowered. The beds on varnished boards or laths, with hair mattresses. In each ward a cistern, basin and towel for the patients . . . and water closets, as at Guy's hospital. . . . Airy rooms and refectories for convalescent patients: one spare and unfurnished ward; each ward to be taken in succession and called the spare ward. The kitchen, wash-house, brew-house and bake-house, out of the house. . . . The wards washed once a week—scraped and lime-washed at least once a year."

There was also to be a convenient bath, and "a piazza and spacious walk to induce patients to take the air and exercise".

Many hospitals came in for severe criticism from Howard, generally because they were dirty, smelly, untidy, noisy, stuffy, and sometimes bug-infested. But the Leeds Infirmary was one hospital which Howard particularly praised:

"This is one of the best hospitals in the kingdom. In the wards, which are fifteen feet eight inches high, there is great attention to cleanliness; and six circular apertures or ventilators open into a passage five feet and a half wide. . . . No bugs in the beds. Many are here cured of compound fractures, who would lose their limbs in the unventilated and offensive wards of some other hospitals."

Among other hospitals described by Howard was the London Hospital of which the plans were published in 1752. Howard said about the London Hospital:

"This spacious building . . . consists of eighteen wards. . . . The wards in general are twenty feet wide, and twelve high, and each contains about eighteen beds. . . . The passages, which are eight feet wide, are dark. . . . Medical and chirurgical patients are together. . . . The wards were not dirty, but the house has not been white-washed for some years; nor has it, within or without, the appearance of neatness."[7]

Howard's views on hospitals were expanded by his friend and collaborator the physician John Aikin, in a book entitled *Thoughts on Hospitals*. Among many interesting observations Aikin said:

"The architect considers it is his business to manage his room and materials in such a manner as to accommodate the greatest number of people in the least possible space. The physician on the contrary would leave as much vacant space, occupied by the fresh air alone circulating freely, as was in any degree compatible with use and convenience. It is to the prevalence of [the architect] above [the physician] . . . that all our complaints are owing. . . .

"It does not belong to my profession to lay down an architectural plan for one of these buildings. . . . But by pointing out what to avoid, we in effect give rules what to aim at."[8]

The ideas on hospital planning and design put forward by Pringle, Howard and Aikin were taken very seriously by the committee entrusted with replanning the Newcastle upon Tyne Infirmary in 1801. The Infirmary was then just fifty years old and had originally been built for its purpose. The committee began work by circulating among the hospital governors a report on the defects of the existing infirmary and proposals for remedying them. The governors were told that

"The principal cause of the contamination of the air in the whole house . . . arises from the long ward on the ground floor . . . (containing twenty beds) and that immediately adjoining (containing seven beds). They [the committee] propose to convert these into physicians' and surgeons' consulting rooms, a waiting hall for the patients, and a dispensary (all of which necessary accommodations are at present very imperfect)."

The committee proposed to replace the twenty-bed ward by three six-bed wards opening on to a well-ventilated gallery; and the number of beds in other wards generally was to be reduced from eleven to seven. A water closet was to replace the *necessary* in each ward.

Because these wards were too hot in summer every window was to have a hinged square pane at the top for ventilation and a strong venetian blind outside. Each ward was also to have an opening in the wall on to the gallery, the opening being opposite one of the gallery windows to ensure cross-ventilation. The double-doors to the wards were to be on swivels "which may if necessary be locked back", the committee said, "to prevent the patients from shutting them". The iron bedsteads were to stand head to the wall, and some in every ward were to have "a screw to raise or lower the back, for altering the position for patients". All this was simply to refurbish the old Infirmary. An extension to the building was planned to provide

"separate rooms for patients under dangerous diseases, and after operations of magnitude; where perfect *quiet* and pure air are so essential to recovery. . . . The new wards will not only enjoy the benefit of every contrivance for ventilation which has already been mentioned but, having a northern aspect, will be protected from the inconvenience of heat in summer. Ventilating cross galleries with a fire-place in each are to be constructed . . . between the new and the old buildings. These are to serve the purpose of dining-rooms . . . and such patients as are able to sit up are to remain in them some hours daily, during which time their bedding is to be carried into the open air, and the wards exposed to ventilation.

"The committee . . . have further recommended that a useful invention . . . should be introduced in the construction of the new building, by which atmospheric air, passing through a square opening made in the wall on a level with the floor in the basement story, is heated by a sand-bath; and is conveyed by earthen tubes placed perpendicularly, into the galleries and thence into the wards. . . . The basement story, 11 feet high, will contain hot, cold, vapour, and shower baths, a laundry and other necessary offices."

The single rooms, each twenty-five feet by twelve feet in area, for dangerously ill and post-operative cases were located on the top floor of the building near the operating-room. A nurse or a convalescent patient would share the room with the patient to look after him.

There was to be a small isolation block including two six-bed wards and two two-bed wards, kitchen, wash-house, and water-closet, to be used for "infectious fevers of accidental occurrence". The planning committee added that:

"Every floor in the new house will have a nurses' room, scullery, and water closet, conveniently situated, and abundantly supplied with water from a large leaden cistern placed on the top of the new building."

When the foundation stone of the new building was laid in September 1801 the subscription to the building fund amounted to £2,817.

An interesting feature of the revised organization in the Newcastle Infirmary was the separation of medical from surgical patients

"and in these two divisions, they are likewise to be arranged according to similarity of disease and wants. For example, there are to be wards appropriate for inflammation and abscess; for sores and ulcers; for casualties; for inflammatory fevers; for pectoral complaints; for patients under a mercurial process (necessary in various obstinate distempers); and for miscellaneous complaints requiring similarity of treatment. . . . In all the above divisions of disease, when a patient's case requires perfect quiet, when he is apt to disturb others, or is afflicted with noisome symptoms, he will be placed in a separate room."[9]

Such enlightened ideas as keeping the groups of patients small and providing enough single rooms to accommodate any patient needing one on clinical or social grounds were fairly rapidly lost sight of during the next few decades. The increasing population of ill-paid workmen and their families crowding into the industrial towns, created slums which in turn fostered all kinds of ailments. The voluntary hospitals bore the brunt of treating the sick and undernourished. Nevertheless the English hospitals, unlike the hospitals in Paris, could not be compelled to find a bed for every sick person who presented himself at the door, and so the wards rarely became grossly overcrowded. Neither Pringle's injunction to keep the beds well-spaced nor his views on the importance of good ventilation were wholly forgotten, though practice no doubt often lagged behind precept.

In the out-patient department the state of affairs was rather different. Every day at a stated time the doors were opened to a large waiting-hall leading to some consulting and treatment rooms and to the dispensary. A crowd of ill and ailing people then surged in for medicine or a surgical dressing and perhaps a little advice. The motives of hospital governors in allowing this daily chaos appear to have been mixed. They all readily stated their charitable motives, and a few admitted that to be able to show a large annual total of out-patient attendances was useful in persuading subscribers to the hospital funds to be generous. Moreover the honorary physicians and surgeons looked to the out-patient department as a source of interesting clinical material.[10]

Before our own day it was scarcely meaningful to speak of *design* in the out-patient department. The characteristic features were the large, top-lit waiting-hall filled with rows of benches to preserve some sort of order in the throng, and a deliberate absence of anything at all which might make the place attractive. For one of the preoccupations of hospital administrators —and of some physicians and surgeons—was how to exclude people who really had enough money to pay for private treatment but who nevertheless "abused" charity by using the hospitals and by the same means defrauded the medical profession of their rightful fees.[11]

Only since the Second World War have we in Great Britain designed out-patient departments with the convenience and sensibilities of patients in mind. But although in the middle years of the nineteenth century hospital planners and administrators intended out-patients to find conditions disagreeable, they were nevertheless genuinely concerned for the comfort and well-being of in-patients. The revelations about the deplorable state of the Crimean hospitals undoubtedly acted as a great stimulus to better planning at home. Florence Nightingale herself, not long after her return from the Crimea, began to publish her own views on the subject.

It was at about this time that attention was attracted to the design of the Hôpital Lariboisière, opened in Paris in 1854.[12] This was the prototype and the most famous example of the *pavilion* plan which stemmed directly from the deliberations, during the 1780s, of the distinguished Commission appointed by the Académie des Sciences to replan the Hôtel-Dieu—the Commission which included La Place and Lavoisier.

Essentially the pavilion hospital was made up of a series of single-storey or two-storey rectangular ward-blocks, usually placed at right-angles to a linking corridor—covered in some hospitals, open to the sky in others, and omitted altogether in fever hospitals. The blocks were fairly widely separated from each other, usually by lawns. Each ward occupied a whole floor of the block and was cross-ventilated through opposite rows of windows reaching from floor to ceiling. Beds were placed head-to-the-wall, one between each pair of windows. This was the kind of ward which Florence Nightingale recommended, and in Great Britain such wards are still commonly known as *Nightingale* wards. She approved particularly of natural cross-ventilation, and like many of her contemporaries disapproved of mechanical systems for artificial ventilation, though she was in favour of the patent grates, originally devised by Count Rumford and improved first by Neil Arnott[13] and afterwards by the military engineer Douglas Galton.[14]

Florence Nightingale in 1857 was preparing herself to give evidence before the Royal Commissioners inquiring into the state of the Army by visiting and studying the plans of a variety of hospitals. She identified "four radical defects in construction: (1) the agglomeration of a large number of sick under the same roof, (2) deficiency of space, (3) deficiency of ventilation, (4) deficiency of light". On her fourth point she said:

> "Second only to fresh air . . . I should be inclined to rank light in importance for the sick. Direct sunlight, not only daylight is necessary for speedy recovery. . . . I mention from experience, as quite perceptible in promoting recovery, the being able to see out of a window, instead of looking against a dead wall; the bright colours of flowers; the being able to read in bed by the light of a window close to the bed-head. It is generally said that the effect is upon the mind. Perhaps so, but it is not less so upon the body on that account. . . . The windows should reach from two to three feet of the floor to one foot of the ceiling. The escape of heat may be diminished by plate or double glass. But while we *can* generate warmth, we cannot generate daylight."

Although Florence Nightingale insisted on impervious surfaces, without interstices, for hospital walls and floors, she reminded planners that "a good colour, and not a dull dirty one, is necessary in all sick wards". And she appreciated the importance of light-coloured walls in reflecting light.[15]

Florence Nightingale was the pioneer of work-study in hospitals. Her observations of nurses at work in wards led her to reject the concept of small wards. Her considered opinion was that about thirty to thirty-two patients was the smallest economical size for the nursing unit; she recommended a ward complement of one sister, two nurses, and one scrubber, provided that, as she said, there were lifts and a supply of hot and cold water laid on all over the hospital. "Other things being equal, it is certain that a ward with the appliances and without the extra attendant, will be better served than a ward without the appliances and with the extra attendant."[16] The authority of her views on nursing organization caused them to be widely accepted and acted upon. Her recommendations on design and construction were often ignored.

Another interesting amateur hospital planner was the surgeon Charles Hawkins who prepared the design for rebuilding Queen Charlotte's Hospital. In his opinion a hospital of about 400 beds "or at most 500 beds, is quite large enough for any one neighbourhood, and for all clinical purposes, and will hold quite as many sick people as ought to be congregated in one building". He added:

> "As in this country the price of land is so enormous that it appears to me to shut out what is called the 'Pavilion' plan, whatever its merits or demerits may be, and it has both, I think the best plan we can adopt is that of the letter H, the wards being only in the wings, and the centre of the building used for . . . necessary rooms and offices. . . . A plan of such a hospital . . . I exhibited last year in the Architectural Exhibition. In this plan, wards have windows on each side, which I consider a *sine quâ non*. The fire-place is placed in the centre of the ward, having two faces. . . . All water-closets to be placed in a portion of the building projecting from the main building, so that they can have windows on both sides."

Hawkins's ancillary rooms included a lavatory with a constant supply of hot and cold water for patients who were able to get up to wash; a room with slate shelves for the patients' provisions—bread, butter, and milk for the day—so that they need no longer be kept on shelves over the beds; and a room for the patients' clothes so that they need not be kept in boxes "close to, or what is worse, under the patients' beds".

Hawkins recommended wards holding twenty to twenty-five beds, and an allowance of from 1,500 to 2,000 cubic feet of space for each patient. Beds were to be at least six feet apart. He also said:

"There is also one other subject well worthy the consideration of governors of hospitals: the desirability of spending a little money in ornamentation of the *wards* . . . to enliven the spirits and hasten the cure of many a patient now doomed to have nothing on which to rest a restless eye than the eternal whitewash of most hospitals. A little shade of colour introduced in the wash for the walls, with a parti-coloured border, is all that is required, with a few well-selected engravings."[17]

A more persuasive account of how to enliven hospital wards had already appeared in the *British Medical Journal* in 1857:

"At Bethlem Hospital there are some convalescent wards which fill with pleasure the mind of the philanthropic physician. Here the patient not only finds cheerful light literature and the current newspapers, but the windows are fitted up with vivaria, fernaries and cages full of birds and the smaller animals. It is impossible to estimate too highly the value of these little aids to pass the vacant hour; yet we venture to say that, in ninety-nine cases out of a hundred, the members of a hospital Board who would propose the introduction of such cheap amusements as these for the patients would be laughed at."[18]

John Bristowe, a physician on the staff of St. Thomas's Hospital and the Dean of the Medical School, and Timothy Holmes, a surgeon on the staff of St. George's, were two more medical men deeply interested in hospital planning. They made a survey of English hospitals and the hospitals of Paris for John Simon, the Medical Officer of the Privy Council, in the early 1860s.[19]

Holmes and Bristowe did not believe that the size of a hospital, reckoned in numbers of beds, had much effect in keeping the hospital "healthy": "Whether it contains a hundred patients or a thousand does not appear to exercise the least influence on the health of any individual in the hospital", they said. Nor did they attach any particular importance to which of the current type-plans—E-shaped, H-shaped, pavilion plan, and so on—was selected, though they were inclined to think that the long walking-distances implicit in the pavilion plan were a formidable disadvantage. They were equally open-minded about the shape and size of wards:

> "To say that this or that shape of ward is the only one that ought to be adopted, is to make an assertion for which there is only little foundation in theory, and still less support in experience. The size of the ward is a subject so directly connected with nursing that it must be considered in connexion with that subject. . . . In hospitals divided into a large number of wards, containing a few beds each, there can be no efficient supervision of the patients, since the number of the nurses is usually below that of the wards."

Bristowe, in an introductory lecture at St. Thomas's at the start of the academic year 1862–3, referred to some statistics which had been compiled by the Resident Medical Officer in connexion with the current rebuilding plans for St. Thomas's. "The place of abode of the in- and out-patients of St. Thomas's Hospital last year [showed] that the great majority came from within a circle round the hospital of two miles radius." From this finding Bristowe reasoned that "the hospital should be placed in the centre of a crowded district, near a leading thoroughfare, and, if possible, not far from one or two railway termini". He disapproved of the current suggestion that hospitals should be in two parts: a "receiving-house" in the town and a hospital for convalescents and chronic cases in the country. He recommended having outlying dispensaries, however, administered by officers appointed by a parent hospital and linked to it by an ambulance service.[20]

During the middle years of the nineteenth century only large wards were planned and built in our hospitals. This was on the grounds both of nursing economy (as Florence Nightingale taught) and of thorough cross-ventilation, which everybody believed in. Nevertheless there still were people who cherished the notion that small wards would be more agreeable to the patients. In 1870 the *Lancet* said in a leader:

"We are not prepared to commit ourselves to a positive asser-
tion, indicating that very small wards, massed together in one
building, are better adapted for the treatment of medical or
surgical cases than those now existing in our newest hospitals.
But, speaking generally, we may safely remark that the small-
ward system has hardly received a sufficient amount of consideration. There are several undeniable advantages to be derived in
wards containing only three or four beds. Isolation, quietude, an
equable temperature, and a sense of comparative privacy to the
patient, are easily attainable. Such wards can also, after occupation by contagious diseases, be cleaned, purified, and kept
empty for some time without detriment to the general working
of the hospital. Presuming that a proper cubic space exists for
each patient, that good ventilation is secured, and that super-
lative care is exercised in the speedy removal of all excreta, foul
bedding, &c., we cannot but believe that a small-ward hospital
possesses much that is recommendable, always excepting the cost
and difficulty of efficient administration."

The leader went on to describe an old hospital, the Seamens'
Hospital at Greenwich, then the only entirely small-ward
hospital in the United Kingdom. The *Lancet* said:

"We take leave to suggest to the officers of the Seamen's
Hospital Society that some useful data may be gleaned for future
use if a continuous general record is kept as to the results of cases. . . .
Is comparative isolation favourable to speedy recovery? Is good
ventilation easily secured? Are hospital gangrene, pyaemia,
erysipelas, and the contagious fevers less liable to spread than in
the wards of other general hospitals? . . . If, after the lapse of a
sufficient time, the above questions can be fully and fairly
answered in the affirmative, we shall have something more to say,
and something whereon to base our own predilections, in
favour of small-ward hospitals."[21]

During the last quarter of the nineteenth century a great deal
of interest was aroused by the notion of building circular wards.
They were proposed in this country by John Marshall who was
professor of surgery at University College Hospital, then being
replanned. He read a paper on the subject to the National
Association for the Promotion of Social Science, at Cheltenham
in October 1878. At that time, so he afterwards said, he was
unaware that a hospital with round wards had just been com-

pleted in Antwerp. Marshall advocated the circular shape on
the grounds that it could be cross-ventilated from all directions,
that "a central source of radiant heat would present the advantage of being equally distant from every patient in bed"—
though this source would probably need to be supplemented by
hot-water pipes round the circumference—and that nursing
supervision would be simplified. He suggested that "moveable
surgical tables and screens might be arranged to travel in a
circular tramway".[22]

Although authoritative voices including that of the *Lancet*
were quickly raised against building circular wards, chiefly
because of increased cost, a few were nevertheless built in
England: at the Victoria Hospital, Burnley, at the East Sussex,
Hastings and St. Leonard's Hospital, and at the Bradford
Children's Hospital.[23] The Bradford Children's Hospital was
described in *Building News* as being "in the Queen Anne style".
Another children's hospital, completed at about the same time
in Gateshead, was described as "domestic early English".[24]

In 1895 the *Lancet* conducted another of its many surveys of
hospital practice. This time it was a Special Sanitary Commission on Ventilation and the Treatment of Infected Air. The
Commission dismissed natural ventilation as "obviously un-
suited for a hospital, since it cannot be placed under control",
and dismissed also mechanical ventilation by "the agitation or
punkah principle". They recommended the plenum system
which drew in relatively clean air at roof level, filtered, warmed
and humidified it and then blew it, at the rate of ten changes an
hour, through the hospital, the windows being kept shut. This
was the system which had been devised by the Glasgow engineer
William Key and installed in the new Birmingham General
Hospital.

The Commissioners referred to the suggestions made a dozen
years earlier, at the time of the Royal Commission on Small-pox,
that infected air from wards should be heat-sterilized before
being allowed to escape from the hospital. The *Lancet's* Commissioners said that this suggestion had actually been imple-
mented, though not with great success, in the new fever
hospitals built for the Nottingham, Barnsley, and Bradford
corporations. A furnace had been built into the outlet shaft

"with the double object of ventilation by extraction and the 'cremation' of the outgoing air".[25]

In the last decade of the nineteenth century H. C. Burdett published his book *Hospitals and Asylums of the World*. Besides classifying the various types of hospital plan customarily adopted by his contemporaries, Burdett's book offered a useful mine of administrative and building know-how. The main divisions of his building classification were:

1. Pavilion hospitals.
2. Block hospitals.
3. Corridor hospitals.
4. Composite or (as Burdett himself described the class) Heap-of-buildings hospitals (e.g. Addenbrooke's, Cambridge, and the Edinburgh Royal Infirmary.

Burdett instanced the Edinburgh Royal Infirmary as an example of a hospital in which convenience has been sacrificed to a grandiose architectural conception. "The water-closets", he said, "are placed in circular turrets at the angles of the ward. These circular turrets are a characteristic feature of Scottish architecture and when forming part of an old castellated mansion are appropriate and of historic interest. But when they are reproduced in a hospital, the only effect is to unduly lengthen the sides of the lobby and to lessen the chance of cross-ventilation effecting its object."

On the general subject of ward provision Burdett noted that one W.C. to ten or twelve patients and one lavatory-basin to every four patients were commonly considered sufficient. Ancillary rooms which he listed included a duty-room and a sluice-room. In the latter room an innovation was a mechanical bed-pan washer called "the McHardy sink" after its inventor, the Professor of Ophthalmology at King's College, London. An ice-box for storing food in the ward was referred to by Burdett as an ordinary requirement. He drew attention to the fact that architects never provided enough cupboards.

On the organizational side, Burdett attacked the still-lingering custom of making the sister sleep in a room overlooking her ward through a kind of judas-window. The nurse off duty should be off the ward, he pointed out, adding that progressive hospitals were building separate nurses' homes.

For main kitchens Burdett recommended the gas-cooker; and he was in favour of the then new trend towards building the whole kitchen department on the top floor of the hospital. Building balconies to wards so that patients, up or in bed, could go out-of-doors was another new trend. And the gas-lighting installations which had been in use for thirty-odd years were being replaced by electric lighting, though this was still something of a nine days' wonder. He and his contemporaries were most favourably impressed by the fact that electric light did not vitiate the atmosphere. An inspection-lamp to plug in at the patient's bed-head had already been invented, and Burdett remarked that it gave light instantly without so much as the turning of a tap.[26]

During and after the Franco-Prussian War the success of German and French surgeons operating under Lister's carbolic spray led to advances in the surgery of the body-cavity which soon required more sophisticated antiseptic techniques. Within the next two decades the use of antiseptics had been wholly replaced in major surgery by the heat sterilization of instruments, dressings, and utensils; and a strict aseptic regime had been evolved for everyone present during an operation.

By 1890 operating theatres on the Continent were built to specifications which have not yet needed to be fundamentally altered. These theatres, which Great Britain began to copy in the early eighteen-nineties, were bare of all furniture except the operating-table—generally a metal frame supporting a glass slab warmed by a water-bath. Walls and floors were covered with impervious materials: terazzo for the floor, marble veneer, enamelled slate, or tiles, for the walls, hard-gloss paint for the ceiling. Angles were rounded off, and there were no ledges anywhere "on which one can even put one's hat", the *British Medical Journal* noted.[27]

In Great Britain, inhalation anaesthesia by specialist anaesthetists was not giving ground to local anaesthesia, done by the surgeon himself with the patient on the table, and so anaesthetic rooms, and often one or two recovery rooms, were included in the theatre suite. At the London Hospital, where the annual number of major operations had increased from 420 in 1881 to 2,711 in 1901, the suite included: one theatre for teaching and

four others; three anaesthetizing rooms, four recovery rooms or
small wards, two sisters' rooms, a nurses' room, a surgeons'
room, a theatre superintendent's room, two attendants' rooms,
and instrument and sterilizing rooms.[28] The new theatre at St.
George's Hospital, opened in 1896, was supplied with warmed
and filtered air at the rate of ten changes an hour.[29]

At the turn of the century hospitals were having to find room
also for one of the new X-ray machines. In the Liverpool Royal
Infirmary, for example, the old theatre was roofed over in 1902
to make an X-ray room below and two operating theatres on
top.[30]

These major innovations in surgical practice and in diagnostic technique were only to be had in hospital. Suddenly the
facilities provided charitably for the poor became superior to
anything which could be arranged for rich people in their own
homes or for more or less well-to-do people in the provident
nursing homes which had been established to meet their needs.
In Continental and American hospitals patients had long been
expected to pay according to their means. Because it would
have been unethical to give them better medical care for their
money, the substantial fees which some of them paid secured
privileges such as privacy, comfortably furnished rooms, and
better food than non-paying patients were given. But on the
Continent and in America the *clinical facilities* of hospitals were
available to anyone. In Great Britain, on the other hand,
hospitals still jealously guarded their status as charitable
institutions for the poor. True, since 1880, St. Thomas's and
some other London teaching hospitals greatly in need of money
had got their statutes changed by Act of Parliament so that they
could accept paying patients.[31] But the fees charged were
beyond what many middle-class and most lower-middle-class
people could afford, though they still earned too much to be
eligible for the public wards. The income barrier was set in most
hospitals at thirty to forty shillings a week for a man with up to
three children under six years old.[32]

In America as early as 1908 the staff of the King's Daughters'
Hospital at Temple, Texas, decided that all the patients whether
they were paying for their care or not ought each to be in a
single room, and the hospital was reorganized accordingly.[33]

Soon after the First World War the superintendent of the Presbyterian Hospital in Chicago, Asa Bacon, wrote:

> "Wards are intended for the poor people, for charity patients or for those who can pay but a small amount. Labour conditions have so changed that the average working man does not want charity. . . . The private room for each patient, with its complete utility equipment, not only provides comfort, but . . . allows the occupancy of *all the beds all of the time.*"

Bacon proposed a hospital which was revolutionary in conception because the whole organization was based on providing a full range of services centrally instead of locally in ancillary rooms reduplicated for each ward unit. Every patient was to have a room to himself with his own toilet facilities in it; and the rooms were to be comfortably furnished as in a hotel rather than a hospital.

The building was to be cruciform in plan with the central-service departments in the basement and on the ground floor, communicating directly by lift with each of the four arms containing the patients' rooms on the upper floors. Bacon was thinking only in terms of the small community hospitals, for 200 beds or less, which the Americans were then planning to build in considerable numbers. So each floor of the building was to contain only about twenty-eight beds—seven in each arm arranged on both sides of a short internal corridor. This meant that the nurse on duty in each wing had very little walking about to do in looking after her patients. Still further to cut down walking, Bacon proposed to install a pneumatic-tube system to carry messages and suitable packaged supplies.[34]

In 1921 a plan was devised for the Beth Israel Hospital in New York, in which pairs of single rooms shared toilet facilities and a nursing-utility room. The superintendent at that hospital wrote:

> "We wish to call specific attention to the fact that without an individual utility room, the private room system may not be feasible economically."

This was because of the time-consuming distances which the nurses would otherwise have to walk in attending to the patients' needs.

In the Beth Israel Hospital single rooms were to be used for seriously ill patients. Convalescing patients were to be removed to an area made up of dormitories and day-rooms, where they could walk to any service rooms directly involved in their treatment and care.[35]

Very soon after 1921 the ideal of a single room for every patient was reluctantly abandoned in America as impracticable. An American architect E. F. Stevens, who had toured European hospitals just before the First World War, wrote in 1922:

> "The old twenty- and thirty-bed wards . . . have gone, let us hope, for ever. . . . [But] it is evident that we must find some middle ground where the patient may have much of the privacy of the single room with the economic efficiency of the open ward. . . . The great intermediate class of patients who, with the 'ward pocketbook', are acquiring the 'private room appetite' must be cared for in such a way as to afford privacy to the patient and economy in cost and administration of the building."

Stevens's solution was to build small wards, sharing main ancillary rooms in pairs. Each ward was to be divided by partitions into bays for three or four beds. This was essentially the layout which Stevens had seen in the wards in the new Rigs Hospital in Copenhagen in 1914.[36]

The partitioned wards in the Rigs Hospital, in which pairs of beds were placed opposite each other and parallel to the window-wall, had been opened in 1910.[37] Stevens recorded that already in 1914 this arrangement had been copied in America in at least one hospital.[38]

In 1929 one of our own architects, Percy Adams, read a paper at the Royal Institute of British Architects on English hospital planning. He said:

> "For many years it has been customary to place the beds in large wards at right angles to the windows. . . . Recently, many doctors have advocated the scheme largely adopted in America of placing the beds parallel to the windows."

Percy Adams went on to describe the ward plan which his firm had devised for a new hospital at Southend. The ward was T-shaped and contained twenty-four beds separated by half-glazed screens into two groups of four beds and one of sixteen, all placed head to the screens and parallel to the windows. Adams and his partners, Holden and Pearson, used this arrangement again in a wing which they added in 1930 to the Sussex Hospital for Women and Children.[39]

When in 1937 the London County Council, in their own hospitals, proposed to standardize the dimensions of what they called "normal" types of wards, describing them as "those in which beds are placed on either side of the ward and project at right angles from the walls", the *Lancet* commented:

"It is not clear . . . whether [the Council] accepts the view that the type of ward described as 'normal' is also the best. Probably it has been thought that wards of a design common in other countries, but rarely seen in our general hospitals, are still at too experimental a stage to permit of standardized dimensions. . . . Apparently, however, the L.C.C. are themselves prepared to experiment, for a scheme for a large extension of the North-Eastern Hospital (for infectious diseases) . . . in 1934, included eight ward blocks each with two wards of twenty beds divided into bays of four beds each by dwarf glazed screens."[40]

After the Second World War when it once more became feasible to think about hospital planning and even building in this country, the climate of opinion here was very much what it had been in America after the First World War. At a practicable level of expenditure the planners wished to give patients as much comfort and privacy as they could and to make working conditions as easy as possible for the nurses.

Until very recently in our hospitals the ancillary rooms were always located as a double row at the entrance to the bed-area with the result that the nurses, to save themselves from constantly running to and fro between their work-rooms and their patients, organized nursing care as a series of ward rounds. A ward round in this context means that a nurse pushes a loaded trolley from one bed to the next dispensing the same things to every patient—it might be a bedpan or a plate of prunes and custard—more or less regardless of any patient's particular needs and preferences at that particular moment.

In 1949 the Nuffield Provincial Hospitals Trust sponsored a research team to investigate the functions and design of hospitals, and they planned wards for what is called group-allocation nursing: the ward complement of nurses divides up into two teams and the patients are thought of as forming two groups, each group being the especial responsibility of one nursing team or the other. This arrangement made the relationship between the nurses and their patients much more personal. The main ancillary rooms were placed centrally in the bed-area so that the walking-distance between the work-rooms and the farthest beds was radial instead of being the whole length of a rectangle as it is in the traditional British open ward. A special study established the proportion of all the beds which were to be in single rooms to ensure that a room was generally available for any patient needing one for clinical or social reasons. The rest of the beds were arranged in open bays for four or six beds. The bays were separated by solid walls to give room-like dimensions. Decorations and furnishings were domestic in character. The beds could be lowered to be no higher than the bed at home. No bed was far from toilet facilities resembling those in an ordinary house. There was a treatment room providing proper aseptic conditions. There was a comfortable dayroom.[41]

The Trust's basic conception of what a ward should be like has certainly influenced planning in Great Britain. That conception seems likely to be displaced by a new plan from America: the "race-track" in which patients' rooms form a hollow square round a core of artificially lit and artificially ventilated work-rooms and lifts bringing virtually all the supplies from centralized service departments at ground level—an arrangement not so very different from what the superintendent of the Presbyterian Hospital in Chicago proposed in 1920.

REFERENCES

1. *Proceedings of the Charitable Society for Relieving the Sick Poor at the Publick Infirmary, Westminster*, London, 1722–35.
2. *An Account of the Proceedings of the Governors of St. George's Hospital from . . . 1733 to . . . 1788; a Defence of the Majority of the Infirmary at Westminster . . . Letter from a Subscriber*, n.d.
3. CLARKE, A. (1737). *A Sermon Preached Before the Governors of the County Hospital*, Winchester.
4. *An Account of the Bristol Infirmary*, Bristol, 1744.

5. HALES, S. (1758). *A Treatise on Ventilators*, pp. 25, 40, London.
6. PRINGLE, J. (1752). *Observations on the Diseases of the Army in Camp and Garrison;* pp. 132–4, London.
7. HOWARD, J. (1752). *An Account of the Principal Lazarettos in Europe; with . . . Observations on . . . Prisons and Hospitals*, 2nd ed., pp. 131, 141–2, 192, London.
8. AIKIN, J. (1771). *Thoughts on Hospitals*, pp. 13, 20, London.
9. *An Account of the Infirmary at Newcastle*, Newcastle upon Tyne, 1801.
10. Investigation into the administration of the out-patient department of the London Hospitals, *Lancet*, 1862, **ii**, pp. 553, 577, 613, 677, 678, 774.
11. *Lancet*, 1862, **i**, 695; *ibid.*, 1863, **ii**, 452; *Brit. med. J.*, 1870, **i**, 635.
12. HUSSON, H. M. (1802). *Etude sur les Hôpitaux*, p. 347, Paris.
13. ARNOTT, N. (1855). *On the Smokeless Fire-place*, London.
14. GALTON, D. (1893). *Healthy Hospitals*, pp. 107, 109, 112, London.
15. NIGHTINGALE, F. (1857 and 1863). *Notes on Hospitals*, 1st & 3rd eds., London.
16. NIGHTINGALE, F. (1863). *Notes on Hospitals*, 3rd ed., p. 54, London.
17. HAWKINS, C. (1862). On the construction of hospitals (letter), *Lancet*, **ii**, 20.
18. The shortcomings of hospitals, *Brit. med. J.* 1857, p. 302.
19. *Sixth Report of the Medical Officer of the Privy Council* (1864). Appendix 15, London.
20. BRISTOWE, J. S. (1862). St. Thomas's Hospital (Introductory lecture), *Brit. med. J.*, **ii**, 388.
21. Construction of Hospitals, *Lancet*, 1870, **ii**, 642.
22. MARSHALL, J. (1878). *On a Circular System of Hospital Wards*, London.
23. A circular system of hospital wards, *Lancet*, 1895, **ii**, 671; Burdett, H. C., Circular hospital wards, *ibid.*, 1885, **ii**, 684.
24. Building News, Building intelligence: Bradford Children's Hospital; Gateshead Children's Hospital. *Building News*, 1888, **55**, 591, 425.
25. Special sanitary commission on the ventilation of hospitals and the treatment of infected air, *Lancet*, 1895, **i**, 1203.
26. BURDETT, H. C. (1893). *Hospitals and Asylums of the World*, vol. iv, pp. 26, 37, 55–8, London.
27. Life saving surgery III. Operating theatre asepsis, *Brit. med. J.*, 1894, **ii**, 818.
28. The new operating department at the London Hospital, *Brit. med. J.*, 1902, **i**, 1305.
29. The new operating theatre at St. George's Hospital, *Lancet*, 1897, **i**, 267.
30. HAMILTON, G. G. (1908). A note on separate operating rooms and their management, *Brit. med. J.*, **i**, 1479.
31. Admission of paying patients to St. Thomas's Hospital, *Lancet*, 1880, **ii**, 19.
32. LOCH, S. (1898). The growth of medical charities, *Charity Organisation Rev.*, N.S., **4**, 240.

33. McReynolds, G. S. (1920). Efficient hospitals; success of private room plan at Temple, Texas, *J. Amer. med. Ass.*, **74**, 479.
34. Bacon, A. S. (1920). Efficient Hospitals, *J. Amer. med. Ass.*, **74**, 123.
35. The open ward vs. single rooms, *Mod. Hosp.*, 1922, **18**, 233.
36. Stevens, E. F. (1914). The ward unit of the general hospital, *J. Amer. med. Ass.*, **62**, 270.
37. *Rigshospitalet i Kjøbenhavn*, Copenhagen, 1911.
38. Stevens, E. F. (1914). The ward unit of the general hospital, *J. Amer. med. Ass.*, **62**, 270.
39. Birmingham hospitals centre, award in design competition, *Lancet*, 1930, **i**, 317; *ibid.*, 1931, **i**, 1382; (1932) Southend General Hospital, *ibid.*, **ii**, 699.
40. Hospital planning and development, *Lancet*, 1937, **i**, 225.
41. Nuffield Provincial Hospitals Trust (1955). *Studies in the Functions and Design of Hospitals*, pp. 4–29, Oxford Univ. Press.

The History of Hospital Finance and Administration

R. R. TRAIL

SOME DOUBT HAS been expressed as to the truth of the common statement that hospital organization as we know it is Christian in origin, although Julian the Apostate is credited with saying that the old religions would lose their hold unless they showed a zeal in the care of the poor equal to that of the early Christians. Be that as it may, we can recognize the beginnings of organization in the fourth-century basilica of St. Basil at Caesarea, modern in its arrangement of separate houses for types of patients and convalescents, nursing and medical staff, and in its attached workshops and industrial schools.

The native story of hospitals in our sense of the term begins with the general hospital of St. John, built by William the Conqueror's Norman Archbishop, Lanfranc, in 1084, in the side of the city walls of York. The first St. Bartholomew's, built by the generosity of a layman, can claim to be our first voluntary hospital; the second, St. Thomas's, this time the foundation of a laywoman, was founded in 1200; its spital, endowed with a yearly income of £343, was given by Peter des Roches, Bishop of Winchester, in 1228.

Before then and until the Reformation houses under the name of "hospitals" were attached to practically every monastery. These were entirely under the control of religious Orders, and followed the pattern of the Saxon institutions known to exist at Flixton in Yorkshire and at St. Albans in 794, and at York in 937, where King Althelstan had founded his St. Peter's. All these houses were for people in need of shelter, such as pilgrims, and the aged and infirm, but some like the lazar houses for lepers and the spital houses for the sick did think a little about the comfort of the body while concentrating on the preparation of the soul for the next world. Probably one of these was the rebuilt St. Peter's which, in addition to its alms-house and its house for orphaned children, is said to have had 224 beds for the sick and poor. If we are tempted to take a supercilious view of the purely religious function of these early foundations it is well to remind ourselves that some of our voluntary hospitals resulting from the new eighteenth-century attitude to the plight of the poor were equally religious in con-ception and others were spitals where treatment was of merely secondary consideration, for the belief that illness was the just reward of sin died hard.

In the monastic houses we have the first appearance of the administrator, the Infirmarer, a non-medical clerk in holy orders, whose rolls recorded all purchases for alterations and repairs, equipment, drugs and herbs. He could call in medical aid as one did when John of Gaddesden went to the Abbey at Abingdon. Similarly we have the first appeals secretary in Alfune, the persistent beggar who brought in the capital for Rahere's foundation of the 1123 St. Bartholomew's. The first public appeal for building came in 1141 in the sermons preached by the Archbishop of Canterbury to get support for the monks of St. Bartholomew's at Buckland, Dover, which in turn had the first scheme for paying patients, mostly wealthy lepers required to deposit one hundred shillings on admission and so augment the income from an annual local fair.

The thirteenth century saw a complete reorganization, especially in the Royal Hospitals, some of which already existed, while others were under construction. They would have shamed many of our nineteenth-century prison-like buildings, for they were of one storey, with large windows, high ceilings and tiled floors, and were near a plentiful water supply which was not again advocated as a prime necessity until the six-teenth century. The chief official was now a master or warden, usually appointed by the patron although we know of some exceptions. For example, the hospital of St. John at Oxford had the right to elect its master from one of three Augustinian chaplains, who with six lay brothers and six sisters formed the main staff. Only rarely were masters physicians. We have the records of two; in 1355 the Duke of Lancaster appointed his own physician as master of the Preston hospital, and the master of St. Nicholas's at Pontefract at the end of the fourteenth century is given as "Louis the physician".

Ultimate responsibility for administration now lay with the King and the bishop of the diocese as official visitors. The King usually deputed his duties to his Chancellor; the bishop had no jurisdiction over royal foundations. Masters were expected to ensure the enforcement of the rules drawn up by the bishop. In the purely ecclesiastical houses a further check was imposed by the weekly chapter, while in all hospitals a local jury could look into serious allegations of mismanagement. Even with all these safeguards there were flagrant misdemeanours, for in 1414 Parliament enacted a Statute calling attention to the finding that "the goods and profits are by divers persons, spiritual and temporal withdrawn and spent to the use of others". Mismanagement could hardly be avoided when several masters lived out, and others were permanently absent, holding several appointments. Moreover, much of the income could be eaten up by patrons, who not only deposited their aged servants but made occasional descents for free lodging for themselves and their retainers.

But there were other uncontrollable causes for financial difficulties. St. Thomas's Hospital is a case in point. When it was rebuilt in Borough High Street, after the original house had been destroyed by fire, it depended for the major part of its income on the rents of donated land. The Black Death not only cut these rents drastically by the loss of labour on the farms but brought in many more patients. By 1357 the position was so serious that the brethren petitioned the Pope to grant indulgences to subscribers. Further troubles came in 1535 when Henry appointed Thomas Cromwell and two visitors to enquire into conditions in all monastic hospitals; they gave what was no doubt the expected report, and in 1540 the hospital was surrendered to the King.

All mediaeval hospitals had collecting boxes at the gate to augment income from the annual endowments of patrons, but there were other sources of capital. Monarchs often supplied wood from their royal forests and alms paid by the county sheriff from the profits of Crown lands. In 1257 Stephen le

Longespeye signed an agreement to give St. Bartholomew's an annual rent of twenty shillings. St. Giles at Norwich owned six manors and the advowsons of eleven churches, and in 1357 had a legacy of twenty marks for the master and brethren, forty pence for the other officials, and two shillings towards the maintenance of each bed.

Most houses appointed a professional beggar known as the "proctor", who wandered near and far, armed with a warrant from the bishop; sometimes in return for alms they gave pardons and indulgences. There were also a few groups of local folk, the forerunners of our present Leagues of Hospital Friends, like the Fraternity of St. John the Baptist at Winchester, each of whom gave one shilling annually.

Special privileges were granted to some favoured hospitals. King John decreed that the lepers of Shrewsbury Hospital could take handfuls of corn from all sacks exposed for sale in the town market. St. Mary's Hospital at Southampton had the right to one penny on every tun of wine imported at the harbour, and St. Leonard's collected a tax of twelve to twenty-four sheaves of corn for every plough in the diocese of the Archbishop of York. Naturally such tolls brought grumblings from the merchants and farmers, but some towns continued their generosity over long periods. The Mayor and Corporation of Carlisle granted local lepers a pottle of ale from every brewhouse in the city, and on Saturdays a farthing loaf from every baker who sold bread. Annual fairs brought in considerable sums; one of the most famous was that for the lepers of St. Mary Magdalene, held at Sturbridge near Cambridge, which was authorized by King John in 1211.

The Dissolution which followed the legislation of 1535–6, and had been heralded by Henry's visitors under Thomas Cromwell, brought further vast changes in administration and in methods of finance. That the King in his haste to deprive the Pope of every vestige of authority did not altogether forget the plight of the poor and infirm is shown in the 1535–6 statute against vagrancy, which required that those who took over the land of disbanded houses should continue hospitality and service for them; for example St. Leonard's at York was to remain as a charity for thirty-one poor people. But the Corporation of

London was so alarmed by the hordes of rowdy beggars that now roamed the streets that it petitioned Henry to grant it the governance of St. Mary's, St. Thomas's and St. Bartholomew's. He made no answer until 1547 when he gave St. Bartholomew's to the Corporation with its land on Smithfield, property, and 500 marks annually, provided the citizens of London made an equal cash donation. By an Act of Common Council the City did so, and in addition paid the expenses of repair so that the hospital could take one hundred patients.

Control was vested in a master and four chaplains, but such was their incompetence that we now see the beginning of a story of administration that goes on for 300 years; the story of a lesson, slowly and unwillingly learnt, of the futility of large boards of governors and the uselessness of the occasional committees set up without executive powers. In 1547 the City authorities appointed a Court of Governors from the aldermen, the Common Council and subscribers, under the presidency of the Lord Mayor. Two special officials, a treasurer and a hospitaller, were appointed. The hospitaller was expected to do some medical work, to arrange religious services and to see to the property and feeding of the patients. The diet throughout the Tudor period was good: generous helpings of beef, pork, mutton and herrings. Milk was not often supplied, and although the water supply was then very good the governors apparently agreed with Andrew Boorde that ale was the natural drink for an Englishman, for they not only gave a daily ration but allowed the matron to augment her salary of £3 5s. 8d. a year by selling it, a privilege that was not withdrawn until 1707. As the daily ration was three pints, which even in the small beer of those days is known to have provided 500 to 600 calories and a good supply of vitamin B, the patients at St. Bartholomew's during the sixteenth and seventeenth centuries were better fed than those in most hospitals of the first half of the nineteenth.

St. Thomas's, surrendered to Henry in 1540, was returned to the Mayor and citizens in 1551 and reopened in 1552. Until 1556 it was subject to the court that ruled St. Bartholomew's, but then had its own, which included three aldermen, the eldest being the president. This court had full and rigorous control, as shown in its *Book of the Government of the Hospital*; for example the court and not the surgeon decided when his patient should have an operation. A physician and a matron were appointed. Members of the court, under the title of almoners, visited the hospital in rotation. Patients who could pay were asked to give one shilling a week, but in 1569 more than half the 203 were unable to do so. The hospitaller who collected these fees had £10 a year and four pints of ale daily. Up to the time when the new court took over, boarding allowances had been paid to the staff and patients so that they could buy their own food.

In 1605 St. Thomas's created a precedent; it appointed the first known Hospital Committee. This was apparently *ad hoc*, to consider building a brick wall in the back yard to replace the broken wooden paling through which the patients had been slipping out in the night time to the local ale house.

In 1629 Charles I criticized the administration. In his opinion the salaries paid to the staff were too small. The costs of drugs and herbs were rising steadily and there had been complaints of their bad quality, which is hardly surprising since the apothecary had to supply them out of his £60 per annum. The raised salaries were evidently still meagre; in 1639 the secretary and matron were jailed for debt, the latter owing £100 as she could not exist on her allowance of 2/4d a week for food.

The usual patients, though they stayed longer than in later times, were now in no sense almsmen. The last attempt to introduce such a patient was made by Queen Elizabeth in 1579. After 1552 the demand for beds for the acutely ill had gradually ousted the aged infirm and also the night-lodgers, described as "Common beggars and rogues, that come nightly for their lodging". From 1635 onwards, however, the numbers applying for admission were getting beyond the financial resources of the Court, which took a very practical interest in the welfare of the discharged patient, for it not only supplied him with clothing, surgical appliances and travelling expenses, but also tried to find him employment. The Great Fire brought further difficulties; it reduced the income from rentals on property by £600 a year. Yet this does not excuse an evident laxity in administration ten years later when the governors failed to find an explanation for a deficiency of £243. Things might have gone better had they continued the experiment of the mid-century by which a Standing Committee was to meet fortnightly to consider day-to-day administration; unfortunately this did not last more than a year. Little seems to have been learnt from the inefficiency of the administration during the remainder of the seventeenth century, for in 1699 forty rules of governance, on much the same lines as those of 140 years before, were enacted or re-enacted.

It looks as if Thomas Guy tried to improve on this form of management when in his will he made provision for the chronic sick and "the incurables" discharged from St. Thomas's. He wished to see control by sixty governors, including a president and a treasurer who with twenty-one others were to form a Court of Committees. We may gather what he thought of the efficacy of treatment from his proposal that the salary of the chaplain at £80 a year should be double that of a physician or surgeon.

The eighteenth is the century of the voluntary hospital movement that was to serve England for 250 years. The backward state of the country which until 1719 had no general hospitals in twenty-three of its principal counties was at last realized. It may well be that the efforts of the College of Physicians and the Society of Apothecaries to do something for London's sick poor in the new dispensaries had some effect on public opinion generally, but there were other basic causes for the philanthropy, religious and precautionary, in a certain sense of fear of the return of the sixteenth-century conditions. London showed the way in the foundation of the new general hospitals of Westminster in 1719, Guy's in 1725, and St. George's in 1736. The provinces saw their first general hospital in the Royal Hampshire County Hospital, opened in 1736; by 1800 there were twenty-four more. But in all of them the same system of government by unwieldy and unyielding boards of governors continued.

The new Westminster Hospital, for which "a charitable proposal" to help the poor of St. Margaret's was made in 1716, is an example. Although this project had failed in its first three months the finances went fairly well afterwards. In 1722, two years after a house had been found at a rental of £22 a year, there was £145 in hand after paying £12 14s., with free board, lodging and beer, for the staff other than the matron; this consisted of one nurse, a maidservant and a messenger boy. Apothecaries had been asked to tender for the supply of drugs. All patients had to deposit burial money on admission. Shortly after frustration appeared, for all subscribers were trustees. They numbered several hundred, and they failed to settle disputes among the medical staff, some of whom formed their own Committee which led to the foundation of St. George's Hospital. Still, the prospect of becoming eligible as a Governor for an annual subscription of £5 brought in substantial sums, so that although the staff costs had gone up to £78 a year in 1736, it was now possible to have a nurse for each ward at £6 a year plus board and lodging, a cook at £7 a year, and to replace an inefficient "secretary and register" by a paid clerk.

In 1760 the governors decided to appoint an official administrator; the quarterly meetings had become chaotic as a result of the system whereby a dozen or so met in turn, rejecting at one meeting what their brethren had proposed at the last. The post was advertised at £25 a year. The successful applicant was to see to daily prayers, occasional sacraments, inventories, dietary and burial arrangements of patients, the supervision of staff, the accounting, and the necessary preparations for board meetings. Apparently he would have to be on duty twenty-four hours a day for he was to ensure the patients did not get drunk or get out at night. There was only one applicant, a publican; he was not appointed. Not till 1801, forty-one years later, was a further attempt made to improve the administration. Four referees recommended that a Committee of twenty-five should be appointed annually to attend conscientiously to the affairs of the hospital; twelve nominated members would attend a weekly board meeting for a month at a time. The Trustees would have nothing to do with such an advanced proposal, which would interfere with their privileges and powers. At last in 1826, one hundred and four years after this cumbrous form of management had been established, several *ad hoc* committees led to the formation of the hospital's first Medical Committee, which met once a month to inspect all bills for drugs and to regulate treatment. Yet it took a further seven years before the first secretary was appointed, and a further two before a House Committee was set up in 1835.

The ups and downs of hospital finance in the nineteenth century are illustrated in the fortunes of Moorfield's Eye Hospital. For seven years after its foundation in 1805 it had a novel but rather grim method of raising capital. At the annual anniversary dinners, heralded by an appeal sermon from an eminent divine on the previous Sunday, patients were exhibited to excite the generosity of the diners, with marked success. In April 1815, although the expensive Napoleonic War was still going on, the invested fund for general purposes stood at £2,415, and the building fund, then but two years old, at £852; by October the former had gained a further £400 and the latter over £300. In 1828 the magnificent sum of £2,309 was raised from a three-day sale in the Egyptian Room of the Mansion House; it had been organized by a committee of ladies and conducted under the patronage of the Lord Mayor and his Lady.

The year 1854, however, told a different tale. Its inadequate total of £236 in subscriptions and donations ushered in bad times that continued until 1900, when the disturbed conditions of the South African War were a factor in the debt of £5,000 that now faced the board. This same year brought a further blow. The hospital had moved to its present site. On the old one the City of London Union had charged rates at the nominal figure of £88 per annum, but now the Holborn Union assessment was £870, an eleventh of the total expenditure for the year. An appeal brought not only the answer that the hospital was no longer a local but a national charity, but also a summons to pay arrears in rates of £324. Temporary relief came when publicity about the summons brought in £300 in three days, but the governors knew something more had to be done to keep their hospital going, and from 1909 onwards every patient was asked to pay what he could for treatment. By this means about £1,500 annually was added to the sum collected from donors.

Whatever the cause, lack of funds, bad nursing, or disinterest in the physical comfort and cleanliness of the patients, many hospital records show that dirt and discomfort were common. Even as late as 1869 the Radcliffe Infirmary was begging for old sheets and rags to make dressings. In 1821 one of its visitors had complained that sheets were kept on the beds for a month even if patients had died in them, and another that they were never washed. This seems a particularly strange attitude to cleanliness when we remember that a number of Regimina on travel in the days of the Crusades advised frequent washing of the body and clothing, and the covering of beds with fresh linen as a protection against vermin. William Buchan had preached it in several editions of his *Domestic Medicine* up to the first decade of the century. Not till 1815 did St. Bartholomew's replace its bug-ridden wooden beds with iron ones, although considerable sums had been spent for years on attempts at disinfestation. In 1828 Westminster Hospital had only cold baths, and when it did put in water-closets they can hardly be described as ideal for they were installed behind thin wooden partitions at the ends of the wards, and one leaked down on the kitchen below.

Nursing remained at a very low standard everywhere until 1860, more than a hundred years after a physician had written that a character was never demanded from applicants, since only the lowest type of woman would undertake such disagreeable work. Sairey Gamps were common. It was hardly to be expected that those employed at night as mere "watchers" should spend their miserable few pence of pay on anything but cheap gin when they had to cook their one ration of bacon on a piece of wood before the kitchen fire and eat it in the scullery. Some hospitals had before then shown a conscience towards them and the patients. In 1838 the Middlesex had advised attracting a better type by offering higher pay, and in 1842 the new Brompton Hospital demanded a higher standard of character, education and cleanliness, refusing the illiterate type the London Hospital had been forced to accept thirteen years earlier. It was now over half a century since Buchan had said "it would tend greatly to prevent the spreading of infectious diseases if proper nurses were everywhere employed to take care of the sick"; but long needed reforms began only with Elizabeth Fry's training house and were accelerated by the opening of Florence Nightingale's School for Nursing at St.

Thomas's Hospital in 1860, although the wise advice to place all nurses under the control of matrons was for many years resisted by the medical staff as undermining their authority. Perhaps working and living conditions could have been improved earlier if less money had been spent on alcohol as an essential item of the patient's diet. The accounts of the Worcester Royal Infirmary show that 6,426 gallons of beer were consumed in the year 1861. At the Salop Infirmary port wine was the panacea. In 1748 the Board of Governors had been so alarmed at its annual cost that it passed a resolution that raisin wine should replace it and be supplied only on the express orders of the medical staff, but to no avail. Forty years later they tried to reduce costs by buying port wine in bulk and demanding that prescriptions for it should be registered with the patient's name and dosage clearly stated. Again they failed. In spite of appeals to the medical staff the amounts used continued to rise. While we may speculate about how much of this palatable medicine ever reached the bedside we are left in no doubt about the value of alcohol in treatment in the opinion of the doctor whose comment on the opening of the Temperance Hospital was "God help the patients!"

As already noted the old type of futile administration went on well into the nineteenth century. In 1835 it took the 900 trustees of the Manchester Hospital three hours to ballot on the election of a surgeon. The successful one of four applicants spent £700 on transport and entertainment.

The establishment of the workhouses that came with the Poor Law Amendment Act of 1834 brought no change. For too many of the poor and the aged infirm they were the only institutions available for treatment. Conditions were disgraceful. These unfortunates were herded in insanitary and ill-equipped buildings with totally inadequate medical and nursing care, and were locked in at night with no help at hand. The 1866 Sanitary Act brought a little improvement, but the first real move to deal with the situation came with the formation of the Association for the Improvement of the Infirmaries of London Workhouses in the same year, and in the Metropolitan Poor Law Act of 1867 that led to the setting up of the Metropolitan Asylums Board.

By the beginning of the nineteenth century many of the general hospitals were in serious financial trouble. In 1798 the Worcester Royal Infirmary was so hard pressed that it took the bold step of publishing the names of all subscribers who were in arrears with their donations, and began charging not less than 7/6d a week to everyone admitted because of road accidents. Interest in the foundation of special hospitals may have been a major cause for this lack of support for the general hospitals; a new one appeared in almost every year of Queen Victoria's reign. Considerable help came with the setting up of the Hospital Sunday and Saturday Hospital Funds, and London's hospitals benefited greatly from the quarter of a million pounds collected in the first year of the Prince of Wales Hospital Fund opened in 1897, when the capital had 700 empty beds. Yet it became evident that something had to be done to improve their administration and finance; they could not remain a collection of dissociated units, competing with one another and with the new charities interested in social services for the poor.

The first step towards a National Health service was taken in the 1920s by a group of public spirited men with ideas of reform. Joined by treasurers, managing bodies of the Metropolitan hospitals, representatives of patients and ratepayers, and medical men, they sent four deputations to the Secretary of State for the Home Department, requesting state intervention. They pointed out that bed-accommodation was imperfectly distributed, that costs varied immensely in every type of hospital, and that funds were being squandered foolishly even in large institutions like Guy's and St. Thomas's. What was needed was efficient management, and sufficient capital to ensure efficient working in the wards, where methods for the control of nursing needed drastic overhauling. They saw no need for the creation of new services but pleaded for readjustment, correlation and development in those already existing. The resulting Government Committee under the chairmanship of Viscount Cave led to the Voluntary Hospitals Commission of 1935, which advised hospital regions, centred on a chosen hospital and co-ordinated by a central body. The rest of the story up to the Appointed Day in 1948 is recent history.

BIBLIOGRAPHY

BONSER, W. (1963). *The Medical Background of Anglo-Saxon England*, Wellcome Historical Medical Library, London.

Brit. Med. J. (1868). Expenses of hospital administration and relief, *Brit. med. J.*, **ii**, 426.

—— (1881). The management of hospitals, *Brit. med. J.*, **i**, 444–6.

—— (1895). The finances of the London hospitals, *Brit. med. J.*, **i**, 31; 91.

BURDETT, H. C. (1884). *Hospital Sunday and Hospital Saturday; Their Origin, Progress and Development . . .*, Kegan Paul, London.

—— (1881). Hospital reform, *Fraser's Mag.*, pp. 501–14.

—— (1882). Administration of hospitals. Is it desirable that hospitals should be placed under state supervision? *Trans. nat. Ass. Promotion soc. Science, 1881*, pp. 498–512, London.

CAMERON, H. C. (1954). *Mr. Guy's Hospital, 1726–1948*, Longmans, London.

CLIFFORD-SMITH, J. L. (1883). *Hospital Management; being the authorized Report of a Conference on the Administration of Hospitals held under the Auspices and Management of the Social Science Association on the 3rd and 4th July 1883*, London.

DAINTON, COURTNAY (1961). *The Story of England's Hospitals*, Museum Press, London.

GAMGEE, J. S. (1868). *Hospital Reform . . .*, Churchill, London.

HOLMES, T. (1881). Remarks on the management of hospitals, *Brit. med. J.*, **i**, 423–5.

Lancet (1869). A project for a reformed system of hospitals, *Lancet*, **i**, 464–7.

—— (1883). Hospital administration, *Lancet*, **i**, 653; 793; 882; 1063: **ii**, 72; 158, 342, 702, 1059.

PARSONS, F. G. (1932–6). *The History of St. Thomas's Hospital*, 3 vols., Methuen, London.

PEACHEY, G. C. (1910–14). *The History of St. George's Hospital, 1123–1923*, Bale & Danielsson, London.

POWER, SIR D'ARCY (1923). *A Short History of St. Bartholomew's Hospital*, St. Bart's Hosp., London.

WILKINSON, J. G. (1870). *Hospital expenditure in London and the Provinces . . .*, London.

The Influence of Professional Nursing on the Development of the Modern Hospital

H. MARJORIE SIMPSON

THE INFLUENCE OF professional nursing on the development of the modern hospital has been profound, all-pervasive and often unperceived. Other members of the hospital staff visit the patient; the nurse is his constant companion. Thus the physical, psychological and social environment for the patient in hospital is largely determined by what the nurse is and does.

What the nurse is and does today stems directly from the leadership of Florence Nightingale. Merton, considering issues in the growth of the profession, says of Florence Nightingale that "she was interested in the evolving role of the nurse in society, and so she proceeded methodically to transform the public image of the nurse. In part, she did this by becoming a one-woman bureau of public relations. But only in part. Beyond this, she undertook to change the public conception of the nurse by remaking the realities of what a nurse actually was".[1]

Her leadership was charismatic in character, suited to meet under crisis conditions the clamouring problems of her day. When her work was over, the hierarchy of the servants' hall characteristic of eighteenth- and early nineteenth-century hospital nursing had given place to a hierarchy based on breeding, education and training. The dedication (and, incidentally, some of the intolerance) of the religious orders had been retained and stiffened by discipline. Nursing duties were carried out at a smarter pace; slovenly techniques had been replaced by rigid rituals. Custody of the patient had given place to care if not yet to cure, and he was lying tidily, passively in bed in a pavilion-type hospital of impeccable cleanliness. Nurses were stepping backwards into the future, their eyes fixed firmly on the receding glories of their golden age.

Even though the picture was not as clear cut as the preceding

245

description implies, the nature of the hospital and of nursing had been radically and rapidly altered under the guiding hand of one woman. These changes and their implications are examined below.

Florence Nightingale as a Charismatic Leader

Charismatic leadership, as analysed by M. Weber, develops in religious, economic and other fields in times of crisis when natural leaders, not office holders or patriarchs, take control by reason of specific personal attributes of body and spirit. The crisis passed, the new ways tend to be solidified into a system as rigid as that which they have replaced.

In the true tradition of charismatic leadership Florence Nightingale was divinely called to her task. "God spoke to me and called me to his service,"[2] she records in her diary on 7th February 1837. She had no regulated career, salary or training. Cecil Woodham-Smith says "Miss Nightingale always denied she had been 'trained' at Kaiserwerth. 'The nursing was nil . . . the hygiene horrible'".[3] She was frequently and vigorously in conflict with authority, had no bureaucratic administrative structure to support her work, and used her own resources and funds collected by friends and well-wishers to finance her innovations. She seized on the tasks of the moment, demanding obedience from her followers, and her success determined allegiance to her and brought recognition.

Social Background to Reforms

If hospital and nursing reform resulted from dynamic leadership, the direction of the changes and the mould into which they set were determined by the pattern of nineteenth-century society.

This was a man's world, "in which the roles of the sexes and their 'natural' attributes were conceived of primarily in terms of masculine needs and convenience".[4] Men held that women needed masculine guidance but had a natural affinity for, and gloried in, drudgery on behalf of the helpless and dependent. Women did not dissent. As late as 1888 a letter of 13th August in the *Daily Telegraph* says "No sensible woman objects to acknowledging what is the fact, that she is physically and intellectually inferior to man". It is not surprising that in a hospital system developing in such a society a doctor should describe to the nursing staff their place in the scheme of things in the following terms: "on your side an unvarying routine, where obedience is the first duty, subordination the fit attitude and a good conscience the sole reward."[5]

As Agnes Hunt makes clear "daughters of the upper middle classes were not supposed to go out into the world to earn their own living".[6] This influenced their suitability for nurse training. The Annual Report of the Nightingale Fund 1862 states that

"Persons of superior manners and education, ladies in fact, are not as a rule the best qualified, but rather women of somewhat more than ordinary intelligence emanating from those classes in which women are habitually employed in earning their own livelihood. Ladies, however, are not excluded; on the contrary, where sufficient evidence is shown that they intend to pursue the calling as a business, and have those qualifications which will fit them to become superintendents, their admission would be considered an advantage".[7]

The ladies had doubts of their own, so had their parents. As Langdon-Davies points out "the care of the sick involves many details that no lady should ever think of".[8] "Ought I to leave Mama?" asks Agnes Jones.[9] "I should lose all chance of getting married and put myself outside the pale of social life", admits another prospective candidate.[10]

The doubts had their foundation in the current conception of hospitals and the nurses in them. "The willingness to become a nurse at a hospital in the eighteenth century was an indication of such probable moral depravity that it was not the custom at Westminster Hospital to ask for characters."[11] Even if nurses were free from vice, they were likely to be illiterate, careless in their personal habits and casual in the services they rendered to the sick.

Hospital living conditions too were not calculated to attract the delicately reared. Nurses had dormitories and sisters rooms off the ward. Sometimes nurses prepared their own food; sometimes it was prepared for them. In neither instance does it sound appetising.

The nature of disease was not well understood; the risk to the nurse's health was considerable. Patients could be despairing, rough, uncouth and dirty.

The New Order

Not all nurses, however, were undesirable either in relation to character or work, and hospitals could be rebuilt. Florence Nightingale systematically investigated the existing scene. She set to work to cull the best from current practice and then to make it the typical rather than the exceptional picture Such a change called for drastic measures. She held that "only in an atmosphere of the strictest discipline could the sure protection, offered hitherto only by religious vows, be secured. Also, only in an atmosphere of devotion to duty could nursing develop as a vocation distinct from the commercial undertaking which it had been."[12]

Under her guidance the new nurse emerged, "clean, quiet and punctual", trained "to undertake the personal care of patients",[13] never to ask "why" and as seldom as possible "how",[14] obedient, deferential, dedicated and respectable.

The new hospital was a cleaner, airier, less overcrowded place than the old, but not all hospitals were new. "In 1875 the National Association for Providing Trained Nurses for the Sick Poor described conditions at a London hospital as being so bad that good nursing was impossible."[15] In 1889 an article in the *Nursing Record* on Life in a Cottage Hospital stated that "the hospital will accommodate thirty patients, or, by putting two in a bed in some of the wards, thirty-eight patients".[16] In 1891 Dr. Allan Gray, the Medical Officer of Health for Leith, reported

> "the hospital contained cases of diphtheria, erysipelas, measles, and a considerable number of scarlet fever cases, besides a family suffering from typhus; and all these cases were attended during the night by one nurse. . . . Thirty-one cases [of typhus] were subsequently recorded . . . and the simple statement is appended that they all sprang from the family above mentioned."[17]

Nursing Duties

Cleaning duties loomed large in the new hospital as in the

old. The nurses waited on the ward sister, made her bed and emptied her bath and slops; they did the washing up in the ward and much polishing of the many brass fittings. There were open fires to be tended. In the old Westminster Hospital every drop of hot water had to be carried up from the basement.[18]

Very cautiously the doctors were entrusting nurses with other duties, counting the pulse for example, "but", said one doctor in 1889, "while you are trusted so far, yet with the character of the pulse, its length, quality and tension you have nothing to do. And so of the administration of drugs. It is not yours wholly. Hypodermic injection for example is, or ought to be, solely in the hands of the doctor."[19] In 1904 Dr. Fenwick, giving evidence to the select committee on the Registration of Nurses, said

"the nurse ought certainly to be able to take the patient's temperature and pulse correctly. . . . Then I consider that she ought to know exactly how to feed the patient, how to keep him and his surroundings clean, how to undertake the ventilation of his room and that she should also be able to understand the symptoms that he presents and be able to accurately report them to the doctor."

This last was of growing importance because as Dr. Fenwick went on to say "the doctor cannot stay always by his patient and it is since we have had these well-trained nurses that abdominal surgery had made the great advances that it has".[20] It is small wonder that the doctors were glad to pass on the task of being always by the patient. "I have not yet forgotten", writes a nurse in 1888, "nursing my first ovariotomy, when it was the rule for one Nurse to take entire charge of the case for the first fifty-six hours."[21] Another states that for forty-eight and often sixty hours consecutively the nurse is left to watch her case minutely, ceaselessly and sleeplessly.[22]

Yet nurses flooded into the voluntary hospitals and a few made their way to the poor law infirmaries where conditions were more difficult and the satisfactions of the work less obvious. "I had a bright death-bed today to cheer me"[23] wrote Agnes Jones, but not everyone had the dedicated spirit that she brought to her work.

The new nurse influenced the development of the modern hospital not only by acquiring new skills and a new personality but also by the cheapness of the labour she provided. An editorial in the *Nursing Record* of May 1889 stated,

"there is no hospital however small, which can continue without its complement of nursing workers; and as, almost without exception, the finances of hospitals are straitened, they must always have a certain number of probationers at work learning their profession and, therefore, receiving smaller remuneration than they could command were they fully trained."

This attitude has never wholly died and hospitals have not been designed to use their labour force economically.

Leadership during the Period of Consolidation and Conservatism

The impact of Florence Nightingale's reforms was immense but there was need for her ideas to be disseminated and her work consolidated. Kopf writes:

"Florence Nightingale may well be assigned a position in the history of social statistics next to those occupied by Quetelet and Farr. Her ardent, genuine sympathy for the sick and distressed was greatly augmented by a positive genius for marshalling definite knowledge of the forces which made for disease and suffering."[24]

Her reforms were the result of painstaking investigations. She had and used devoted and influential friends to further her schemes and she accomplished a revolution.

During the ensuing period of consolidation and conservatism, nurse leaders used other tactics. "I am much amused", wrote Agnes Jones, "at the way in which I get all I ask for. . . . We parted amicably. I felt a load off my mind though bodily weary—standing two and a half hours after a long day's work."[25] Another persistent reformer was Miss Lückes: "She would accept defeat for the moment if she could not get what she thought right, and would just begin working for it again. She would never make a compromise by accepting anything less than what was right."[26] On the other hand Mrs. Strong, told she had gone too far in asking for a nurses' home, said, "as I knew the work could not advance without it, I resigned".[27]

It was the gay reformer Agnes Hunt who took the drastic step of sending smallpox patients to put their own complaints to members of the hospital committee. Both she and Sister Dora assisted with the financing of their own hospital buildings.

Finally, there was the approach through committees. Miss MacManus affords an example of a matron working this way. She writes, "To the House Committee every week the three chief executive members of the hospital staff—the Superintendent, the Clerk to the Treasurer . . . and the Matron— brought their business. It had been laid down years before by that far-seeing administrator Cooper Perry that the matron, as one of the chief executive trio, should understand the business of the hospital as a whole."[28]

Steadily the work went forward, advanced now by one method, now by another. The pattern had been set, the task was to make its application universal. The battle for registration was fought and won, ensuring that the new style nurse became the standard nurse, in short supply perhaps but at least an identifiable product.

Modern Developments

Yet even as the nursing world struggled to assimilate and disseminate the new pattern of hospital care, events moved on. Miracles of medical discoveries eliminated the old diseases and called for nurses versed in ever more complicated technical procedures. Nurses were better educated but so were their patients; reliance on formula and ritual became less acceptable. The dedicated spinster making the hospital her whole world was giving place to married non-resident nursing staff, and men were joining women in the work. Other employment opportunities opened up for women. The hospital team itself expanded, disturbing the old doctor-nurse-patient relationship with the addition of dieticians, social workers, physiotherapists, technicians and domestic supervisors. The very old replaced the very young, and the mentally sick replaced the fever patient as the major challenges to nursing skill. Nurses, still trying to perfect themselves on a standard formula after events had swept away the conditions that that formula was designed to meet, were caught and moulded by the swirling currents of social change.

Merton claims that Florence Nightingale, if read aright, had this to say: "First, that a profession requires the formulation of far-reaching goals; second, that to achieve these goals, a profession must help shape its history rather than merely to adapt to the course of events; third, that research is indispensable for the advancement of the profession; fourth, that only as the standards of training and practice are perpetually raised will the public image of the profession be reshaped in accord with the changing reality; fifth, that all basic changes in the profession will produce discomfort in various quarters, for change requires readjustment both within the profession and among neighbouring professions and occupations."[29]

There are signs that nurses are moving away from their preoccupation with traditional practice and are pausing to review their tasks objectively. If this is so they may be expected, not to lead a new revolution or to provide a static element in a changing situation, but to work as partners in developing the modern hospital to meet the needs of a modern age.

REFERENCES

1. MERTON, R. K. (1958). Issues in the growth of a profession, in American Nurses' Association, *Issues in the Growth of a Profession*, 41st Convention of the Amer. Nurses Ass., pp. 5–6.
2. WOODHAM-SMITH, C. (1955). *Florence Nightingale*, p. 21, Penguin Books, London.
3. *Ibid*, p. 72.
4. DEVEREUX, G. and WEINER, F. (1950). The occupational status of nurses, *Amer. sociol. Rev.*, 15, 629.
5. STURGES, O. (1889). Nurses and doctors, *Nursing Rec.*, 2, 214.
6. HUNT, AGNES (1938). *This is My Life*, p. 80, Blackie, Glasgow.
7. DUNBAR, V. M. (1936). *The Origin and Early Development of Two English Training Schools for Nurses*, Florence Nightingale International Foundation (Typescript), p. 34.
8. LANGDON-DAVIES, J. (1952). *Westminster Hospital*, p. 123, John Murray, London.
9. JONES, A. E. (1872). *Memorials of Agnes Elizabeth Jones by her Sister*, p. 31, Strahan, London.
10. HALLOWES, R. M. (1955). Alice Sophia Gregory, *Nursing Mirror*, 101, p. V.
11. LANGDON-DAVIES, J., *op. cit.*, p. 123.
12. DUNBAR, V. M., *op. cit.*, p. 15.
13. Lancet (1932). Commission on Nursing. Final Report, *Lancet*, 24.

14. MOLLETT, Miss (1888). Discipline, *Nursing Rec.*, **1**, 99.
15. LANGDON-DAVIES, J., *op. cit.*, p. 140.
16. KEMP, H. M. (1889). Life in a cottage hospital, *Nursing Rec.*, **3**, 6.
17. Nursing Echoes (1891). *Nursing Rec.*, **6**, 273.
18. LANGDON-DAVIES, J., *op. cit.*, 239.
19. STURGES, O. (1889). Nurses and doctors, *Nursing Rec.*, **2**, 198.
20. *Select Committee on Registration of Nurses Report (1905)*, pp. 3–4, H.M.S.O., London.
21. Hospital sketches (1888). The Sister, *Nursing Rec.*, **1**, 256.
22. Nursing echoes (1890). *Nursing Rec.*, **4**, 295.
23. JONES, A. E., *op. cit.*, p. 358.
24. KOPF, E. W. (1961). Florence Nightingale as a statistician, *Quart. Publ., Amer. statist. Ass.*, N.S. **15**, 404.
25. COPE, SIR ZACHARY (1961). *Six Disciples of Florence Nightingale*, p. 6, Pitman, London.
26. HOLLAND, SYDNEY, VISCOUNT KNUTSFORD (1910). *Eva C. E. Lückes*, p. 8, privately published.
27. COPE, SIR ZACHARY, *op. cit.*, p. 29.
28. MACMANUS, EMILY E. P. (1956). *Matron of Guy's*, p. 145, Andrew Melrose, London.
29. MERTON, R. K., *op. cit.*, p. 6.

Bibliography of Hospital History

COMPILED BY E. GASKELL

INTRODUCTION

THE EXTENT AND variety of hospital literature make it extremely difficult for anyone to bring it under bibliographical control. Hospital history, however, is one small segment which easily lends itself to an orderly arrangement. This subject has already a considerable literature and several societies have been created in Europe to promote further study and research. In France, M. Candille has set a fine example by his bibliographies currently appearing in *L'Hôpital et l'Aide sociale à Paris*. The historian in Britain would probably benefit most from a retrospective bibliography showing the extent to which the subject has already been treated and thus suggesting topics and problems for further research.

The present bibliography was compiled with this purpose in mind. It is selective, and with a few exceptions the latest and most comprehensive publications appear to the exclusion of earlier articles. It is for the reader to build up his own exhaustive bibliography, if the need for one is felt, by using the key works in the following pages. A comprehensive version of the bibliography may be consulted in the Wellcome Historical Medical Library.

Each section of the bibliography has been allotted four possible subdivisions—a, Bibliographies; b, Subject histories; c, Hospital histories in general; d, Hospital histories by locality. The entries in each of these subdivisions are arranged chronologically by publication-date, but in (d) the primary order is alphabetical by name of hospital, after which the chronological order is followed. In the section on military hospitals there is a deviation from this rule, and the entries are in order of military campaign.

The bibliography includes the more important background

works essential for any student of hospital history. In addition it may be useful to mention here a few of the more general bibliographical guides to British history which provide starting points for the hospital historian. Reference sources of constant value are the *Bibliography of British History* (1928–59); Gross's *Bibliography of British Municipal History* (1915); the *Bibliography of the History of Wales*, 2nd ed. (1962); Hancock's *Bibliography of Works Relating to Scotland 1916–50* (1959–60); Carty's bibliographies of Irish history (1936–40), and O'Neill's *Sources of Irish Local History* (1958). Nor should one forget the breviates of parliamentary papers by P. & G. Ford, or the histories of public health (e.g. Frazer, 1950) and of the National Health Service (Ross, 1952; Eckstein, 1959; Lindsay, 1962).

Arrangement of Sections

1. General Hospital History in England and Wales.
2. General Hospital History in Scotland.
3. General Hospital History in Ireland.
4. Mediaeval Hospitals.
5. Dispensaries.
6. Cottage Hospitals.
7. Naval Hospitals.
8. Military Hospitals.
9. Hospital Teaching.
10. Hospital Administration.
11. Hospital Design.
12. Special Hospitals.
    (i) Hospitals for Burns.
    (ii) Cancer Hospitals.
    (iii) Children's Hospitals.
    (iv) Ear, Nose and Throat Hospitals.
    (v) Eye Hospitals.
    (vi) Hospitals for Fistula.
    (vii) Heart Hospitals.
    (viii) Hydropathic Hospitals.
    (ix) Hospitals for Incurables.
    (x) Isolation Hospitals.
    (xi) Maternity Hospitals.
    (xii) Mental Hospitals.

(xiii) Hospitals for Nervous Diseases.
(xiv) Orthopaedic Hospitals.
(xv) Skin Hospitals.
(xvi) Hospitals for Stone.
(xvii) Surgical Hospitals.
(xviii) Hospitals for Tropical Diseases.
(xix) Tuberculosis Hospitals.
(xx) Hospitals for Venereal Diseases.

SECTION 1

GENERAL HOSPITAL HISTORY IN ENGLAND AND WALES

a. *See* BURDETT, H. C., *infra.*
   HOUSE OF LORDS, *General Index to the Reports on Metropolitan Hospitals,* London, 1892.
c. BURDETT, H. C., *Hospitals and Asylums of the World; their Origin, History, Construction, Administration, Management, and Legislation,* 4 vols., London, 1891–3. (Vol. 4 is a comprehensive bibliography.)
   EVANS, A. D. *and* HOWARD, A. G. R., *The Romance of the British Voluntary Hospital Movement,* London [1930].
   IVES, A. G. L., *British Hospitals,* London, 1948.
   DAINTON, C., *The Story of England's Hospitals,* London [1961].
d. *Bangor* INGMAN, J., The early days of the Caernarvonshire and Anglesey Hospital, with notes on some of Bangor's medical practitioners, 1772–1856, *Trans. Caerns. Hist. Soc.,* 1950, **11,** 61–72.
   Bath BAYLIES, W., *An Historical Account of the Rise, Progress, and Management of the General Hospital or Infirmary in the City of Bath,* Bath, 1758. (This evoked two anonymous pamphlets in 1759, *A Short Answer* and *A Full Reply.*)
   Birmingham JONES, J. E., *A History of the Hospitals and Other Charities of Birmingham,* London [1909].
   WYNN, W. H., The General Hospital, Birmingham, *Med. Press,* 1939, **202,** 365–370.
   Bristol SMITH, G. M., *A History of the Bristol Royal Infirmary,* Bristol, [1917].
   DOPSON, L., A history of pharmacy at Bristol Royal Infirmary, *Chem. & Drugg.,* 1956, **165,** 622–4; **166,** 171–3, 222–3, 256–7, 441–3.
   Cambridge HAYNES, G. S., Addenbrooke's Hospital, Cambridge, *Med. Press,* 1942, **207,** 72–76.
   Canterbury BERESFORD-JONES, A. B., The Kent and Canterbury Hospital, 1790 to 1940, *Med. Press,* 1941, **205,** 328–31.

Cardiff   SHEEN, A. W., Cardiff Royal Infirmary, *Med. Press*, 1942, **207**, 306–310.

Carlisle   MACLAREN, N., Cumberland Infirmary; past, present and future, *Brit. med. J.*, 1952, **ii**, 967–969.

Chichester   STEER, F. W., *The Royal West Sussex Hospital: the First Hundred Years, 1784–1884*, Chichester, 1960.

Exeter   HARRIS, J. D., *The Royal Devon and Exeter Hospital*, Exeter, 1922.

Gloucester   FRITH, B., *The Story of Gloucester's Infirmary*, Gloucester, 1961.

Greenwich   POLAND, J., *Records of the Miller Hospital and Royal Kent Dispensary*, Greenwich, 1893.

Hereford   LANGFORD, A. W., [History of Hereford General Hospital], *Trans. Woolhope Nat. Fld. Cl.*, 1960, **36**, 149–160.

Hull   LOWSON, K. J., *The Story of the Hull Royal Infirmary 1782–1948* [Hull, 1948].

Leamington   CHEYNE, A. I., The History of the Warneford Hospital, Leamington Spa, *Bgham. med. Rev.*, 1958, **20**, 415–9.

Leeds   ANNING, S. T., The apothecaries of the General Infirmary at Leeds, *Med. Hist.*, 1961, **5**, 221–238.

ANNING, S. T., *The General Infirmary at Leeds. Vol. I: 1767–1869*, London, 1963.

Lincoln   SYMPSON, T., *A Short Account of the Old and of the New Lincoln County Hospital*, Lincoln, 1878.

Liverpool   PEMBERTON, H. S., David Lewis Northern Hospital, *Sphincter*, 1956, **18**, 51–60.

BICKERTON, H. R., Royal Infirmary, Liverpool, *Med. Press*, 1941, **206**, 114–119.

MACALISTER, C. J., *The Origin and History of the Liverpool Royal Southern Hospital*, Liverpool, 1936.

London   POWELL, Sir G. A., *The Metropolitan Asylums Board and its Work, 1867–1930*, London, 1930.

COLEMAN, R. *and* DALEY, W. A., The development of hospital services with particular reference to the municipal hospital system of London, *Proc. roy. Soc. Med.*, 1942, **35**, 741–752.

COURT OF COMMON COUNCIL, *Memoranda, References and Documents, Relating to the Royal Hospitals of the City of London.* [and] *Supplement*, 2 vols., London, 1836 [repr. 1863] –1867.

HUNTER, W., *Historical Account of Charing Cross Hospital and Medical School (University of London) . . . with which is Included Some Account of the Origin of the Other Hospitals and Schools in London*, London, 1914.

ANDERSON, L. G., *Elizabeth Garrett Anderson, 1836–1917*, London, 1939.

French Hospital and Dispensary, [London, 1868].

DAMMERT, F., History and importance of the German Hospital in London, *Münch. med. Wschr.*, 1937, **84**, 1179–1184.

BROCK, R. C., *The Life and Work of Astley Cooper*, Edinburgh, 1952. (Surgeon to Guy's Hospital.)

CAMERON, H. C., *Guy's Hospital, 1726–1948*, London, 1954.

History of the Italian Hospital in London, 1884–1906, London, 1906.

AVERY, H., La storia dell'Ospedale Italiano di Londra, *Attualità osped.*, 1958, **3**(6), 41–42.

LYLE, H. W., *King's and some King's Men: Being a Record of the Medical Department of King's College, London, from 1830 to 1909 and of King's College Hospital Medical School from 1909 to 1934. [and] Addendum . . . to 5th July, 1948*, 2 vols., London, 1935–1950.

CLARK-KENNEDY, A. E., *The London: a Study in the Voluntary Hospital System. Vol. I: The First Hundred Years, 1740–1840*, London, 1962. *Vol. II: The Second Hundred Years, 1840–1948*, London, 1963.

METROPOLITAN HOSPITAL [Brief History from 1836 to 1889] [London, 1890].

SAUNDERS, H. ST. G., *The Middlesex Hospital 1745–1948*, London, 1949.

BETT, W. R., *Sir John Bland-Sutton, 1855–1936*, Edinburgh, 1956. (Surgeon to the Middlesex Hospital.)

PARSONS, J., *A Short History of Queen Mary's Hospital for the East End, Stratford* [1962].

RIDDELL, Lord, *Dame Louisa Aldrich-Blake*, London, 1926. (Dean of the Royal Free Hospital 1914.)

THORNE, M., Royal Free Hospital, *Med. Press*, 1940, **204**, 106–110.

JEWESBURY, E. C. O., *The Royal Northern Hospital 1856–1956: the Story of a Hundred Years' Work in North London*, London, 1956.

MOORE, Sir NORMAN, *The History of St. Bartholomew's Hospital*, London, 1918.

POWER, Sir D'A., St. Bartholomew's Hospital, 1880–1930, *Glasgow med. J.*, 1932, **118**, 73–102.

THORNTON, J. L., *John Abernethy: a Biography*, London, 1953. (Surgeon to St. Bartholomew's Hospital.)

KERLING, N. J. M., *St. Bartholomew's Hospital. List of Archives to 1850*, [London, 1962].

HOLMES, T., *Sir Benjamin Brodie*, London, 1898. (Surgeon to St. George's Hospital.)

PEACHEY, G. C., *History of St. George's Hospital*, pts. 1–6, London, 1910–14.

BLOMFIELD, J., *St. George's 1733–1933*, London, 1933.

LOCKHART-MUMMERY, J. P., St. Mark's Hospital, *Med. Press*, 1941, **205**, 450–454.

WILLCOX, W., St. Mary's Hospital, *Med. Press*, 1941, **206**, 348–352.

McINNES, E. M., *St. Thomas's Hospital*, London, 1963.

NIXON, N. H., *North London or University College Hospital: a History of the Hospital from its Foundation to the Year 1881*, London, 1882.

University College Hospital and Medical School: a Record 1914–1919, 2 vols., London, 1922.

[B., G.] *University College Hospital: the Story of the Past Century, 1833–1933* [London, 1933].

WELLS, C., *Recollection of the West London Hospital; Being the Presidential Address Delivered before the West London Medico-Chirurgical Society*, London, 1891.

LANGDON-DAVIES, J., *Westminster Hospital: Two Centuries of Voluntary Service 1719–1948*, London, 1952.

Luton   LEE, H. B., The end of the Alexandra Hospital, [1867–1958] *St. Bart's. Hosp. J.*, 1958, **62**, 10–11.

Manchester BROCKBANK, W., *Portraits of a Hospital, 1752–1948*, [Royal Infirmary] London, 1952.

Mexborough WILSON, D. M., *A Short History of the Montagu Hospital, Mexborough, 1889–1925*, Mexborough, 1926.

Newcastle HUME, W. E., *The Infirmary, Newcastle-upon-Tyne, 1751–1951: a Brief Sketch*, Newcastle, 1951.

Norwich EADE, Sir P., *The Norfolk and Norwich Hospital, 1770–1900*, London, 1900.

  CLEVELAND, A., *A History of the Norfolk and Norwich Hospital from 1900 to the End of 1946*, Norwich, 1948.

Nottingham JACOB, E. H., *A History of the General Hospital near Nottingham, Open to the Sick and Lame Poor of Any Country*, Bristol, 1951.

Oxford GIBSON, A. G., *The Radcliffe Infirmary*, London, 1926.

Reading DORMER, E. W., Ed., *The Story of the Royal Berkshire Hospital 1837–1937*, Reading, 1937.

Rochester GREENWOOD, E. J., *The Hospital of St. Bartholomew, Rochester*, Rochester, 1962. (England's oldest hospital.)

St. Albans Bart's in Herts [Hill End Hospital, St. Albans], *St. Bart's. Hosp. J.*, 1961, **65**, 197–200.

Salisbury. SALISBURY AND DISTRICT INFIRMARY AND HOSPITAL LEAGUE, *The History of Salisbury Infirmary Founded by Anthony, Lord Feversham A.D. 1766*, Salisbury, 1922.

Sheffield LEADER, J. D., *Sheffield General Infirmary. A Brief Sketch of a Century's Work, 1797–1897 . . . Together with Reminiscences and Biographical Notices of the Medical Staff by Simeon Snell*, Sheffield, 1897.

Shrewsbury HOWIE, W. B., The administration of an eighteenth-century provincial hospital: the Royal Salop Infirmary, 1747–1830, *Med. Hist.*, 1961, **5**, 34–55.

  HOWIE, W. B., Finance and supply in an eighteenth-century provincial hospital 1747–1830 [The Salop Infirmary], *Med. Hist.*, 1963, **7**, 126–146.

Stamford WRIGHT, H. P., *The Story of the 'Domus Rei' of Stamford (Hospital of William Browne)*, London, 1890.

Sunderland ROBINSON, W., *The Story of the Royal Infirmary, Sunderland*, Sunderland, 1934.

Taunton HUGO, T., *The History of the Hospital of St. Margaret, Taunton*, London, 1874.

Windsor MCAULEY, J. E., *The Hospital at Windsor: a Brief History of Windsor Dispensary and Infirmary and King Edward VII Hospital 1818–1939*, Windsor, 1960.

Worcester MCMENEMEY, W. H., *A History of the Worcester Royal Infirmary*, London [1947].

SECTION 2

GENERAL HOSPITAL HISTORY IN SCOTLAND

b. COMRIE, J. D., *History of Scottish Medicine*, 2nd ed., 2 vols., London, 1932.
FERGUSON, T., *The Dawn of Scottish Social Welfare: a Survey from Medieval Times to 1863*, London, 1948.
FERGUSON, T., *Scottish Social Welfare, 1864–1944*, Edinburgh, 1958.
d. *Aberdeen* History of the Aberdeen Royal Infirmary, Dundee, 1904.
LYALL, A., The case of Dr. Memis v. Managers of Aberdeen Royal Infirmary, *Med. Hist.*, 1960, **4**, 32–48.
Dumfries McDOUGAL, J. W., *The Dumfries and Galloway Royal Infirmary: a Brief Pictorial Survey, 1776–1948*, [Dumfries, 1948].
Dundee GIBSON, H. J. C., *Dundee Royal Infirmary, 1798 to 1948: the Story of the Old Infirmary, with a Short Account of More Recent Years*, [Dundee], 1948.
Edinburgh TURNER, A. L., *Story of a Great Hospital: the Royal Infirmary of Edinburgh, 1729–1929*, Edinburgh, 1937.
ROBERTSON, D., The Royal Infirmary of Edinburgh: payments by patients in the 18th century, *Edin. med. J.*, 1942, **49**, 643–8.
Glasgow COWAN, J. M., *Some Yesterdays. With a Note upon the Development of Hospitals by J. Ferguson*, Glasgow, 1949.
PATRICK, J., *A Short History of Glasgow Infirmary*, Glasgow, 1940.
The Victoria Infirmary of Glasgow: Historical and Financial Summary, 1878–1895, Glasgow, 1895.
DOWNIE, J. W., *The Early Physicians and Surgeons of the Western Infirmary Glasgow*, [Glasgow], 1923.
POWER, W., *The Western Infirmary of Glasgow: a Short History Written on the Occasion of the Jubilee*, Glasgow, 1924.
MURRAY, D., *The David Elder Infirmary, Govan; the Gift of his Son Alexander Elder*, Glasgow, 1927.
Inverness MACKENZIE, T. C., *The Story of a Scottish Voluntary Hospital*, Inverness, 1947.

SECTION 3

GENERAL HOSPITAL HISTORY IN IRELAND

b. FLEETWOOD, J., *History of Medicine in Ireland*, Dublin, 1951.
c. JOHNSON, Z., The provincial hospitals of Ireland, *Dublin J. med. Sci.*, 1891, **91**, 217–226.
d. *Cork* CUMMINS, N. M., *Some Chapters of Cork Medical History*, Cork, 1957. (Mainly a narrative of hospital history.)
Dublin KIRKPATRICK, T. P. C., The origin of some of the hospitals of Dublin, *Dublin J. med. Sci.*, 1914, **137**, 98–109.

COSGRAVE, E. M., Drumcondra Hospital; a short history, *Dublin J. med. Sci.*, 1916, **142**, 386–400.

STOKER, W. T., The hospitals of the House of Industry; a historical sketch, *Dublin J. med. Sci.*, 1885, **80**, 469–486.

MACNAMARA, D. W., The Mater—1914–1919, *J. Irish Med. Ass.*, 1961, **49**, 147–157.

ORMSBY, *Sir* L. H., *Medical History of the Meath Hospital and County Dublin Infirmary*, Dublin, 1888.

[A series of four articles on the history of Mercer's Hospital], *Irish J. med. Sci.*, 1935, pp. 1–23.

CLERY, A. B., The Richmond Hospital, Dublin, *Med. Press*, 1943, **210**, 242–245.

A Century of Service [St. Vincent's Hospital], Dublin, 1934. (Founded by Sisters of Charity.)

CANAVAN, J. E., *The Irish Sisters of Charity*, Dublin, 1941.

MOORHEAD, T. G., *A Short History of Sir Patrick Dun's Hospital*, Dublin, 1942.

KIRKPATRICK, T. P. C., *The History of Dr. Steevens' Hospital, Dublin, 1720–1920*, Dublin, 1924.

Belfast MALCOLM, A. G., *The History of the General Hospital, Belfast, and the Other Medical Institutions of the Town*, Belfast, 1851.

MARSHALL, R., *Fifty Years on the Grosvenor Road: an Account of the Rise and Progress of the Royal Victoria Hospital, Belfast . . . 1903–1953* [Belfast 1953].

MCMECHAN, E. W., A tribute to our surgical pioneers: a history of surgery and surgeons of the Royal Victoria Hospital, Belfast, from 1792 to 1920, *Ulster med. J.*, 1955, **24**, 81–91.

SECTION 4

MEDIAEVAL HOSPITALS (inc. LEPER-HOUSES)

b. KNOWLES, D. *and* HADCOCK, R. N., *Mediaeval Religious Houses of England and Wales*, London, 1953.

c. CLAY, R. M., *The Mediaeval Hospitals of England*, London [1909].

MERCIER, C. A., *Leper Houses and Mediaeval Hospitals: Being the Fitzpatrick Lectures*, London, 1915. *Also in Glasg. med. J.*, 1915, **83**, 1–20, 81–103.

FLEMMING, P., The medical aspects of the mediaeval monastery in England, *Proc. roy. Soc. Med.*, 1928, **22**, 771–782.

HAMMOND, E. A., Physicians in mediaeval English religious houses, *Bull. Hist. Med.*, 1958, **32**, 105–120.

BULLOUGH, V. L., A note on medical care in mediaeval English hospitals, *Bull. Hist. Med.*, 1961, **35**, 74–7.

d. *Cumberland* BARNES, H., Leprosy and local leper hospitals, *Trans. Cumberland Westm. Arch. Soc.*, 1889, **10**, 95–123.

Durham ROBSON, H. L., The mediaeval hospitals of Durham, *Sunderland Antiq. Soc.*, 1960, **22**, 33–56.

Gloucestershire PARKER, G., Early Bristol medical institutions. The mediaeval hospitals and barber-surgeons, *Trans. Bristol Glouc. Arch. Soc.*, 1922, **44**, 155–178.

FULLER, E. A., Cirencester hospitals, *Trans. Bristol Glouc. Arch. Soc.*, 1892–3, **17**, 53–8.

Kent GODFREY, W. H., Some mediaeval hospitals of East Kent, *Arch. J.*, 1929, **86**, 99–110.

Shropshire MAXWELL, C., The mediaeval hospitals of Bridgnorth, *Trans. Shrop. Arch. Soc.*, 1920–1, pp. 49–56.

Suffolk ROWE, J., The mediaeval hospitals of Bury St. Edmunds, *Med. Hist.*, 1958, **2**, 253–263.

Scotland DURKAN, J., Care of the poor: pre-Reformation hospitals, *Innes Review*, 1960, **10**, 268–80.

DILLON, W. J., The spittals of Ayrshire, *Ayrshire Arch. & nat. Hist. Coll.*, 1961, **6**, 12–42.

Ireland BELCHER, T. W., Notes on the mediaeval leper hospitals of Ireland, *Dublin quart. J. med. Sci.*, 1868, **46**, 36–45.

SECTION 5

DISPENSARIES

a. ROYAL COLLEGE OF PHYSICIANS, *Some British Hospitals and Dispensaries*, London, 1962. (The College possesses minute books of the Western and Westminster General Dispensaries.)

c. RENTOUL, R. R., The growth and progress of provident dispensaries, *Brit. med. J.*, 1887, **i**, 1351–3.

KING, F. A., Self-supporting dispensaries of the early nineteenth century, *Med. Ill.*, 1955, **9**, 654–6.

d. *Leicester* LEICESTER AND LEICESTERSHIRE PROVIDENT DISPENSARY, *Its History, Prospects, Present Position, and Requirements*, Leicester, 1878.

London ROSENBERG, A., The London Dispensary for the Sick-Poor, *J. Hist. Med.*, 1959, **14**, 41–56.

London's earliest health centre [i.e. Westminster General Dispensary], *Chem. & Drugg.*, 1957, **167**, 696–8.

LETTSOM, J. C., *Medical Memoirs of the General Dispensary in London, etc.*, London, 1774.

SCHUSTER, N. H., *The Western General Dispensary, St. Marylebone*, London, 1961.

SMITH, A., *An Historical Sketch of the Finsbury Dispensary*, London, 1870.

Northampton BECKE, J., *Provident Dispensaries: Sketch of the Facts Connected with the Establishment of the Royal Victoria Dispensary, Northampton, with a Short Summary of the Results of the Working of that Institution, During a Period of Twenty Six Years, and Practical Suggestions for the Conduct of Similar Institutions,* Northampton, 1872.

York ALLEN, O., *History of the York Dispensary, Containing an Account of its Origin and Progress to the Present Time, Comprising a Period of Fifty-Seven Years,* York, 1845.

Scotland PORTER, I. A., *Alexander Gordon, M.D., of Aberdeen, 1752–1799,* Edinburgh, 1958. (Chap. 3 (pp. 21–28): A. Gordon, dispensary physician.)

SECTION 6

COTTAGE HOSPITALS

c. BURDETT, H. C., *The Cottage Hospital, its Origin, Progress, Management, and Work. With an Alphabetical List of Every Cottage Hospital at Present Opened, and a Chapter on the Hospitalism in Cottage Hospital Practice,* 3rd ed., London, 1896.

BURDETT, H. C., *The Cottage Hospital: its Origin, History, Value and Advantage,* London, 1901.

d. *Bourton-on-the-Water Centenary of the Bourton-on-the-Water Cottage Hospital, 1861–1961,* Bourton, 1961.

Mildenhall REES, H. G., St. M., A note on the Mildenhall Cottage Hospital, *Med. Hist.,* 1962, **6**, 185–7.

Portsmouth Portsmouth Cottage Hospital, [Portsmouth, 1885].

Sudbury HOLDEN, J. S., *History of a Cottage Hospital,* Sudbury, 1889.

SECTION 7

NAVAL HOSPITALS

b. *History of the Second World War. The Royal Naval Medical Service, by J. L. S. Coulter. Vol. 1: Administration,* London, 1954. (see Chap. 8, pp. 97–123, Hospital Ships. Chap. 14, pp. 310–385, Hospitals.)

KEEVIL, J. J., *Medicine and the Navy, 1200–1900. Vol. 1: 1200–1649, vol. 2: 1649–1714,* Edinburgh, 1957.

LLOYD, C. and COULTER, J. L. S., *Medicine and the Navy, 1200–1900. Vol. 3: 1714–1815, vol. 4: 1815–1900,* Edinburgh, 1961–3.

d. *Chatham* Jubilee of the Royal Naval Hospital, Chatham, *J. roy. Nav. Med. Serv.,* 1955, **41**, 185–8.

Greenwich A Description of the Royal Hospital for Seamen with a Short Account of the Establishment of the Royal Naval Asylum, London, 1858.

JAMES, R. R., The medical officers of Greenwich Hospital from A.D. 1695 to 1800, *J. Roy. Nav. Med. Serv.*, 1934, **20**, 164–73.

Origin and Progress of the Hospital for Sick and Diseased Seamen in the Port of London, on Board the Dreadnought, Moored off Greenwich, London, 1878.

Haslar TAIT, W., *History of Haslar Hospital*, Portsmouth, 1906.

RODDIS, L. H., *James Lind: Founder of Nautical Medicine*, New York, 1950. (*See* Chap. 8, pp. 120–145, The first physician of the Royal Hospital at Haslar.)

Plymouth HURFORD, A., The early history of Plymouth hospital: obtained from Admiralty records, documents and local records, *J. roy. Nav. Med. Serv.*, 1935, **21**, 40–47, 138–151, 249–52.

SECTION 8

MILITARY HOSPITALS

a. IRVING, J., A concise view of the progress of military medical literature in this country; being a chronological arrangement of authors, with critical remarks on their works, *Edin. med. & surg. J.*, 1845, **63**, 83–98, 285–302; **64**, 115–129, 375–389; 1846, **65**, 34–49. (Also published separately, Edinburgh 1846. Covers the years 1563 to 1844.)

c. STEWART, D., Disposal of the sick and wounded of the English Army during the sixteenth century, *J. roy. Army Med. Corps*, 1948, **90**, 30–8. (Shows the existence of military hospitals in Ireland circa 1600; primary sources used.)

FIRTH, C. H., The sick and wounded in the Great Civil War, *Cornhill Mag.*, 1901, n.s. **10**, 289–299.

KEMPTHORNE, G. A., Some notes on the medical service of the Restoration Army, *J. roy. Army Med. Corps*, 1939, **72**, 340–6.

KEMPTHORNE, G. A., The medical services of William the Third's Army, *J. roy. Army Med. Corps*, 1937, **69**, 372–82.

ABELL, F., *Prisoners of War in Britain, 1756 to 1815*, London, 1914. (Numerous refs. to hospitals in index.)

KEMPTHORNE, G. A., The Army medical services at home and abroad, 1803–8, *J. roy. Army Med. Corps*, 1933, **61**, 144–150.

HOWELL, H. A. L., The British medical arrangements during the Waterloo campaign, *Proc. roy. Soc. Med., Sect. Hist. Med.*, 1923–4, **17**, 39–50.

McGRIGOR, *Sir* J., *The Autobiography and Services*, London, 1861. (Lived 1771 to 1858. Director of the Army Medical Department.)

McLAREN, E. S., *Ed.*, *A History of the Scottish Women's Hospitals*, London, 1919.

History of the Great War Based on Official Documents. Medical Services, 12 vols., London, 1921–31.

History of the Second World War, United Kingdom Medical Series, ed. Sir A. S. MacNalty, London, 1953. (*See* especially Administration, Vol. 1: Emergency Medical Services, Vol. 1.)

d. *London*   THOMPSON, C. J. S., *The Story of "Homleigh" Auxiliary Military Hospital, Harrow on the Hill*, London, 1919.

LORD, J. R., *The Story of the Horton (Co. of London) War Hospital: Epsom. Its Inception and Work and Some Reflections*, London, 1920.

S., C. I., *King Edward VII's Hospital for Officers, Beaumont House: an Historical Record (the First Fifty Years), 1899–1950*, [London, 1952].

ROLLO, J., *A Short Account of the Royal Artillery Hospital at Woolwich, etc.*, London, 1801.

SECTION 9

HOSPITAL TEACHING

b. NEWMAN, C., *The Evolution of Medical Education in the Nineteenth Century*, London, 1957.

c. THOMSON, Sir A., History and development of teaching hospitals in England, *Brit. med. J.*, 1960, **ii**, 749–51.

d. *Birmingham*   BIRMINGHAM MEDICAL REVIEW, Special no.: *The History of the Birmingham School of Medicine, 1825–1925*, Birmingham, 1925.

MORRISON, J. T. J., *William Sands Cox and the Birmingham Medical School*, Birmingham, 1926.

Bristol   CROSS, F. R., Early medical teaching in Bristol: the Bristol Medical School and its association with the University College, *Bristol med.-chir. J.*, 1927, **44**, 73–112.

Liverpool   HAY, J., The centenary of the Liverpool School of Medicine, *Liv. med.-chir. J.*, 1934, **42**, 57–68.

London   SINGER, C. *and* HOLLOWAY, S. W. F., Early medical education in England in relation to the pre-history of London University, *Med. Hist.*, 1960, **4**, 1–17.

GORDON-TAYLOR, Sir G. *and* WALLS, E. W., *Sir Charles Bell: His Life and Times*, Edinburgh, 1958. (*See* Chap. 14, pp. 140–153: Founding of Middlesex Hospital Medical School.)

COOK, C., History of Moorfields Medical School, *Brit. J. Ophthal.*, 1961, **45**, 241–50.

COPE, Sir Z., *The History of St. Mary's Hospital Medical School, or A Century of Medical Education*, London, 1954.

St. Thomas's Hospital Medical School, *St. Thos. Hosp. Rep.*, 1897, **24**, 1–118.

COWELL, G., Some account of Westminster Hospital and its Medical School, *Westm. Hosp. Rep.*, 1885, **1**, 1–18.

Manchester   BROCKBANK, E. K., *The Foundation of Provincial Medical Education in England and of the Manchester School in Particular*, Manchester, 1936.

Newcastle TURNER, G. *and* ARNISON, W. D., *The Newcastle-upon-Tyne School of Medicine, 1834–1934*, Newcastle, 1934.

Scotland STEWART, G., Sketch of the history of the Royal Infirmary and of the development of clinical teaching, *Edinb. Hosp. Rep.*, 1893, **1**, 1–17.

Ireland KIRKPATRICK, T. P. C., Early medical teaching in Ireland, *Med. Press*, 1947, **218**, 281–5.

MACAFEE, C. H. G., The history of the Belfast School of Obstetrics, 1793–1933, *Ulster med. J.*, 1942, **11**, 20–50.

O'RAHILLY, R., *A History of the Cork Medical School, 1849–1949*, Oxford, 1949.

SECTION 10

HOSPITAL ADMINISTRATION

(Inc. DIET, FINANCE, STATISTICS & WELFARE)

For individual hospitals, see other Sections

c. STEELE, J. C., The mortality of hospitals, general and special, in the United Kingdom, in times past and present, *J. statis. Soc.*, 1877, **40**, 177–261.

BURDETT, H. C., *Hospital Sunday and Hospital Saturday: Their Origin, Progress and Development*, London, 1884.

BURDETT, H. C., The Hospital Sunday and Saturday Funds, *J. Hosp. Assoc.*, London, 1884, pp. 57–85.

POWER, *Sir* D'A., Some early hospital statistics, *Proc. roy. Soc. Med., Sect. Hist. Med.*, 1920–1, **14**, 21–22.

LONG, F. D., *King Edward's Hospital Fund for London: the Story of its Foundation and Achievements, 1897–1942*, London, 1942.

NUFFIELD PROVINCIAL HOSPITALS TRUST, *A Report on the Purpose and Activities of the Trust, 1939–48*, Oxford, 1949.

RABENN, W. B., Hospital diets in eighteenth-century England, *J. Amer. diet. Assoc.*, 1954, **30**, 1216–1221.

BELL, E. M., *The Story of Hospital Almoners*, London, 1961.

SECTION 11

HOSPITAL DESIGN

YOUNG, K. D., *On the Evolution of Hospital Design*, London, 1910.

ELCOCK, C. E., Hospital building—past, present and future, *Proc. roy. Soc. Med.*, 1941, **35**, 359–74.

SECTION 12

SPECIAL HOSPITALS

c. KERSHAW, R., *Special Hospitals: Their Origin, Development, and Relationship to Medical Education; Their Economic Aspects and Relative Freedom from Abuse*, London, 1909.

SECTION 12 (i)

HOSPITALS FOR BURNS

d. *Scotland* SIMPSON, D. C. *and* WALLACE, A. B., Edinburgh's first Burn Hospital, *J. roy. Coll. Surg. Edinb.*, 1956, **2**, 134–143.

SECTION 12 (ii)

CANCER HOSPITALS

d. *London* HURDON, E., Das Marie Curie Hospital in London: seine Ursprung und seine Ausgaben, *Strahlentherapie*, 1938, **63**, 679–81.
COUPLAND, S., The Cancer Charity of the Middlesex Hospital, 1792–1902, *Rep. Cancer Res. Lab., Middlesex Hospital*, 1902, 1, 1–42,
ROYAL CANCER HOSPITAL, *The Royal Cancer Hospital, Fulham Road, London, 1851–1951*, London, 1951.
SANDWITH, F., *Surgeon Compassionate: the Story of William Marsden*, London, 1960. (Founder of the Royal Cancer Hospital.)
Manchester CHRISTIE HOSPITAL AND HOLT RADIUM INSTITUTE, *The Results of Radium and X-ray Therapy in Malignant Disease*, Edinburgh, 1950. (*See* Historical survey on pp. 5–8.)

SECTION 12 (iii)

CHILDREN'S HOSPITALS

b. ABT, I. A., *ed.*, *Paediatrics*, vol. I, Philadelphia, 1923. (*See* pp. 120–121 for list of hospitals with dates of foundation.)
d. *Birmingham* WATERHOUSE, R., *Children in Hospital: a Hundred Years of Child Care in Birmingham*, London [1960].

Bristol UNITED BRISTOL HOSPITALS, *The Bristol Royal Hospital for Sick Children*, Bristol [1960].

London MALONEY, W. J., *George and John Armstrong of Castleton: two Eighteenth Century Medical Pioneers*, Edinburgh, 1954.

POYNTER, F. N. L., A unique copy of George Armstrong's printed proposals for establishing the dispensary for sick children, London, 1769, *Med. Hist.*, 1957, **1**, 65–6.

DAVIS, J. B., *Annals Historical and Medical, During the First Four Years of the Universal Dispensary for Children . . . Founded in 1816, etc.*, London, 1821.

GILBERT, J., *The History and Results of a Dispensary for Sick Children Threatened with Chronic Disease*, London, 1884.

HIGGINS, T., "*Great Ormond Street*" *1852–1952*, London, 1957.

STANTON, B. M., *Story of the East London Hospital for Children*, London, 1920.

BACK, F. H., *and* LEVIN, S., Paediatrics of the past. A note on practice over the past 60 years in the Queen Elizabeth Hospital for Children, [Formerly the East London Hospital for Children and Dispensary for Women], *Brit. med. J.*, 1954, **ii**, 406–8.

Sheffield ILLINGWORTH, R. S., The changing pattern of paediatrics in a children's hospital 1876–1961, *Proc. roy. Soc. Med.*, 1961, **54**, 1011–3.

Taunton HUGO, T., *The History of the Hospital of St. Margaret, Taunton*, London, 1960.

Scotland GUTHRIE, D., *The Royal Edinburgh Hospital for Sick Children, 1860–1960*, Edinburgh, 1960.

Ireland HUNTER, R. H., The Belfast Hospital for Sick Children, *Ulster med. J.*, 1937, **6**, 46–50.

MARSHALL, R., The story of the Ulster Hospital, *Ulster med. J.*, 1959, **28**, 118–147.

SECTION 12 (iv)

EAR, NOSE and THROAT HOSPITALS

b. POLITZER, A., *Geschichte der Ohrenheilkunde*, 2 vols., Stuttgart, 1907–13.

STEVENSON, R. S. *and* GUTHRIE, D., *A History of Oto-Laryngology*, Edinburgh, 1949.

c. KERSHAW, R., British ear and throat clinics historically considered, *J. Laryngol.*, 1913, **28**, 421–7.

d. *London* STEVENSON, R. S., James Yearsley and the Metropolitan Ear, Nose and Throat Hospital, *Brit. med. J.*, 1938, **i**, 464.

SEMON, *Sir* F., The *Autobiography*, ed. H. C. Semon and T. A. McIntyre, London, 1926. (1st Physician for Throat Diseases at St. Thomas's Hospital.)

STEVENSON, R. S., *Morell Mackenzie: the Story of a Victorian Tragedy*, London, 1946. (Founded the Throat Hospital.)

ORMEROD, F. C., The Centenary of the Golden Square Hospital and the 75th anniversary of the founding of the journal, *J. Laryngol.*, 1962, **76**, 357–8.

Ireland　Benn Ulster Eye, Ear and Throat Hospital, *Ulster med. J.*, 1937, **6**, 119–122.

SECTION 12 (v)

EYE HOSPITALS

b. WOOD, C. A., *ed.*, *The American Encyclopedia and Dictionary of Ophthalmology*, Vol. 8, Chicago, 1916. (Pp. 6391–3 contain a list of British institutions arranged by date of foundation.)

c. SORSBY, A., Nineteenth century provincial eye hospitals (with special reference to those no longer extant), *Brit. J. Ophthal.*, 1946, **30**, 501–546.

d. *Bradford*　Bradford Royal Eye and Ear Hospital, 1857–1957, *Brit. med. J.*, 1957, **ii**, 157.

Bristol　UNITED BRISTOL HOSPITALS, *The Bristol Eye Hospital, Founded 1810*, Bristol, 1960.

London　SORSBY, A., Defunct London eye hospitals, *Brit. J. Ophthal.*, 1936, **20**, 77–98.

SORSBY, A., *The Royal Eye Hospital 1857–1957*, London, 1957.

COLLINS, E. T., *The History and Traditions of the Moorfields Eye Hospital. One Hundred Years of Ophthalmic Discovery and Development*, London, 1929.

LYLE, T. K., Some of the great historical figures associated with Moorfields, *Brit. J. Ophthal.*, 1961, **45**, 251–8.

GRIMSDALE, H., G. James Guthrie, F.R.S., 1785–1856, founder of the Royal Westminster Ophthalmic Hospital, *Brit. J. Ophthal.*, 1919, **3**, 145–152.

Sunderland　ROBINSON, W., *The Centenary History of the Durham County and Sunderland Eye Infirmary, 1836–1936*, Sunderland, 1936.

Swanley　SORSBY, A., The origin and development of White Oak Hospital, *Annual Report of the [London County] Council*, 1935, Vol. 4, pt. 3, (Medical supplement) p. 11.

Ireland　SOMERVILLE-LARGE, L. B., The development of ophthalmology in Ireland, *Irish J. med. Sci.*, 1960, pp. 97–129.

SOMERVILLE-LARGE, L. B., Dublin's eye hospitals, *Irish J. med. Sci.*, 1944, pp. 485–497.

WILSON, T. G., *Victorian Doctor: Being the Life of Sir William Wilde*, London, 1942. (Founder of St. Mark's Hospital, Dublin.)

SECTION 12 (vi)

HOSPITALS FOR FISTULA

d. *London*　St. *Mark's Hospital for Fistula and Other Diseases of the Rectum: the History of St. Mark's Hospital, 1835–96*, London, 1897.

SECTION 12 (vii)

HEART HOSPITALS

d. *London*　BUTTERWORTH, *Lady* D. M., *The Story of a City Hospital, 1848–1925*, London [1925]. (City of London Hospital for Diseases of the Heart and Lungs.)

WHITNEY, R., *The Place of Hearts: Being a History of the National Hospital for Diseases of the Heart, 1857–1937*, London, n.d.

CAMPBELL, M., The National Heart Hospital, 1857–1957, *Brit. Heart J.*, 1958, **20**, 137–9.

SECTION 12 (viii)

HYDROPATHY AND HOSPITALS FOR RHEUMATISM

d. *Bath*　GORDON, R. G., *& others., A Survey of Chronic Rheumatic Diseases: Contributed by Contemporary Authorities in Commemoration of the Bicentenary of the Royal National Hospital for Rheumatic Diseases, Bath, 1738–1938*, London, 1938.

London　MULLETT, C. F., Public baths and health in England, 16th–18th century, *Bull. Hist. Med.*, Supp. no. 5, Baltimore, 1946. With bibliography of 238 items, up to 1880.

Margate　ABRAHAM, J. J., *Lettsom: His Life, Times, Friends and Descendants*, London, 1933. (Founder of the Sea-Bathing Hospital.)

Southport　FENN, S. B., The 19th century "water cure" in England. 1. An early hydro-therapeutic hospital [at Southport]. 2. John Smedley of Matlock [by R. MacLelland], *Arch. med. Hydrol.*, 1934, **12**, 229–230.

SECTION 12 (ix)

HOSPITALS FOR INCURABLES

d. *London*　*Some Account of the Royal Hospital for Incurables*, London, 1872.

CLARKE, *Mrs.*, *Helpless: History of the British Home for Incurables*, London, 1894.

Ireland　BRADY, C., *Dublin Hospital for Incurables*, Dublin, 1865.

SECTION 12 (x)

ISOLATION HOSPITALS (inc. CHOLERA, FEVER, SMALLPOX)

a. BILLINGS, J. S., *Bibliography of Cholera*, Washington, 1875.

b. CREIGHTON, C., *A History of Epidemics in Britain*, 2 vols., Cambridge, 1891–4.

MULLETT, C. F., A century of English quarantine (1709–1825), *Bull. Hist. Med.*, 1949, **23**, 527–45.

McDONALD, J. C., The history of quarantine in Britain during the 19th century, *Bull. Hist. Med.*, 1951, **25**, 22–44.

MILLER, G., *The Adoption of Inoculation for Smallpox in England and France*, Philadelphia, 1957. (*See* especially pp. 146–156. Extensive bibliography on pp. 294–339.)

c. LOCAL GOVERNMENT BOARD, *10th Annual Report, 1880–1. Supplement Containing Report and Papers Submitted by the Board's Medical Officers*, London, 1882.

LOCAL GOVERNMENT BOARD, *40th Annual Report, 1910–11. Supplement . . . Containing a Report on Isolation Hospitals. By H. F. Parsons*, London, 1912.

d. *London* GREGORY, G., *Some Account of the Hospital for Smallpox and Vaccination, at Battle Bridge, St. Pancras*, London, 1830.

GUY, W. A., Two hundred and fifty years of smallpox in London, *J. statis. Soc.*, 1882, **45**, 399–443.

Scotland POYNTER, F. N. L., Thomas Anderson (1743/4–1813): pioneer of vaccination in Scotland, *Scott. Soc. Hist. Med.*, *Report of Proceeding*, 1959–60, pp. 12–21.

Ireland MacARTHUR, Sir W. P., Medical history of the famine, in *The Great Famine (1845–50)*, ed. R. D. Edwards and T. D. Williams, Dublin, 1956, Chap. 5, pp. 263–315.

CUMMINS, N. M., The Cork Fever Hospital, *J. Irish med. Assoc.*, 1955, **37**, 385–9.

MOORE, D. B. D. K., Building of a hospital, 1804–1940 [Fever Hospital in Cork Street], *Irish J. med. Sci.*, 1941, pp. 1–6.

SECTION 12 (xi)

MATERNITY HOSPITALS

b. SPENCER, H. R., *The History of British Midwifery from 1650 to 1800*, London, 1927. (Appendix II, pp. 179–182, has a list of British Lying-in Institutions and their staffs during the late 18th and early 19th centuries.)

KERR, J. M. M., *and others, Historical Review of British Obstetrics and Gynaecology, 1800–1950*, Edinburgh, 1954.

d. *Bristol* UNITED BRISTOL HOSPITALS, *The Bristol Maternity Hospital*, Bristol [1961].
London RYAN, T., *The Origin, History, Work, and Present State of Metropolitan Lying-in Hospitals*, London, 1888.
An Account of the British Lying-in Hospital for Married Women . . . Situated in Brownlow-street, Longacre. From the Time of its Institution, in Nov., 1749, to the 31st Dec., 1804, [London] 1805.
WOOD, J. S., *A Brief Chronological Sketch of the Foundation and Work of the Chelsea Hospital for Women*, [London, 1883].
RYAN, T., *The History of Queen Charlotte's Lying-in Hospital*, London, 1885.
OXFORD, A. W., *The History of the Samaritan Free Hospital. With an Appendix on the London Hospitals and Infirmaries*, Cambridge, 1931,
Manchester BRIDE, J. W., *A Short History of the St. Mary's Hospitals, Manchester, and the Honorary Medical Staff: from the Foundation in 1790 to 1922*, Manchester, 1922.
BRIDE, J. W., *The Manchester School of Obstetrics and Gynaecology: an Analysis of Obstetric Work at St. Mary's Hospitals, Manchester, from the Registers, 1875 to 1920*, Manchester, 1951.
Scotland STURROCK, J., Early maternity hospitals in Edinburgh (1756–1879), *J. Obst. Gynaec.*, 1958, **65**, 122–131.
MILLER, D., A short record of the Edinburgh Royal Maternity and the Simpson Memorial Hospital, *Trans. Edin. Obst. Soc.*, 1937–8, **97**, 1–12.
JARDINE, R., The Glasgow maternity hospitals; past and present, *Trans. Glasgow Obst. Gynaec. Soc.* (1900–1902), 1903, **3**, 13–28. *Also: Glasgow med. J.*, 1901, **55**, 28–42.
Ireland KIRKPATRICK, T. P. C., The Coombe Lying-in Hospital, 1826–1926, *Irish J. med. Sci.*, 1926, pp. 393–402.
CLARKE, J., Abstract of a registry kept for some years in the Lying-in Hospital of Dublin, *Trans. Ass. King's & Queen's Coll. Phys. Ireland*, 1817, **1**, 367–403.
KIRKPATRICK, T. P. C., *The Book of the Rotunda Hospital, an Illustrated History of the Dublin Lying-in Hospital from its Foundation in 1745 to the Present Time*, edited by Henry Jellett, London, 1913.
BROWNE, O'D. T. D., *The Rotunda Hospital, 1745–1945*, Edinburgh, 1947.
HUNTER, R. H., The Royal Maternity Hospital, Belfast, *Ulster med. J.*, 1937, **6**, 211–216.

SECTION 12 (xii)

MENTAL HOSPITALS

a. BURDETT, H. C., *Hospitals and Asylums of the World. Vol. II: Asylum Construction*, London, 1891.

LAEHR, H., *Die Literatur der Psychiatrie, Neurologie und Psychologie von 1459–1799*, 3 vols., Berlin, 1900. (The bibliography in vols. I and II is arranged chronologically. Vol. III, the subject index, refers to hospitals under the heading 'Anstalten'.)

b. NICHOLSON, D., A chapter in the history of criminal lunacy in England, *J. ment. Sci.*, 1877–8, **23**, 165–85.

HUNTER, R. A. *and* MACALPINE, I., *Three Hundred Years of Psychiatry, 1535–1860*, London, 1963.

LEIGH, D., *The Historical Development of British Psychiatry, vol. I: 18th and 19th century*, Oxford, 1961.

c. WALK, A., Some aspects of the 'moral treatment' of the insane up to 1854, *J. ment. Sci.*, 1954, **100**, 807–837.

JONES, K., *Lunacy, Law and Conscience 1744–1845: the Social History of the Care of the Insane*, London, 1955. (Chapter on criminal lunatics. Extensive bibliography with separate listing of statutes and reports.)

HUNTER, R. A., *and others*, The country register of houses for the reception of 'lunatics', 1798–1812, *J. ment. Sci.*, 1956, **102**, 856–863.

WALK, A., The history of mental nursing, *J. ment. Sci.*, 1961, **107**, 1–17.

JETTER, D., Ursprung und Gestalt panoptischer Irrenhäuser in England und Schotland, *Sudhoffs Arch. Gesch. Med.*, 1962, **46**, 27–44.

d. *Birmingham*   WINSON GREEN MENTAL HOSPITAL, *Centenary Brochure of the City of Birmingham Mental Hospital, Winson Green*, [Birmingham, 1947].

CRICK, H. A., *The Story of Mental Nursing and of Rubery Hill and Hollymoor Hospitals*, Birmingham, [1958?].

Bristol   HEMPHILL, R. E., *Bristol in the Evolution of Mental Health, 1696–1961*, [Exhibition Catalogue], Bristol, 1961.

Broadmoor   PARTRIDGE, R., *Broadmoor: a History of Criminal Lunacy and its Problems*, London, 1953.

Cambridge   Fulbourn Hospital, near Cambridge: centenary reflections, *Nurs. Times*, 1958, **54**, 1341–4.

Caterham   GIBSON, J., *St. Lawrence's Hospital, Caterham, Surrey, 1870–1956*, Caterham [1957?].

London   O'DONOGHUE, E. G., *The Story of the Bethlehem Hospital, from its Foundation in 1217*, London [1914].

WHITTAKER, D., Seven hundredth anniversary of Bethlem, *J. ment. Sci.*, 1947, **93**, 740–747.

MORRIS, A. D., *The Hoxton Madhouses*, Cambridge, 1958.

FRENCH, C. N., *The Story of St. Luke's Hospital*, London, 1951.

Manchester   BROCKBANK, E. M., *A Short History of Cheadle Royal from its foundation in 1766 for the Humane Treatment of Mental Disease*, Manchester, 1934.

Norwich   BATEMAN, Sir F. *and* RYE, W., *The History of the Bethel Hospital at Norwich*, Norwich, 1906.

Ticehurst   Some incidents in the history and practice of Ticehurst Asylum, *J. ment. Sci.*, 1901, **47**, 62–71.

Wakefield BOLTON, J. S., The evolution of a mental hospital—Wakefield, 1818–1928, *J. ment. Sci.*, 1928, **74**, 587–633.

Worcester COOKE, E. M., A review of the last twenty years at the Worcester County and City Asylum, with some conclusions derived therefrom, *J. ment. Sci.*, 1895, **41**, 387–408.

York TUKE, D. H., *Reform in the Treatment of the Insane. Early History of the Retreat, York*, London, 1892.

    STRONG, L. A. G., *Light through the Cloud; the Story of the Retreat, York, 1796–1946*, London [1946].

    [GRAY, J.] *History of the York Lunatic Asylum, with Appendix Containing Minutes of the Evidence on the Cases of Abuse lately Enquired into by the Committee, etc. Addressed to William Wilberforce Esq.*, York, 1815.

Scotland THOMSON, J. B., Criminal lunacy in Scotland from 1846–70, both inclusive, *Edinb. med. J.*, 1871–2, **17**, 21–9.

    MacNIVEN, A., The first Commissioners [of the Board of Lunacy]: Reform in Scotland in the mid-nineteenth century, *J. ment. Sci.*, 1960, **106**, 451–71.

    EASTERBROOK, C. C., *The Chronicle of Crichton Royal (1833–1936): Being the Story of a Famous Mental Hospital*, Dumfries, 1940.

    Some Account of the Rise, Progress, and Present State of the Lunatic Asylum at Edinburgh, with Some Remarks on the General Treatment of Lunatics, Pointing out the Advantages of Avoiding all Severity, Edinburgh, 1812.

Ireland KIRKPATRICK, T. P. C., *A Note on the History of the Care of the Insane in Ireland up to the end of the Nineteenth Century*, Dublin, 1931. (The Acts of Parliament dealing with Ireland are listed on pp. 39–40. Bibliography of books on pp. 41–43.)

    CRAIG, M. J., *The Legacy of Swift. A Bi-centenary Record of St. Patrick's Hospital, Dublin*, [Dublin], 1948.

SECTION 12 (xiii)

HOSPITALS FOR NERVOUS DISEASES

a. TEMKIN, O., *The Falling Sickness: a History of Epilepsy from the Greeks to the Beginnings of Modern Neurology*, Baltimore, 1945. (*See* pp. 245–259, 'The hospitalization of epileptics.' Bibliography of 706 references.)

d. *London* FEILING, A., *A History of the Maida Vale Hospital for Nervous Diseases*, London, 1958.

    BOLL, R. E. M., May Sinclair and the Medico-Psychological Clinic of London, *Proc. Amer. Philos. Soc.*, 1962, **106**, 310–26. (The first public clinic in England for psycho-analytic treatment. Information also about the Tavistock Clinic for Functional Nervous Disease.)

    HOLMES, *Sir* G. M., *The National Hospital, Queen Square, 1860–1948*, Edinburgh, 1954.

    Queen Square and the National Hospital, 1860–1960, London [1960].

HUNTER, R. A. *and* HURWITZ, L. J., The case notes of the National Hospital for the Paralysed and Epileptic, Queen Square, London, before 1900, *J. Neurosurg. Psychiat.*, 1961, **24**, 187–194.

SECTION 12 (xiv)

ORTHOPAEDIC HOSPITALS

b. OSMOND-CLARKE, H., Half a century of orthopaedic progress in Great Britain, *J. Bone Jt. Surg.*, 1950, **32B**, 620–675.
VALENTIN, B., *Geschichte der Orthopädie*, Stuttgart, 1961. (Pp. 158–185 on England. With copious references.)
d. *Hinckley* VALENTIN, B., Robert Chessher (1750–1831): an English pioneer in orthopaedics, *Med. Hist.*, 1958, **2**, 308–13. (Founder of the first orthopaedic institute in England.)
Liverpool LE VAY, D., *The Life of Hugh Owen Thomas*, Edinburgh, 1956.
London THORNTON, J. L., Orthopaedic surgeons at St. Bartholomew's Hospital, London, *St. Bart's Hosp. J.*, 1955, **59**, 195–204.
Oswestry HUNT, A. G., *This Is My Life*, London, 1947. (*See* Chap. 8, pp. 122–63: The Story of Baschurch.)
WATSON, F., *The Life of Sir Robert Jones*, London, 1934.
MALKIN, S. A. S., The conquest of disability, *Ann. roy. Coll. Surg. Engl.*, 1957, **20**, 99–111. (Mainly about Sir R. Jones and the hospital service which he built up.)
Windermere PLATT, *Sir* H., Richard Watson (1737–1816), Bishop of Llandaff, Hunterian Trustee: a chapter in the history of orthopaedics, *J. Bone Jt. Surg.*, 1956, **38B**, 46–53. (The Ethel Hedley Hospital, Windermere, and its development out of the Bishop's private residence.)

SECTION 12 (xv)

SKIN HOSPITALS

b. GRAHAM-LITTLE, *Sir* E., A retrospect of dermatology in Great Britain, in *De Dermatologia et Dermatologis*, Ed. L. Nékam, Budapest, 1936, pp. 141–152.
GRAHAM-LITTLE, *Sir* E., Celebrated British dematologists of the past fifty years, *Brit. J. Derm. Syphil.*, 1938, **50**, 503–518.
d. *London* BECHET, P. E., The City Hospital: a history of its dermatologic division, *Arch. Derm. Syphil.*, 1939, **39**, 672–8.
RUSSELL, B., *St. John's Hospital for Diseases of the Skin, 1863–1963*, Edinburgh, 1963.

History of St. Mark's Hospital, in *Collected papers of St. Mark's Hospital, London. Centenary volume 1835–1935,* London, 1935, pp. 1–20.
Scotland WALKER, N., The past of dermatology in Edinburgh, *Brit. med. J.,* 1906, **ii,** 1437–9.

SECTION 12 (xvi)

HOSPITALS FOR STONE

d. *London* MORSON, C., *St. Peter's Hospital for Stone, 1860–1960,* Edinburgh, 1960.

SECTION 12 (xvii)

SURGICAL HOSPITALS

d. *London* WARDROP, J., [West London Hospital of Surgery], *Irish J. med. Sci.,* 1956, pp. 271–275.
Scotland PATERSON, R., *Memorials of the Life of James Syme,* Edinburgh, 1874. (Set up his own private surgical hospital in Edinburgh in 1829.)

SECTION 12 (xviii)

HOSPITALS FOR TROPICAL DISEASES

d. *London* MANSON-BAHR, P. H., *The Life and Work of Sir Patrick Manson,* London, 1927. (Albert Dock Hospital.)
MANSON-BAHR, Sir P., *History of the School of Tropical Medicine in London (1899–1949),* London, 1956. (*See* Chap. 4, pp. 15–27: The Source (Seamen's Hospital Society); Chap. 13, pp. 85–87: Hospital for Tropical Diseases.)

SECTION 12 (xix)

TUBERCULOSIS and CHEST HOSPITALS

b. KAYNE, G. G., *The Control of Tuberculosis in England, Past and Present,* London, 1937. (*See* Chap. 3, pp. 24–36: The voluntary system; Chap. 6, pp. 50–55: Sanatoria. With good bibl. on pp. 174–7.)
c. LOCAL GOVERNMENT BOARD, *Sanatoria for Consumption and Certain Other Aspects of the Tuberculosis Question. Supplement in Continuation of the Report of the Medical Officer for 1905–6, to the 35th Annual Report of the Local Government Board 1905–6,* By H. T. Bulstrode, London, 1908.

(Chap. 8, pp. 119–130: 'The evolution of the sanatorium idea' is
essential reading. Contains an index to sanatoria in England and
Wales.)

WILLIAMSON, D. J., The anti-tuberculosis dispensary movement, *Brit. J.
Tuberc.* 1910, **4**, 157–168.

HARTSTON, W. *and* WHEELER, W. F., First tuberculosis dispensary, [With
subsequent correspondence by G. Lissant Cox, A. R. Robertson,
Harley Williams and P. J. Bishop], *Brit. med. J.*, 1958, **i**, 339, 402,
519, 647, 1005–6.

d. *London*   DAVIDSON, M. *and* ROUVRAY, F. G., *The Brompton Hospital: the
Story of a Great Adventure*, London, 1954.

SIMMONDS, F. A. H., *A History of Clare Hall Hospital [Formerly the
Smallpox Hospital, South Mimms]*, Barnet, 1962.

Royal Hospital for Diseases of the Chest. Its Origin and Progress, 1814–1883,
[London, 1883]. (Founded by Isaac Buxton.)

SCHUSTER, N. H., Isaac Buxton, 1773–1825, *Proc. roy. Soc. Med., Sect.
Hist. Med.*, 1955, **48**, 326–8.

Papworth   VARRIER-JONES, Sir P., *Papers of a Pioneer*. Coll. by P. Fraser,
London, 1943. (Chap. 5, pp. 43–58 on Papworth village settle-
ments.)

Sutton Coldfield   CYRIAX, R. J., The pioneer of the sanatorium treatment
of pulmonary tuberculosis, [George Bodington], *Brit. J. Tuberc.*,
1925, **19**, 1–16. (Introduced sanatorium treatment into England.)

Scotland   The Edinburgh tuberculosis scheme, *Edin. med. J.*, 1937,
4, 285–297. (Contains much information on Sir R. Philip and
his dispensary from which the Scheme evolved. With a bibliography of Philip.)

PHILIP, Sir R. W., The Victoria Hospital for Consumption, Edinburgh; its rise and outlook, *Edin. Hosp. Rep.*, 1895, **3**, 13–20.

*Sir Robert W. Philip, 1857–1939: Memories of his Friends and Pupils One
Hundred Years after his Birth*, London, 1957. (Established the
Victoria Dispensary for Consumption in Edinburgh, the first of
its kind in the world, which later became the Royal Victoria
Hospital.)

Ireland   BARR, A., *A Social Account of Tuberculosis in Ireland* [Thesis],
Belfast, 1953.

BARR, A., The development of the tuberculosis service in Northern
Ireland, *Irish J. med. Sci.*, 1955, pp. 512–22.

SECTION 12 (xx)

HOSPITALS FOR VENEREAL DISEASE

a. PROKSCH, J. K., *Die Litteratur über die Venerischen Krankheiten. Bd. 1*, Bonn,
1889, [and] *Supplement 1*, Bonn, 1900.

b. FESSLER, A., Venereal disease and prostitution in the reports of the Poor
   Law Commissioners, 1834–1850, *Brit. J. vener. Dis.*, 1951, **27**,
   154–157. (Venereal wards in workhouse infirmaries.)
d. *Leicester* BLAKESLEY, H. J., The male venereal clinic at the Royal
   Infirmary, Leicester; an account of its origin, development and
   work, *Brit. med. J.*, 1921, **i**, 619.
London PEACHEY, G. C., William Bromfield, 1713–1792, *Proc. roy. Soc.
   Med., Sect. Hist. Med.*, 1915, **8**, 103–25. (Founder of London
   Lock Hospital.)
   HIGHAM, A. R. C., The history of St. Paul's Hospital, London, *Proc.
   roy. Soc. Med.*, 1957, **50**, 164–6.
Nottingham BUCKLEY, J. C., The Nottingham Venereal Diseases Clinic;
   its work and its history, as illustrating principles upon which
   schemes for dealing with V.D. problems should be based, *J. roy.
   San. Inst.*, 1923–24, **44**, 21–26.
Scotland LEES, R., The "Lock Wards" of Edinburgh Royal Infirmary,
   Brit. J. vener. Dis., 1961, **37**, 187–9.

Index

281